Principles of

Psychophysiology

PRINCIPLES OF

PSYCHOPHYSIOLOGY

AN INTRODUCTORY TEXT AND READINGS

RICHARD A. STERNBACH
DEPARTMENT OF PSYCHIATRY
UNIVERSITY OF WISCONSIN
MADISON, WISCONSIN

ACADEMIC PRESS   New York and London

ACADEMIC PRESS INC.
111 Fifth Avenue, New York, New York 10003

United Kingdom Edition published by
ACADEMIC PRESS INC. (LONDON) LTD.
Berkeley Square House, London W.1

LIBRARY OF CONGRESS CATALOG CARD NUMBER: 65-26410

PRINTED IN THE UNITED STATES OF AMERICA

To My Mother

Preface

This volume is meant to serve two purposes: to be a text for an undergraduate course in psychophysiology and to provide an introduction to the field for those in clinical areas who would like to become involved in psychophysiological research.

As we show in the Introduction, psychophysiology differs from physiological psychology. The latter now encompasses so many subdisciplines that the burgeoning literature necessitates separate treatment of neuropsychology, psychophysiology, behavioral endocrinology, etc. This is shown in the many specialized seminars already given at the graduate level. It is clear that the current undergraduate course in physiological psychology provides a superficial survey of many topics, or else gives adequate treatment to too few areas. However, by considering separately the several fields which have emerged as functionally autonomous, as this book does, each of them can receive good coverage.

Two factors may have contributed to the lag in programming a course such as this text is designed to serve. The first is the inevitable weight of tradition and reluctance to make curricular innovations for what may turn out to be a "fad." The second is the lack of any text that gives organization to the mass of published materials in this field, which places a discouraging burden on the instructor who would otherwise be willing to initiate such a course. We can do nothing about the first problem. As for the second, it is hoped that this text will provide a solution. I have selected the major findings in the literature and have organized them in a sequence which follows the basic principles which, so far, seem to have emerged or are in the process of doing so. The Readings in the Appendix are, like all Readings, designed to supplement the text by providing illustrative reports without duplicating the descriptions given in the text. The Readings are included within these covers to keep costs down and to spare students the almost impossible task of finding all the sources in the library. The selections included in the Appendix, aside from their intrinsic worth, also give historical perspective to the field.

This volume should be especially helpful to medical students since courses in psychophysiology are being given more often now in medical schools. In departments of psychiatry the subject matter is used as a bridge between the students' knowledge of physiology and the more tenuous clinical psychiatry to which the students will later be exposed. Since this text selectively covers the literature, it presents the essentials without adding greatly to the medical students' already too-long list of readings.

Clinical psychiatrists and psychologists have been strongly attracted to psychophysiological research because it uses man as its subject and readily permits correlation between clinical and physiological phenomena. Also, whether the physiological variables are used to indicate or to validate clinical variables, the physiology being sampled offers a comforting reduction to a "lower" or "more basic" level of discourse, or so it seems. For such clinicians there has been no ready collection of psychophysiological work to which they could turn for an introduction to the field. This text offers such an introduction, and with the References, Readings, and the references cited in the Readings there should be enough details and further leads to the literature to enable an investigator to embark on a research project.

To my knowledge, this is the first textbook in the field of psychophysiology. I hope it will stimulate more teaching, reading, and above all, more research in this rewarding area. The reader will see that there are still unanswered questions remaining in each topic covered, and this book should provide a means of organizing the mass of known data so that interesting problems can be formulated and more good research generated.

I am greatly indebted to the authors and publishers who have permitted the reproduction of tables and figures, and the articles included in the Readings. Specific acknowledgments are made where these materials appear. Betty Gardner and Michael Smith contributed original illustrations, and Mary White, Phyllis Fedie, and Patricia Wolley typed the manuscript; I am much indebted to them all for their talents and help. My wife, Diana, and our children, Jennifer and David, have been encouraging, amusedly tolerant, and comforting to a sometimes discouraged author.

I am grateful to Professor M. A. Wenger of UCLA for introducing me to this fascinating field. I have tried to emulate his high standards. I am grateful, too, to the following colleagues who read the manuscript and whose comments and suggestions were most helpful: A. A. Alexander, Ph.D.; Lorna S. Benjamin, Ph.D.; J. J. Chosy, M.D.; David T. Graham, M.D.; Frances K. Graham, Ph.D.; Norman S. Greenfield, Ph.D.; William C. Lewis, M.D.; and David G. Rice, Ph.D.

February 1966   RICHARD A. STERNBACH

Contents

Preface vii

    I. Introduction: The Nature of Psychophysiology 1

   II. An Orientation to
      the Autonomic Nervous System 11

  III. Autonomic Balance 27

  IV. Law of Initial Values 43

   V. Activation, Adaptation, and Rebound 57

  VI. Stimulus-Response Specificity 79

 VII. Individual Response-Stereotypy 95

VIII. Explicit Sets 111

  IX. Implicit Sets 127

   X. Psychosomatic Diseases 139

     References 158

Appendix: Some Important Readings
            in Psychophysiology 163
            Notes on the Readings 163

The Mechanism of Emotional Disturbance
of Bodily Functions 165

   W. B. Cannon
   The New England Journal of Medicine **198,** 877 (1928)

The Effect of Emotion, Sham Rage and
Hypothalamic Stimulation on
the Vago-Insulin System 173

    E. Gellhorn, R. Cortell, and J. Feldman
    American Journal of Physiology **132,** 532 (1941)

Physiological and Clinical Tests of
Autonomic Function and Autonomic Balance 183

    Chester W. Darrow
    Physiological Reviews **28,** 1 (1943)

Response Patterns 219

    R. C. Davis
    Transactions of the New York Academy of Sciences **19** (2), 731 (1957)

Individual Patterns of Physiological Activity
As a Function of Task Differences and
Degree of Arousal 228

    Morris M. Schnore
    Journal of Experimental Psychology **58,** 117 (1959)

Autonomic Response Patterns
During Intravenous Infusion of
Epinephrine and Nor-Epinephrine............................. 240

    M. A. Wenger, T. L. Clemens, M. L. Darsie,
    B. T. Engel, F. M. Estess, and
    R. R. Sonnenschein
    Psychosomatic Medicine **22,** 294 (1960)

Habituation of the Orienting Response
in Alert and Drowsy Subjects 254

    David G. McDonald, Laverne C. Johnson,
    and David J. Hord
    Psychophysiology **1,** 163 (1964)

BODY IMAGE AND PHYSIOLOGICAL PATTERNS
IN PATIENTS WITH PEPTIC ULCER AND
RHEUMATOID ARTHRITIS.. 265
    Robert L. Williams and Alan G. Krasnoff
    Psychosomatic Medicine **26,** 701 (1964)

GOALS AND METHODS OF PSYCHOPHYSIOLOGY 274
    Albert F. Ax
    Psychophysiology **1,** 8 (1964)

INDEX 293

Principles of

Psychophysiology

I

Introduction:
The Nature of Psychophysiology

Psychophysiology, as we will be using the term, is not the same as physiological psychology. Both refer to the study of the relationships between mental and bodily events, but the means of studying them and the kinds of relationships studied are different. It is probably not possible to make a formal definition of either field that will delimit it from the other, but since in the end the disciplines are defined by the activities of those who call themselves psychophysiologists and physiological psychologists, let us examine these activities.

Physiological psychology is the older of the two fields in the sense that it was "founded" a century ago; the term has been used for laboratories, texts, journals, and college courses. Although physiological psychologists originally used humans as subjects, it is now far more common that other animals are used. This is because many of the answers to questions asked require procedures which cannot be employed on humans, and because since Darwin it has been assumed that there is an essential continuity between man and the lower animals which makes the animal findings applicable to humans. Most psychophysiological studies, however, use humans as subjects. Yet because there is some overlap in each field in the kinds of subjects used, this cannot be the differentiating criterion.

Most traditional physiological psychology has proceeded by manipulating some physiological variable, observing changes in behavior, and then postulating an intervening internal event to

1

account for the results. For example, animals trained to run a maze or press a lever may be deprived of food or water, or given a drug, or have some operation performed on their nervous system, and then the effects of this procedure on their performance will be noted. Although this experimental routine is not without exceptions, it is a good example of traditional physiological psychology. On the other hand, the usual psychophysiological experiment has reversed the process. Mental or emotional or behavioral activities are made to occur while physiological events are being observed; correlations between these activities and the observed physiological events are noted, and then some intervening internal event is postulated. Stern has listed examples of these differences, which are shown in Table I (Stern, 1964). This comparison of typical experimental methods comes a little closer to differentiating the fields, but it is possible to show that there are exceptions on both sides, in the activities of those who call themselves physiological psychologists or psychophysiologists.

Another difference which exists in emphasis, but which also has exceptions, has to do with the technique of recording observations.

TABLE I[a]

SOME EXPERIMENTAL VARIABLES USED IN TWO DISCIPLINES

	Independent variable	Dependent variable
Physiological psychology	Brain lesion	Learning—behavioral
	Brain stimulation	Performance
	Drug administration	Conditioning
	Diet manipulation	Food selection
	Auditory stimulation	Habituation of orienting response
Psychophysiology	Vigilance experiment	EEG evoked response
	Sleep deprivation	Background EEG
	Psychologic or psychiatric state (fear, anxiety, depression etc.)	Conditionability of physiological system
	Dreaming	Physiological correlates

[a] From Stern, 1964. Courtesy of the author and Williams & Wilkins Co.

Physiological psychologists may use a wide variety of recording techniques depending upon the behavior and the species they are observing. Psychophysiologists, on the other hand, typically have employed a polygraph, or some similar device, to record the physiological activity in which they are interested. Although there are exceptions, as we have said, it is interesting to note that the journal *Psychophysiology,* which is the official organ of the Society for Psychophysiological Research, was preceded by the Society's *Psychophysiology Newsletter* and that, in turn, began as the *Polygraph Newsletter.* Yet because of the exceptions, this polygraphic recording technique also cannot be the differentiating criterion.

A final difference in emphasis may be considered. By definition and tradition, a physiological psychologist is a psychologist, that is, one who has his degree (Ph.D.) from a department of psychology. Now, anyone else who is interested in the relationships between the physiological and psychological aspects of behavior, and who does research in the field, cannot call his work physiological psychology. Whether he has his Ph.D. in physiology, or he has an M.D., he cannot call himself a psychologist, even if he does feed drugs to rats and watch them run a maze. Consequently many investigators who do what physiological psychologists do have taken to calling themselves psychophysiologists in order to indicate that they are not psychologists. Yet this criterion is obviously an unsatisfactory one for differentiating the two fields. Some non-psychologists are performing research that is physiological psychology, and perhaps half of those in psychophysiology *are* psychologists.

Although our failure to find a single criterion that defines psychophysiology may be confusing or discouraging, we can clarify things somewhat by putting together the several attributes we have been considering. *Psychophysiology is the study of the interrelationships between the physiological and psychological aspects of behavior. It typically employs human subjects, whose physiological responses are usually recorded on a polygraph while stimuli are presented which are designed to influence mental, emotional, or motor behavior; and the investigator need not be a psychologist.* This description covers the great majority of the research studies in psychophysiology to date. Although it is not an adequate formal definition, it is a rather fair operational one, and until you have read the rest of this book it should serve to orient you to the kinds of research with which we will be concerned.

Now let us consider what is meant by "principles of psychophysiology." By no means does this text attempt to deal with all or even most of psychophysiological research. It is not an attempt to review the field. Rather it is a highly selective presentation organized around some of the basic concepts which have emerged and which have been discussed by psychophysiologists. These concepts are called principles, because they seem to enable one to organize the data in such a way that they are meaningful, and enhance our understanding and ability to predict events in human beings. Consequently a great many psychophysiological studies are not cited, not because they are not good ones or not important, but only because they are not directly relevant to the principles with which we are concerned. Also, in some cases, experiments which are directly relevant have not been cited because they would be superfluous; only those which seem necessary to prove a point or illustrate a theme are used. The intent of this text is to enable one who is unfamiliar with the field to comprehend, as simply as possible, the essential nature of the current state of psychophysiology, with as little diversion into extraneous matters as possible.

The principles with which we shall be concerned are those whose names constitute the chapter headings in the Contents. These principles, as it turns out, represent the unique contribution of psychophysiology to the understanding of how human beings function. They are analogous to earlier principles of mass action and vicarious functioning contributed by physiological psychology, or massed vs. spaced learning and schedules of reinforcement contributed by learning theory. The principles of psychophysiology represent another way of looking at human functioning than has been usual in the past, and so are somewhat different from the kinds of information obtainable in other, more traditional texts.

Because of the uniqueness of the psychophysiological approach, no attempt will be made here to "integrate" these principles with all the rest of psychology or physiology. We will not be concerned with the problems of emotion, cognition, motivation, learning, etc., nor with the neurophysiological or biochemical aspects of cell functioning. The older, traditional ways of categorizing functions in psychology are not very useful to psychophysiologists, and the more molecular approaches of modern physiology are not very helpful in understanding total, organized functioning. It therefore seems irrelevant, and in some ways premature, to attempt to show how the principles of psychophysiology add new information to the old problems or encompass new findings in other fields.

One omission from the list of principles may surprise some: conditioning is not given a separate heading. The reason for this is that it is already amply covered in many texts, and in volumes devoted exclusively to the phenomenon. Conditioning of the peripheral effectors of the autonomic nervous system is an especial interest of psychophysiologists, yet because it is not new, nor a unique contribution from the field, and is well covered elsewhere, it is not given separate consideration. Instead the fact of conditioning is used in an explanatory and an illustrative way in discussions of the other principles.

In mentioning the autonomic nervous system (ANS) we come to a topic that might have been mentioned earlier in describing the field of psychophysiology. Most psychophysiological research has been concerned with the factors that influence autonomic functioning, and this has usually involved recording (on the polygraph) peripheral effects of this functioning. Some of the measures commonly used are the sweating and temperature of the skin, the rate and force of cardiac contractions, blood pressure and gastric contractions, etc. However, many psychophysiologists also record measures of central nervous system activity, either in the form of the electroencephalogram (EEG; brain wave) or in the form of its peripheral effects on the electromyogram (EMG; muscle tone). Some workers have attempted to correlate these measures, recording ANS, EEG, and EMG activity simultaneously in order to understand the ways in which such functions are integrated or coordinated in the body. We will discuss some of this work in the section on Activation. Yet it is true that most psychophysiological research has involved only ANS activity, and the principles which we will be discussing apply primarily to the ANS. For this reason we make no extensive mention of the other measures; and for this reason, too, we provide an orientation to the ANS in the next chapter, assuming the reader knows practically nothing about it.

SOME HISTORICAL DEVELOPMENTS

Although psychophysiology has been a formal scientific discipline for only a short time, psychophysiological observations are as old as recorded history. Whenever we note that someone blushes with embarrassment, or flushes with anger, this is a psychophysiological observation. So it is, too, when you note that your palms get so sweaty during an examination that you make the test papers damp. In these instances, the observations establish a relationship between certain physiological (autonomic) changes, and some inferred emotion. The inference about the emotion is usually based on a knowledge of the stimulating conditions that produced the observed changes; yet our experience with many such situations and responses in everyday life often enables us to use only the physiological events themselves to infer the emotion. For example, when a person blushes, we assume embarrassment, and are the more convinced the louder the person protests otherwise.

Even experimental attempts to discover the relationships between emotions and physiology are not new. The remarkable Emperor Frederick II performed the following study (among others) as reported by the historian Salimbene in the 13th century:

> . . . the sixth curiosity and folly of Frederick, as I have said in my other chronicle, was that at a certain luncheon he had two men very well beaten, and then sent one of them to sleep and the other to hunt, and on the following evening, he had them defecate in his presence, because he wanted to know which of them had digested the better. And it was decided by the doctors that he who had slept had enjoyed the better digestion. [Ross, J. B. and McLaughlin, M. M. (eds.), A Portable Medieval Reader, New York: Viking, 1949, p. 366.]

However, two developments were necessary to turn psychophysiological experimentation into the discipline it is today. The first was the development of the polygraph as an instrument of research. By the 1920's, the old Einthoven string galvanometer had been developed into a sensitive and precise instrument for recording a number of bioelectric potentials simultaneously. The inpetus for this came from the electroencephalographers; once Hans Berger had demonstrated, in the 1930's, the feasibility and usefulness of recording the EEG, the demand for such a technique became quite strong from the clinical neurology services. Clinical

EEG machines came to be standard equipment in hospitals everywhere, and with some slight modification for recording DC changes (skin resistance, temperature) these machines could serve very well as polygraphs.

What was important about the availability of polygraphs was that for the first time it was possible to record permanently and to measure objectively a number of physiological systems at the same time. For example, the electrocardiogram (EKG), galvanic skin response (GSR), skin temperature, the EEG, etc., could all be made to appear as simultaneous squiggles on a moving strip of paper. This chart became an objective and permanent record of the subject's physiological activity at the time. And since it was possible to calibrate the sensitivity of the polygraph's amplification system and to record at a known and constant paper speed, then quite precise determinations of the amplitude and rate of physiological activity could be made. A disadvantage of the system was that it required the subject to lie or sit quietly, in order not to disturb the pickup electrodes or entangle the many wires on him, which might produce artifacts or "noise" on the record. Figure 1 illustrates the appearance of a typical record.

Some recent developments have changed somewhat the traditional polygraph usage. One is the use of telemetering devices which do away with the need for wires, permitting the subject to move around and thus making possible the use of more "real life" experimental situations. Another is the use of data-recording magnetic tape which can be converted into digital data and fed into a computer for analysis, greatly simplifying and making more objective the handling of data, and making the paper record superfluous except for display purposes. Also, there is now an increased sensitivity, reliability, and range of response variables available, due to advances in electronic technology.

The second development which enabled psychophysiology to become a scientific discipline was the availability of statistical techniques for analyzing the data obtained. Previously, physiological research had to be satisfied with demonstrating the existence of a phenomenon (such as the relationship between felt hunger pangs and stomach contractions) on a few subjects. However, when psychophysiologists asked questions such as, What is the *degree* of

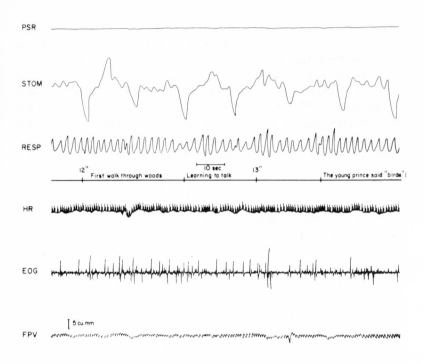

FIG. 1. Sample polygraph tracings. The top tracing is palmar skin resistance, followed by gastric motility, respiration, signal pen (used to identify scenes in a movie being watched by the subject), heart rate, eye blinking, and finger pulse volume. A magnetometer was used to pick up the peristaltic movements of an ingested magnet. (From Sternbach, 1962. Courtesy of Pergamon Press.)

the relationship? or, To what *extent* do individual differences exist? then more sophisticated forms of experimental designs and data analysis became necessary. At about the same time answers were being provided to similar questions raised by those working with individual differences in intelligence and aptitude testing. Methods for obtaining correlations, testing for significance of obtained differences, and performing factor analyses were developed, and quickly adopted by psychophysiologists for use on their physiological data.

With polygraph instrumentation and statistical data analysis, psychophysiological publications began to appear in the 1930's and 1940's. Only a few workers consistently made this kind of research their full-time endeavor—most notably C. W. Darrow, R. C. Davis, and M. A. Wenger. After World War II, A. F. Ax and J. I. Lacey made important contributions, and in 1955 Ax began to circulate the *Polygraph Newsletter* among laboratories as a vehicle for an informal exchange of ideas and solutions to technical problems. In a few years this led to the founding of the Society for Psychophysiological Research (1960) which held its first annual meeting in 1961, and the journal *Psychophysiology* appeared under Society sponsorship in 1964. These latest developments reflect not only the increased interest in the field, but also the burgeoning of research findings which necessitated a new journal, and which make it important now to have an introductory text which surveys the major developments.

While we have described the nature of psychophysiology in a general way, and the typical form of the research, there remains to be specified the kinds of questions usually asked by psychophysiologists. In stating these we will be pointing out at the same time some of the historical factors which, along with technological and methodological innovations, have contributed to the formation of the field of psychophysiology.

SOME IMPORTANT QUESTIONS

Perhaps the most basic question, implicit in the definition of the field, is: What is the relationship between the mind and the body? This is a philosophical problem which has engendered metaphysical speculation for centuries, and about which there is little agreement. In the field of psychophysiology, however, we have virtually the only *experimental* attempt to find answers. When physiological psychology abandoned human for animal subjects in order to obtain better methodological controls, the possibility of dealing with the "mind" was also abandoned.

However much the mind-body problem may exist in the back of the minds of psychophysiologists, it is not the sort of question which can be formulated directly as an experimental hypothesis. More specific kinds of questions have been raised, however. For example, What are the physiological differences among the emotions? This question draws on traditional interests of both psychology and physiology, both with respect to the nature of emotions and to the adequate stimuli for physiological changes. Similarly with another common question: To what extent do individuals differ in their physiological functioning? Here the traditional interest of the psychologist in individual differences unites with the interest of the physiologist in normal functioning. However, another discipline is also interested in this question: medical researchers have been concerned with the problem of where normal functioning leaves off and pathological functioning appears. That is, the whole question of whether abnormal conditions differ from normal in kind or in degree can find a focus in the study of individual differences in physiological activity. Another series of questions also have a primarily medical source: What are the psychosomatic diseases? How do they occur? What information about normal functioning can we obtain from the study of these abnormal conditions? This last question has led psychologists and physiologists to the study of the psychosomatic disorders, just as the question about individual differences has led physicians to study normal physiological responses.

The crossing over of disciplinary boundaries is one of the interesting (and rewarding) aspects of psychophysiological research. Psychologists, physiologists, psychiatrists, and internists are all involved with similar problems and projects and find it useful to exchange information and ways of thinking about these things. But there is another group whose participation in this area may surprise you: bioelectronic and computer engineers. These physical scientists originally became involved to help solve the problems of recording and analyzing hard-to-get-at physiological activity. But quickly they became intrigued with questions of how to duplicate human functions in certain kinds of hardware, for example, in computers and in space systems. Remembering, problem-solving, learning, and perceiving are some of the functions which have been built into machinery, and now the other disciplines have become interested in these models as potentially fruitful ways of thinking about human functions, and this has led to the development of a new field—cybernetics. This constant information exchange is proving useful to all involved.

II

An Orientation
to the Autonomic Nervous System

This chapter is not meant to cover in detail either the anatomy or physiology of the autonomic nervous system (ANS), but merely to sketch out some of the more important facts so that you will have a general orientation to the sources of the responses we will be considering in later chapters. The single best-detailed work on the ANS is probably the book by Kuntz (1953).

When the entire body is being classified into parts or functions for ease of studying, we talk of "systems," such as the skeletal, muscular, cardiovascular, endocrine, and nervous systems (see Fig. 2). The same is done when focusing on the nervous system itself. One division frequently made is that between the central nervous system (CNS) comprised of the brain, brain stem, and spinal cord, and the peripheral nervous system, made up of all nerve fibers leaving and entering the brain stem and spinal cord to and from the rest of the body. In this scheme the ANS is one of the peripheral systems (see Fig. 3).

Another way of looking at the nervous system is to make a division according to functions served. Here we can think of a somatic system and a vegetative or visceral system. The somatic is made up of the CNS and peripheral fibers that conduct messages to and from the sense organs and striated (striped) muscles of the body; we have "voluntary" control of most of these functions. The visceral nervous system is composed of the ANS and its centers in the brain stem and spinal cord, and it innervates the internal organs, glands, smooth muscles, and heart and lungs. These

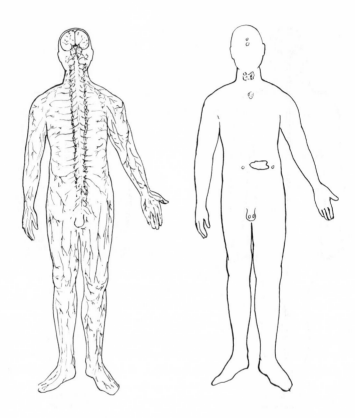

FIG. 2. This and the next five figures are meant to orient the reader, who may be totally unfamiliar with human anatomy, to the several ways of classifying the nervous system. This illustration shows the first major subdivision, which distinguishes the nervous system from the other major systems of the body, such as the endocrine system. The nervous system (here shown very schematically) consists of cells specialized for conduction, which are distributed throughout the body; the endocrine system, consisting of cells specialized for secretion, can have localized organs because the blood stream circulates their products.

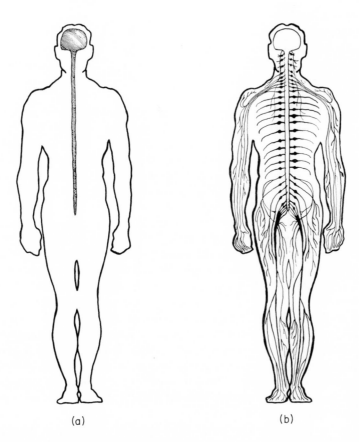

(a)   (b)

FIG. 3. One typical way of subdividing the nervous system itself is into the central and peripheral nervous systems. Using this anatomical classification, the central nervous system would consist of the brain, brain stem, and spinal cord, while the peripheral nervous system would be made up of all the other fibers. The autonomic nervous system is usually considered as part of the peripheral, although it has efferent and afferent fibers originating and terminating in the central. The central and peripheral nervous systems are here represented schematically in (a) and (b), respectively.

activities are largely involuntary, and we are usually unaware of them (see Fig. 4).

Thus the autonomic is generally a peripheral, viscerally-involved system, and it serves to regulate the internal milieu of the body. It functions primarily to maintain optimum internal conditions despite increases or decreases in the demands made on the body (homeostasis).

The ANS itself is further divided into a sympathetic nervous system (SNS) and a parasympathetic nervous system (PNS). The SNS fibers leave the spinal cord in the middle (chest and saddle) regions, and so it is sometimes referred to as the thoracolumbar system. The PNS fibers emerge above and below (*para*sympathetic), from the brain stem and tail areas, and thus the term craniosacral system is sometimes used (see Fig. 5).

As the ANS is classified into thoracolumbar (SNS) and craniosacral (PNS) systems to show their relative anatomic discreteness, it can also be analyzed into functional components, again as we did for the nervous system as a whole. In this view it has been called an adrenergic (SNS) and a cholinergic (PNS) system. This is because generally (not always) the sympathetic fibers stimulate the organs they serve with a substance similar to noradrenaline and adrenaline —the hormones secreted by the adrenal glands; and also because the effects of SNS activity are very similar to changes, such as increased cardiac output, produced by a natural release or artificial injection of adrenaline. The parasympathetic fibers, on the other hand, stimulate end organs with acetylcholine, hence the adjective cholinergic (see Fig. 6).

Now to illustrate the kinds of interaction that occur between systems, there are two additional labels that are sometimes applied (and then we will stop classifying). The SNS is occasionally called the sympathico-adrenal system (Cannon, 1928). This blurring of the artificial boundaries between the nervous and endocrine systems is to remind us of the similarities of the effects of stimulation of the SNS and the adrenal glands. This similarity is no accident, because the adrenal medulla (the core of the adrenal gland), which secretes adrenaline and noradrenaline, is actually a collection of SNS cells which, in the course of evolution, seems to have developed especially to provide the body with a supply of these hormones.

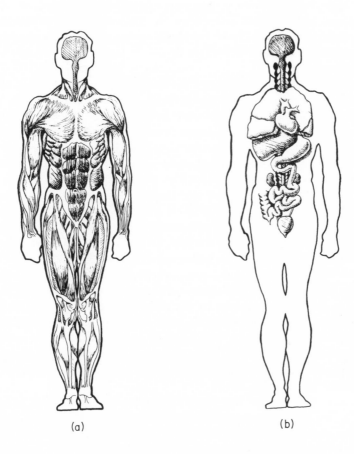

(a)   (b)

FIG. 4. When looked at according to function rather than structure, the nervous system is frequently classified into the somatic and visceral nervous systems The somatic consists of the motor fibers running to the striped muscles, and the traditional sensory fibers. The visceral (autonomic) is made up of the fibers going to and from the hollow organs (viscera) concerned with regulating the internal environment of the body. These are shown in (a) and (b), respectively.

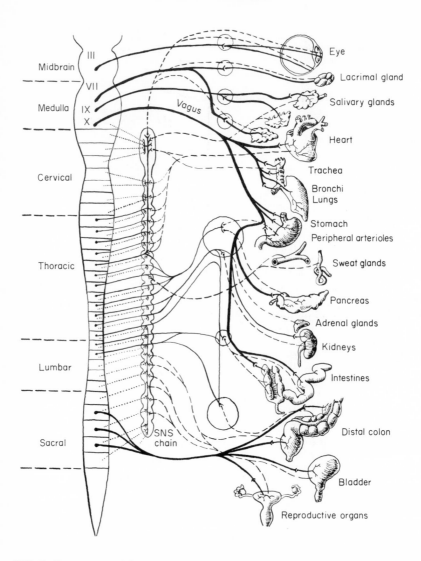

FIG. 5. On a structural basis, the autonomic nervous system itself is divided into the sympathetic and parasympathetic nervous systems. The sympathetic is made up of those fibers whose origins are in the chain of ganglia distributed in the thoracic and lumbar regions of the spinal cord (dashed lines). The parasympathetic consists of those originating in the cranial (brain stem) and sacral regions (solid lines).

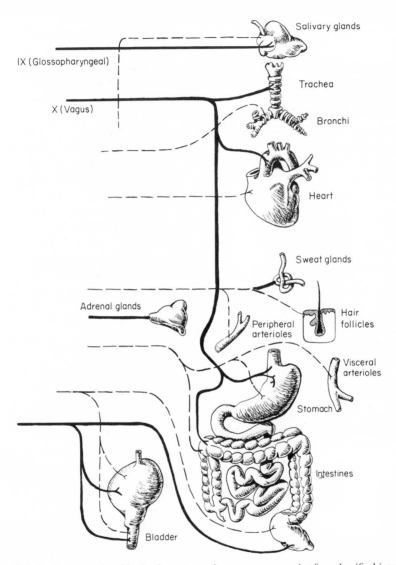

FIG. 6. On a functional basis, the autonomic nervous system is often classified into adrenergic and cholinergic systems. The adrenergic system (dashed lines) is that in which the transmitter substance from fiber to end-organ is similar to adrenaline. The cholinergic system (solid lines) is that in which the transmitter substance is acetylcholine.

In the same way that the SNS is called the sympathico-adrenal system, some workers have referred to the PNS as the vago-insulin system (Gellhorn, Cortell & Feldman, 1941). This is because the Xth cranial nerve, the vagus, which is perhaps the single most important branch of the PNS, seems to stimulate the secretion of insulin from the islet cells of the pancreas; and conversely, the secretion of insulin sometimes appears to potentiate the effects of vagal activity. This relationship is not so close or so clear as that between the SNS and the adrenals, but both terms — sympathico-adrenal and vago-insulin — should help us keep in mind the reciprocal relationships and interdependence between the autonomic and endocrine systems. As a general rule of thumb, the ANS produces faster, adjustive responses to stressful stimuli, but these are short-acting; then the endocrines' hormonal secretion comes into the picture, and their effects last longer (see Fig. 7).

The two subsystems of the ANS are for the most part antagonistic. That is, both SNS and PNS fibers run to most of the autonomically-modulated organs, and these oppose each other in effect. For example, SNS fibers are cardiac accelerators, PNS fibers are cardiac decelerators; on the other hand, PNS activity serves to increase gastric peristalsis (rhythmic waves of contraction), while SNS activity inhibits it. Table II summarizes SNS and PNS effects on some major structures.

Now there are some structural differences between the SNS and PNS which we must consider, in order to understand some specific functions and exceptions to general principles.

Autonomic fibers do not run directly from a central nucleus to an end organ; they synapse. This means simply that one nerve cell (neuron) forms a junction (synapse) with another, and it is the second which transmits the stimulation to the organ. Groups of nerve cells at which such junctures occur are called ganglia, and the fibers which enter and those which leave are called preganglionic and postganglionic fibers, respectively. There are several reasons for making a distinction. In the ANS the preganglionic fibers look thick and white as compared with the postganglionic fibers, which look thin and gray. This is because the preganglionics have myelin sheathing, a fatty substance around them. The myelin serves as an insulator around the fibers, preventing cross-talk or interference

among signals, as in electric cables. It also serves to support regeneration of the neuron in case of injury: regeneration is common
if preganglionic fibers are cut, but not if the unmyelinated postganglionic fibers are cut.

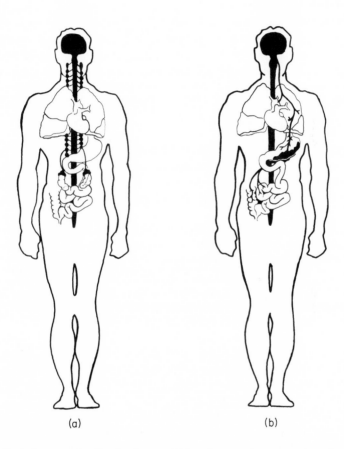

(a)   (b)

FIG. 7. A frequent classification is one which unites certain autonomic and endocrine components on the basis of similarity of function. Thus the sympathetic and
adrenal glands are considered together as the sympathico-adrenal system (a);
similarly the vagus nerve and the pancreas, as the vago-insulin system (b).

TABLE II[a]

SOME PROMINENT FACILITATIVE AND INHIBITORY AUTONOMIC FUNCTIONS

Structure	PNS effect	Function	SNS effect
Eyes { Iris	+	Constriction	−
Eyes { Lens	+	Accommodation	−
Lacrymal glands	+	Tears	−(?)
Nasal mucosa	+	Secretion, dilation	−
Salivary glands	+	Salivation	−(?)
Gastro-intestinal tract	+	Peristalis	−
Stomach glands	+	HCl, pepsin, and mucus	0
Pancreas (islet cells)	+	Insulin	0
Heart (rate)	−	Acceleration	+
Lungs (bronchia)	−	Dilation	+
Adrenal medulla	0	Adrenaline	+
Pheripheral blood vessels	?	Vasoconstriction	+
Sweat glands	0	Sweating	+
Pilomotor cells	0	Piloerection	+
Internal sphincters Bladder } Intestine }	−	Contraction	+
Bladder wall } Lower bowel }	+	Contraction	−
Genitalia	+	Erection	−

NOTE: In the table (+) indicates a facilitative effect and (−) an inhibitory effect. Note that the upper portion of the table emphasizes facilitative effects of the cranial parasympathetics, that the bottom portion separates the sacral parasympathetic effects, and that the central portion emphasizes sympathetic facilitative effects.

[a] From Wenger, Jones and Jones, 1956. Courtesy of the authors and publisher.

In the SNS, most of the thick white preganglionic fibers are short. The synapses form a chain—the sympathetic ganglia—just to the side of the spinal cord. From here long postganglionic fibers travel to the target organs. But there is much intercommunication. Every preganglionic fiber connects to several ganglion cells, the one at its level of exit from the spinal cord and one or two above and below. It has been estimated that just one preganglionic neuron makes contact with 20 to 30 postganglionic cells. Furthermore, there are actually more ganglia than spinal segments. These anatomical features mean that SNS activity is likely to be quite diffuse. That is, central stimulation of any SNS center or nerve will result in widespread changes through much of the body.

The PNS, on the other hand, functions much more discretely. The myelinated preganglionic fibers are long and run right up to near the end organ. Then a comparatively short postganglionic fiber contacts the organ. There is very little opportunity for inter-connections among fibers here. Furthermore, the cranio-parts of the PNS, deriving from the cranial nerves in the brain stem, are separated from the cells originating in the sacral portion by the length of the spinal cord. This further discourages any unity of action. You can think of the SNS as having a mass-action, shotgun approach, while the PNS—like a rifleman—selects its target organs quite specifically. But there are still other reasons for this.

When the preganglionic fibers stimulate the postganglionics at the synapse, they do so by secreting a transmitter substance called acetylcholine (ACh). This applies to both the SNS and PNS fibers. As a matter of fact, it seems to be the general rule throughout the entire nervous system that ACh serves as the interneuron chemical transmitter. But the important exception is SNS postganglionic stimulation of end organs. This is done by a substance called noradrenaline, similar to that secreted by the adrenal medulla. So we have both SNS and PNS preganglionic fibers secreting ACh at the ganglia; and cholinergic stimulation by PNS postganglionic fibers; but adrenergic stimulation by SNS postganglionic fibers.

Here we see another reason for the diffuse nature of SNS re-sponses as compared to the PNS. Any sympathetic activity which increases the secretion of adrenaline and noradrenaline from the adrenal medulla into the blood stream, will result in increased sympathetic activity in all the other end organs normally stimulated by the SNS transmitter substance. So there is a chemical as well as a structural interconnectedness in the SNS, compared with the PNS.

There are several interesting exceptions to SNS adrenergic innervation. One we have mentioned: the adrenal medulla itself, although an end organ, is stimulated by SNS preganglionic fibers and therefore by ACh. It acts like a postganglionic SNS collection of cells—which it is.

Another and more unusual exception are the sweat glands. They are innervated solely by SNS postganglionic fibers, yet the transmitter substance is ACh. This means that the sweat glands do not participate in the mass innervation of SNS activity caused by adrenal medullary secretions. Sweat glands seem to be the only SNS-innervated effectors which do not respond to infusions or injections of adrenaline and noradrenaline. In a way this is too bad for researchers, because sweat responses on the palms are very easy to measure electrically and occur readily to all kinds of "mental" or "emotional" stimuli, and so are a favorite dependent variable for psychologists. Yet you see how atypical this effector is, and how unreasonable it would be to generalize from sweat responses to activity in the rest of the SNS.

Incidentally, the sweating we are talking about here is that which occurs in the so-called "emotional sweating areas," which are the palms of the hands, soles of the feet, armpits and groin; sometimes the forehead and upper lip participate. The rest of the skin surface is part of the "thermoregulatory sweating areas" and responds to excessive environmental or body temperature. Its adaptive function is cooling; the adaptive function of emotional palmar sweating is unclear, although speculations about getting a good grip on objects have been made.

Now there are some more exceptions to the general principles with which we started this chapter. We said that for the most part each autonomically-innervated organ received both SNS and PNS fibers, whose functions were antagonistic, and this is so. But there are a few which receive only single, not dual innervation. We already mentioned that the sweat glands receive only SNS fibers (and cholinergic ones at that). In addition, the hair follicles receive only SNS (adrenergic) innervation. The pilomotor response —goose bumps—is primarily a heat-conserving one, but may also occur in a fear-like shudder.

But perhaps the most important of the singly-innervated organs are the blood vessels. Almost all of them receive SNS innervation exclusively; and this means that sympathetic fibers account for both vasoconstriction and vasodilatation. On this account it is sometimes assumed that there are two kinds of adrenergic substances in these instances; an excitatory (constricting) form, and an inhibitory (dilatating) form. These seem to correspond with what is known of the differences in effects between the adrenaline and noradrenaline produced by the adrenal medulla, but there is some doubt about the nature of this correspondence.

Now let us consider what some of the specific functions of the ANS consist of. You know that it serves primarily homeostatic functions. A person could live all right without an autonomic system, but to make up for the lack of internal compensators he would require a very constant and benign external environment, with moderate temperature, minimal threats, etc.

The SNS in general serves to provide "emergency" responses, and strong SNS activity has been called a "flight or fight" reaction. This is what happens. The heart beats faster, and increases the amount of blood pumped out with each beat. Superficial blood vessels and those going to the gastrointestinal tract constrict and blood pressure increases. The arteries serving the large muscles dilate and so their blood supply is increased. The pupils of the eyes dilate, increasing the amount of light impinging on the retina and thus improving visual acuity. The adrenal medulla secretes adrenaline which, besides reinforcing the other SNS effects as it circulates in the blood, also causes the liberation of blood sugar from the liver, thus making available a larger energy source for the muscles. Breathing becomes faster and deeper, the bronchioles of the lungs dilate, the secretion of mucus in the air passages decreases, and so more oxygen is available for the metabolism of the increased carbohydrates going to the muscles.

These effects, the breakdown of stored supplies and the rapid increase of metabolism, are called catabolism, and SNS functions are therefore sometimes called catabolic. The opposite effect, the restoration of supplies and slowing of metabolism, is called anabolism, and when PNS functions dominate, this anabolic process is said to occur. There is no specific emotion, like fear or rage, which clearly demonstrates this, but what happens during sleep is close enough.

During sleep the cardiovascular functions are reduced. The heart beats slower, and the volume of blood pumped with each stroke is less. The blood flow to the periphery of the body is minimal, but that supplying the gastrointestinal tract and the

other abdominal organs is greater. Blood sugar is stored in the
liver as glycogen. The production of mucus is increased in the
eyes and nose, mouth and throat, lungs and alimentary canal.
Digestive processes are likewise increased, both in the movement
of the gastrointestinal tract and the flow of digestive juices. Altogether the picture is one of rebuilding, or restoring, and is
quite the opposite of the massive expenditures of energy seen in
catabolic (SNS-dominated) states.

Now a word of caution before we leave this area of SNS-PNS
differences: we have emphasized, in our brief description, two
extremely different processes which highlight the activities of the
two branches of the ANS. But we must not assume that in a state
of panic, for example, the PNS ceases to function and the SNS
begins to work harder; or that in sleep the SNS takes time out
while the PNS begins its shift. Both branches of the ANS, as in the
entire nervous system, are always active. Electrodes placed in
nerve fibers anywhere, anytime, will record activity. It is the amount
of electrochemical fluctuations in the system which varies, and the
variation occurs in two ways. First, the frequency of discharge
along a fiber may increase up to a maximum capacity for the
particular fiber. And second, the total number of fibers involved
in discharging to an end organ may increase up to the amount
anatomically present.

Since both the SNS and PNS are always active in varying degrees,
it is not always possible to tell from an end organ's responses
which branch is immediately responsible for the effects you observe. For example, suppose you take someone's pulse for two
consecutive minutes, and notice that his heart beat increases from
72 the first minute to 84 the next. From this fact alone you cannot
really assume an increase in the activity of SNS cardiac accelerators.
That might be the case, but it might also be that there was a decrease in the activity of the PNS decelerators. Either condition
could account for the higher heart rate, and without other evidence
you cannot say which one it was.

For this reason, in the subsequent chapters we will make extensive use of the word *apparent*, to refer to effects which would
occur from an increase in the activity of one or the other branch
of the ANS. So an increase in heart rate will be called an *apparent*

effect of SNS activity; a cardiac deceleration will be an *apparent* PNS effect, and so on. Frequently, when recording a large number of physiological variables on a polygraph, it is possible to judge from the pattern of responses whether in fact one is observing an excitation or inhibition in one branch or the other. But we will defer a discussion of patterns of responses until later.

Since we mentioned the fact that similar effects may occur from different causes, it is interesting to note some practical applications that are made of this. When an ophthalmologist is examining your eyes and wants to take a good look at your retinas, he needs to have the pupils open wide. Dilatation of the pupils is a function of SNS fibers, as we mentioned before; the antagonistic PNS fibers, if left to their own devices, would markedly constrict the pupils. But the ophthalmologist does not attempt to excite your sympathetic system, instead he atropinizes the eye. A few drops of atropine blocks the action of the PNS fibers, and the unopposed SNS fibers open the pupil wide.

On the other hand, the M.D. faced with an acute attack of asthma in a patient takes a different course. The asthmatic patient has his lungs and windpipe congested with mucus—an apparent effect of PNS activity. Instead of giving large amounts of atropine, the doctor's treatment of choice is an injection of a form of adrenaline, which quickly enables the patient to breathe again.

Can you understand why, in these two examples, the particular medication is used? To figure it out, you must remember what was said about diffuse and discrete innervation, and transmitter substances.

III
Autonomic Balance

Let us begin by considering the state of a young man at rest. He is lying on his back on a cot in a quiet room. His eyes are closed, he is still, but not asleep. He is relaxed, breathing slowly and regularly. And although he may not be aware of it, he is demonstrating to us a kind of homeostasis.

Homeostasis, as we mentioned before, is the tendency of organisms to maintain internal equilibrium, or balance. For example, if our young man thinks an exciting thought and (among other things) his heart starts to pump faster, compensatory mechanisms will operate to return his heart rate to about its former level. As a matter of fact, this sort of reflex is going on all the time. Homeostasis is not a fixed state in the organism, but a continuous oscillation of increase and decrease in amount of functioning around some "ideal" level. If we were to observe the young man's heart rate on the polygraph, as in Fig. 1, we would see that, although his average pulse might be 70 beats per minute, in fact at any moment it might vary from 65 to 75 even though no unusual demands for changes in cardiac output are being made.

The heart is only one of the many organs whose activities are modulated by the ANS. We say "modulated" because some, like the smooth muscles of the gastro-intestinal tract and the cardiac muscles of the heart, have their own intrinsic excitability and will be active even in the absence of stimulation by these nerves. The ANS serves to impose a rate of functioning on these muscles in accordance with the needs of the body.

It should be obvious, however, that if we had a different person on the cot, the heart rate we were recording might not be the same at all. The fact of individual differences in functioning extends to ANS activity as it does to virtually every measurable aspect of human behavior. Around the turn of the century an attempt was made to classify people on the basis of the differences in reactivity of the two branches of the ANS. This classification resulted in the concepts of vagotonia and sympathicotonia.

It had been noticed that there were some individuals who showed unusually strong SNS responses to injections of adrenaline, but only slight PNS responses to pilocarpine and atropine. Normally pilocarpine enhances PNS activity, producing slowing of the heart, pupillary constriction, drooling of thin, watery saliva, etc. Atropine, as we mentioned in the previous chapter, inhibits such PNS effects. Consequently, a person who showed a ready response to SNS stimulation, but little or sluggish PNS reactivity, was called sympathicotonic. Sympathicotonia means simply a hyperexcitability — exaggerated tonus — of the SNS.

On the other hand there were some who showed relatively slight responses to sympathomimetic (adrenaline) and sympatholytic (ergotamine) drugs, but excessive reactions to parasympathomimetic (pilocarpine) and parasympatholytic (atropine) drugs. Such persons were called vagotonic — emphasizing the exaggerated readiness to respond of that important branch of the PNS, the vagus nerve.

You may have noticed that we kept the preceding discussion in the past tense. This was because, since Eppinger and Hess (1915) first formulated these ideas over 50 years ago, much has been learned to indicate that these terms are not very useful. It has been shown, for example, that there are some who demonstrate strong reactions to both SNS and PNS drugs; and some with diseases suggesting dominance of the SNS (Raynaud's disease) or PNS (bronchial asthma) may show very strong "tonus" of the opposite branch. We will discuss such disorders further in the chapter on psychosomatic diseases.

A modification and extension of the Eppinger and Hess notions have been made by Wenger (1941), and his work has been helpful in understanding the nature of individual differences in autonomic balance. He began by proposing these hypotheses: because of the differences between the adrenergic and cholinergic branches of the ANS, one branch might be predominant in function over the other; this predominance, or autonomic imbalance, may be chronic (continuous) or phasic (a response to some stimulus), and either branch might be the dominant one; finally, the extent of such autonomic imbalance, when measured in an unselected population, should be distributed continuously around some central tendency which could then be defined as autonomic balance.

Two interesting modifications are represented in this restatement of the original Eppinger and Hess hypothesis. One is that the concept of ANS branches is put in terms of adrenergic and cholinergic, rather than SNS and PNS. Wenger presumed, from the work on drugs that had been done, that the adrenergic-cholinergic concept of the ANS would be a more accurate description of ANS functions than the traditional anatomical (SNS-PNS) classification. The other modification was the idea of a continuous distribution of individuals around an average, so that a few might be found at the extremes (vagotonic and sympathico-tonic, in the old terminology), but that most would bulk towards the middle.

The hypotheses were tested by taking measurements of twenty physiological variables of 62 children 6 to 11 years of age, under resting conditions. Twelve of these variables were those presumably mediated at least in part by the ANS. Correlations among the variables were obtained, and a factor analysis performed. This factor analysis permitted a grouping of those variables which seemed to have certain variance in common; and it also permitted the assigning of weights to the variables in proportion to their contribution to the factor (Wenger, 1941, 1942; Wenger & Ellington, 1943).

Seven of the variables Wenger measured—and he did this study three times over a 3-year period, finding very good reliability of the measures—grouped themselves into a clear autonomic factor. These measures, in the order of their beta weights (loadings on the factor) are: salivary output; palmar conductance; heart period; pulse pressure; dermographic (skin flare) persistence; volar forearm conductance; and respiration rate. We will discuss some of these variables and what they mean shortly.

Meanwhile it is interesting to note that, as Wenger observed, these variables which contribute to the autonomic factor can more logically be said to represent an SNS-PNS continuum than a division of the ANS into adrenergic-cholinergic systems, thus supporting the original Eppinger and Hess conception better than Wenger's restatement of it. Secondly, when a score is computed for each individual, a distribution of such scores is found to be close to normal, thus supporting the second part of the hypothesis.

This score is called an estimate of autonomic balance ($\bar{A}$; say "aybar"). An individual's $\bar{A}$ score is a composite of the values obtained from him on each of the seven autonomic variables we listed. We will not go into the details of how the score is computed (obtainable from the references), but we will mention here that lower scores are designed to reflect apparent SNS dominance, and higher scores reflect apparent PNS dominance. You should note that the single $\bar{A}$ score obtained for a particular individual is meaningful only in relationship to the rest of the individuals on whom the study is based; his score shows the amount and direction of his difference from the group's average.

Now Fig. 8, which describes the distribution of $\bar{A}$ scores for the children studied, can be understood in terms of what we just said. Individual $\bar{A}$ scores run from the forties to the nineties, with a mean of about 70 and a standard deviation of about 8. Roughly two-thirds of the sample have scores between 62 and 78. Consequently, we have here a good statistical definition of autonomic balance: it is simply the mean of the obtained $\bar{A}$ scores for the individuals sampled. To the extent that the sample is an unselected (randomly chosen) one, it is representative of the larger population. In this instance it is a representative sample of children from 6 to 11. With a mean $\bar{A}$ for the group of 70, and a standard deviation of 8, a child whose $\bar{A}$ score is 55 may be said to show marked apparent SNS dominance; one whose score is 85 may be said to exhibit strong apparent PNS dominance.

This conclusion has been confirmed by a much larger study on adults. Wenger had the opportunity to apply an even larger battery of physiological tests to several hundred young male aviation cadets (Wenger, 1948). After weeding out some individuals who were physically ill he was left with a sample of 468. Again the procedure

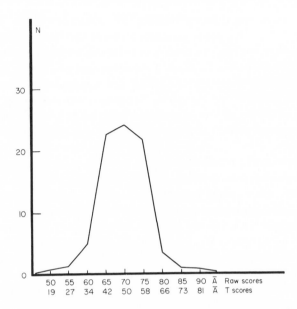

FIG. 8. The frequency distribution of the mean $\bar{A}$ scores (estimates of autonomic balance) for 87 children ages 6 to 12. (From Wenger, Jones & Jones. 1956. Courtesy of the authors and publisher.)

of performing intercorrelations and a factor analysis was followed, again a clear autonomic factor was obtained, and again a normal distribution of $\bar{A}$ scores resulted, with a mean of about 69 and a standard deviation of about 8. Clearly this is a reproducible method for estimating relative autonomic balance.

The physiological variables which contributed to the autonomic factor in the adult male sample are a little different from that in the children's sample. These are as follows: heart period, sublingual temperature, diastolic blood pressure, log conductance change (a measure of sweat response), salivary output, volar forearm conductance, and palmar conductance.

Still another more recent study has been done on 245 young adult females (college students). Again an autonomic factor was derived which in many ways is similar to the other two (Wenger, personal communication).

Now, what are these physiological variables? What do they represent? Are they really representative of the functioning of the ANS? We are asking whether $\bar{A}$ is valid, as well as reliable, as an estimate of autonomic balance. To do this we need first to examine the variables themselves, and then the methods used to assess them. We will describe here only the four measures which appear in all three of the child, adult male, and adult female analyses — salivary output, palmar conductance, volar conductance, and heart period.

Salivary output. There are three salivary glands — the parotid, sublingual, and submaxillary glands. Each receives dual innervation, that is, fibers from both the SNS and the PNS. For each gland the effect of PNS stimulation is to increase the production of thin, watery saliva. SNS effects are the opposite: salivary flow is decreased, the mouth feels dry, and such saliva as is present is thick and mucous. Since this is true of each of the three glands, it follows that the total amount of saliva present in the mouth represents the balance of SNS-PNS activity. More saliva indicates apparent PNS dominance of these glands; less saliva indicates apparent SNS dominance. (Remember the reason for "apparent"? It is because, for these dually innervated structures, one cannot tell from the end product whether it is the result of the dominance of one branch or the inhibition of the other.)

The way salivary output was measured in these studies is quite simple. A small tube is placed just in front of the teeth, between the lips. A pump at the other end creates suction, and the saliva is allowed to be collected in a test tube calibrated in milliliters (cubic centimeters). The individual is urged to force as much saliva as he can to the front of his mouth, to work at producing all the saliva he can, and the collection lasts for three minutes as timed by stopwatch. This turns out to be a very reliable procedure, in that when it is repeated on individuals on different days, the results are usually quite similar (the correlation between days is very high), and it is one of the most stable of the physiological measures used.

This 3-minute forced ejection of saliva is, as we mentioned, one of four variables included in all three of the child, adult male, and adult female estimates of autonomic balance (the others being palmar and volar sweating, and heart period. In the adult male sample, the average amount of saliva produced was 4.2 cc, with a standard deviation of 1.7 cc. Thus if a young adult male could produce only 2.5 cc he would be said to show apparent SNS dominance in this variable — *as compared to the others;* and apparent PNS dominance if he could produce 6.0 cc. Of course, if the subject were a child or young adult female, the performance would be compared with that of the appropriate normative group.

Palmar conductance. This measure of sweating of the palms is an interesting one. You will recall that in the last chapter we described the innervation of the sweat glands as solely an SNS function, and that these SNS postganglionic fibers are unique in that their transmitter substance is ACh, rather than noradrenaline. We also mentioned that sweating of the palms seems to occur in emotional situations, rather than as a heat regulatory response. At any rate, it is clear that the amount of sweating of the palms is a reflection of the degree of activity of palmar SNS fibers.

Now it happens that a salty solution like sweat conducts electricity very well, and this fact makes possible a quantitative measure of sweating. If you pass a slight electric current through skin, a certain amount of resistance will be met. But the more salty solution present, the lower the resistance encountered.

The relationship among these electrical factors is expressed in Ohm's law, which can be stated in three ways:

$$\text{Voltage} = \text{Current} \times \text{Resistance}$$

or

$$\text{Resistance} = \frac{\text{Voltage}}{\text{Current}}$$

or

$$\text{Current} = \frac{\text{Voltage}}{\text{Resistance}}$$

You will remember that if two of these components are known, it is simple to calculate the third, so that if the voltage and current are known, the resistance of the skin is easily determined.

It is this principle that is used to measure palmar sweating. Placing an electrode on each palm, Wenger passed an electrical current through the subjects. He was using a circuit that delivered exactly 40 microamperes of current (this is such a slight amount that not only is it not felt by the subjects, but it is not possible to detect any effects on the body). At the same time he was able to read on a voltmeter exactly how many volts were being delivered. This would fluctuate, according to the subjects' skin resistance, but whatever the voltage at any given moment, that voltage and the 40 microamperes of current were the data which enabled the skin resistance at that moment to be calculated.

The technique Wenger used was to have the subjects stand, relaxed and still, hands at their sides, for 2 minutes, and a measure of the palmar skin resistance at the end of the first and second minutes was obtained.

From what we have said before you will remember that the less sweating, the higher the resistance to the electrical current; the more sweating, the lower the resistance. In order to have a unit of measure which parallels the degree of sweating activity, rather than an inverse measure, some investigators express their results in conductance units. It is the reciprocal of resistance, that is, conductance is 1/resistance. Resistance is measured in units called ohms; conductance in units called mhos (ohms backwards). So, mhos = 1/ohms. By expressing it this way, it is possible to say that the greater the amount of sweating, the higher the conductance.

So each of the two measures of resistance, obtained at the end of the first and second minutes, are converted into conductance units (mhos) and the two are averaged. This average conductance is compared with all the others in the group and converted to a standard score (so this measure can then be compared with salivary output, heart rate, etc.).

Since palmar sweating is a SNS function, a greater amount of sweating indicates a greater amount of SNS activity; this should be represented by a lower score, so it will be placed further to the left on the SNS-PNS continuum. But the more sweating, the higher the conductance measure. We can get around this by "reflecting" the score, that is, subtracting it from 100. This result is then multiplied by the weight for palmar conductance, and added to the other measures to produce an $\bar{A}$ for the individual.

At this point you may well ask whether all these statistical jugglings of an electrical measure can really represent the amount of sweat on the palms. The answer is simply that it can, and does. It correlates very well with other, clumsier techniques, such as counting the number of droplets of sweat or filled pores as shown in microphotographic strips; or the density of iodide stains on the palms; or the amount of moisture in air blown across the palmar surface; or the baseline electrical potential of the sweat glands. Not only does this measure give results similar to the others, but (except for sweat gland potentials) it is much simpler to obtain and yields nicely manipulable numerical results. As for the statistical manipulations themselves, although they seem quite involved, they are mathematically permissible, yield reliable results, and on the face of it the scores do seem to represent the physiological functioning and the individual differences therein. What more could one ask?

Volar conductance. The volar surface of the forearm is the inner part, the one that rests on the desk when you write. Like the palms and the other skin surfaces of the body it contains sweat glands innervated by SNS fibers transmitting ACh. Unlike the palms, however, the sweat glands in the volar forearm do not usually react with a sweating response to "emotional" stimulation. I say "usually" because there seems to be an interesting differentiation that takes place with physiological maturation.

Infants show emotional sweating responses over large areas of the body, but as they grow older the areas become progressively more restricted to the palms, soles of the feet, groin, armpits, and face as we described before. Most preadolescent children will show sweat responses on the palms and lower forearms, but not higher on the forearms. And in adolescents, reactive sweating of the upper limbs seems to occur only on the palms. But there are individual differences, and physiological age does not always correspond to chronological age, so that there are exceptions in young adults whose forearms react as do their palms. (An interesting continuation of the normal differentiation process is that in middle-aged people palmar sweating in response to stimulation occurs mostly in the fingers, and in old age only on the fingertips.)

At any rate this variable has shown itself to be important in the analysis of resting functions, if only because in each of the studies it has been one of those which comprises the autonomic factor. It is obtained by placing an electrode about 2 inches below the inside of each elbow and, as with the palmar measure, impressing a 40 microampere current. Wenger's procedure was to obtain four samples of the skin resistance, at 3-minute intervals, while the subject was reclining on a cot. The highest of the four was converted to a conductance measure and this constituted a raw score. Sometimes a correction factor would be added to take account of the room temperature (remember, this is a variable whose activity is usually a heat-regulatory one).

Heart Period. In both the large samples studied—adult males and adult females—the single variable which contributed most to the autonomic factor was the heart rate. We mentioned previously that although cardiac muscle has its own intrinsic excitability, its rate of contraction is the result of the influences from both accelerator (SNS) and decelerator (vagal, PNS) fibers. The influence of these fibers is, in turn, the consequence of the interaction of a number of reflexes, including those provided by feedback from the carotid sinuses, which are sensitive to blood pressure changes. And one's blood pressure is a function of the heart's stroke volume (how much blood it pumps out at each contraction) and the resistance it meets in the peripheral blood vessels (their degree of constriction or dilation). In fact, matters are even more complicated than this, because factors like oxygen tension and circulating adrenaline are also involved, and these are both consequences and causes of autonomic reflexes.

All in all one would expect that heart rate would be a sensitive indicator of the ongoing activities in both branches of the ANS and, since it is partially influenced by substances coursing in the blood stream to and from all parts of the body, heart rate will reflect this entire system's functioning. That this may be so is suggested by the fact that heart period received the greatest loading (highest weight) of the variables comprising the autonomic factor.

Now heart rate of course is simple enough to measure. You probably have had doctors and nurses hold your wrist and look at their watch and count the number of pulses they feel in 30 seconds; by doubling this they have your heart rate. Try it yourself.

Most psychophysiologists prefer to record the heart rate on a polygraph, however, because there is less chance for error. Two electrodes are placed on opposite sides of the heart (the two arms, an arm and leg, earlobe and arm) and these detect the electrical potentials given off by the contracting heart muscles. With the paper chart moving at a known and constant rate, it is easy to see what distance on the chart constitutes a one-minute period, and to count the number of blips (electrical analogs of pulses) in that period.

In his studies, Wenger sampled the heart rate four times at 3-minute intervals with the subject reclining. These rates were averaged, and the average number of beats per minute was then divided into 10,000. This gives heart period, or the number of milliminutes per ten beats. The reason for this transformation, as we mentioned earlier, was to obtain a distribution of scores more appropriate to work with than could be obtained from heart rate scores alone. Actually there is some argument as to whether heart rate (the number of beats per unit of time) or heart period (the number of seconds per unit of pulses) is the more appropriate measure, but there is no need to discuss the problem at this point. It is enough now to add that the heart period score obtained in Wenger's procedure was converted to a standard score to be weighted and added to the other variables, and thus to contribute to an estimate of an individual's autonomic balance, his $\bar{A}$.

We have spent a good deal of time in describing one investigator's approach to autonomic balance. This is because, to our knowledge, Wenger is the only one who has systematically gone after the problem of individual differences in the resting state. But two important points need to be made in this connection, one having to do with the conditions under which the studies were conducted, and the other concerned with the concept itself.

The subjects who participated in the studies we have described were resting. This is important to remember. Measurements were made during the day following "a good night's sleep," so fatigue would not be a complication. It was at least 24 hours since taking any drugs or alcohol, two hours since the last meal or beverage, and 1/2 hour since smoking and since drinking water. And measurements were taken while the subject was standing, sitting or reclining quietly. Consequently these measures are "basal" in the sense that minimum demands are made on the ANS. They are quite different from the conditions under which the original Eppinger and Hess studies were conducted, because in their studies a determination of apparent SNS or PNS dominance was made in observing responses to drugs—they were in essence re-activity studies. We will be considering how the ANS responds to stimulation in subsequent chapters, but for now we want to em-phasize that most of our information concerning individual differences in autonomic balance comes from studies made under the resting conditions we have described.

The other point we need to make is that this concept of auto-nomic balance is a statistical one. It describes the apparent relative dominance of SNS or PNS activity only in comparison with a reference or standardization group. Now this must not be con-strued as a criticism, but simply a point to be remembered. It is similar to the notions physicians have about body temperature, which are both statistical and individual. If *average* body tempera-ture is 98.6°F, then an individual who produces a reading of 96° or 101° may be cause for concern. Yet 98.6°F is only an average, and there are individuals who consistently show a higher or lower temperature when they are well, and so any determination of the significance of a given reading must take into account what is typical for the person. Of course Wenger was not attempting to provide a way of determining the healthiness of any single person, but rather to investigate the ways in which individuals differ among each other in ANS functioning under resting conditions. And although it may not be possible to tell by these tests whether a person demonstrates homeostasis, it is possible now to compare him with a group to which he is similar. So in a manner of speaking, Wenger's $\bar{A}$ is like the temperature scale: it gives the group average and distribution (like the 98.6°F), and any one person's $\bar{A}$ can be compared to the group.

At this point you may wonder whether there is any significance to scores of relative autonomic balance other than the statistical one. That is, are such scores related to any other characteristic of individuals? From other work it appears that various diagnostic groups can be differentiated from the control reference group by these $\bar{A}$ scores. It has been shown that patients with "operational (battle) fatigue" (Wenger, 1948), with psychosis (Gunderson, 1953), with tuberculosis, even when the disease is arrested (Mark-well, 1961, 1962), and with psychosomatic disorders (Wenger *et al.,* 1962), all have scores indicating apparent strong sympathetic dominance. It is not clear, of course, precisely what this means. It may be that individuals with low $\bar{A}$ scores (apparent SNS dominance) are more susceptible to the kinds of stress represented by these disease categories. On the other hand it is equally likely that the scores represent the individual's physiological responses to the disease or symptoms. The fact that there is a relationship between certain diseases and apparent sympathetic dominance does not, in itself, provide us with enough information to determine which influenced the other, or whether both disease and low $\bar{A}$ scores are determined by still a third factor. Only a follow-up study of normal subjects, some of whom later became ill, could determine whether the apparent SNS dominance was antecedent, and therefore possibly causal.

It is interesting, too, that no disease has been reported to be associated with either apparent PNS dominance, or with $\bar{A}$ scores within the normal range. It may be that not enough abnormal groups have been studied, but from the variety of disorders already sampled it seems that any abnormality is likely to be asssociated with strong apparent sympathetic dominance in the resting state.

With respect to other personality factors, it has been argued by some that the estimate of autonomic balance reflects degree of neuroticism. Wenger (1947) found that for children on the extremes of the $\bar{A}$ distribution, there were significant relationships with certain personality characteristics. Those with strong apparent PNS dominance ("vagotonics") showed more emotional inhibition, less emotional excitability, a lower frequency of activity with less fatigue, and more patience and neatness than those with marked apparent SNS dominance ("sympathicotonics"). In reviewing these data, Eysenck (1953) argues for the view that neuroticism, as defined by factorially derived personality tests, is correlated with the degree of deviation from autonomic balance in either direction. That is, the extent to which an individual's $\bar{A}$ score differs from the group mean either in an apparent SNS or PNS direction reflects the extent of his neuroticism. On the other hand, Eysenck believes that extraversion and introversion are related to the direction of the deviation from autonomic balance. Those with apparent SNS dominance, presumably, would be more extraverted, while those with apparent PNS dominance would be more introverted.

There have been other approaches to the problem of autonomic balance, and we need to consider these briefly. For the most part they differ in two essential features from the approach we have described: they are typically studies of ANS reactivity, employing neurological or pharmacological stimulation as a technique; and the attempt is made to determine the factors influencing or regulating homeostasis within a single organism.

Most of this kind of work has involved animals, because of the nature of the neurological or drug stimulation technique employed. As a result of this animal research we have acquired much information about how our own autonomic systems remain in balance, and the ways in which it can become unbalanced.

It has become apparent that the coordinating center for autonomic activity is the hypothalamus. Although there are autonomic centers which are lower in the nervous system (spinal cord and medulla) and some which are higher (parts of the brain's temporal lobes and inner surfaces of the hemispheres), the hypothalamus seems to be the one place where autonomic balance within the individual is maintained (Gellhorn & Loofbourrow, 1963). Hypothalamic cells receive impulses from the peripheral autonomic fibers and also from other areas of the brain, and in turn they send out "downward" and "upward" discharges. There is good evidence too that the hypothalamus is sensitive to circulating adrenaline and to the acid-base balance in the blood.

One example of how individual autonomic balance may be maintained is the reflex regulation of blood pressure. If blood pressure is decreased (usually a PNS type response) by artificial means, such as by administering a drug like ACh, certain nerve cells in the blood vessel walls change their pattern of firing. These pressure-sensitive cells are called baroreceptors, and they are located chiefly in the aorta and in the carotid sinuses. When the blood pressure drops, a decrease in impulses occurs in fibers going to the medulla and hypothalamus. This decrease sensitizes the hypothalamic cells which influence sympathetic activity, causing an increase in heart rate and constriction of the peripheral blood vessels. Such an effect, of course, raises the blood pressure back to normal. On the other hand, an increase in blood pressure produces an increase in afferent impulses from the baroreceptors and a sensitization of medullary and hypothalamic parasympathetic cells, resulting in cardiac deceleration and a lowered blood pressure.

You can see that this example of autonomic balance is the same as our earlier example of homeostasis. In the sense that we are discussing the mechanisms of optimum functioning within an individual, autonomic balance is a particular instance of homeostatic functioning. As we saw before, homeostasis of autonomically innervated functions is facilitated by the dual innervation of most of the organs and glands involved. What we wish to emphasize here is that the reciprocal action of the SNS and PNS is not a matter of many independent local struggles for supremacy at various loci throughout the body, but rather it is a coordinated and integrated process (in healthy persons) governed by central centers—the hypothalamus particularly. In addition we may note in passing that there is good evidence for localization within the hypothalamus itself. In general it appears that the anterior and some lateral hypothalamic cells regulate sympathetic activity, while the posterior portions of the hypothalamus are concerned with parasympathetic functions.

While there is a great deal more to be said concerning the central mechanisms maintaining autonomic balance, we are not going to take them up here, as it would take us too much into the details of neurophysiology. However, we will return to consider some central processes in the chapter on psychosomatic diseases. And in the next chapter we will see how homeostatic mechanisms form an important bridge in considering the relationship between resting conditions and responses to stimulation.

IV
Law of Initial Values

Early last chapter we left a young man resting on a cot, and somehow never returned to him. It is time to do so, briefly, and consider what happens when stimulation occurs.

If while he is resting we were to fire off a blank pistol in the room, a number of responses would occur. The young man would blink and his head would move forward and his shoulders would hunch up. His arms and legs would flex, and he would gasp. On the polygraph we would detect a big sweating response from his palms, an increase in his heart rate and blood pressure, a decrease in the amount of blood flowing in his fingers, and there would be a dilatation of his pupils. Altogether these responses are called the startle reflex (Sternbach, 1960a, b). They begin in a fraction of a second following the shot, and are over within a few seconds (there are differences in speed of response and rate of recovery among these variables; striped muscle responses like the eye blink are much faster, while other responses like sweat gland secretion are slower).

Now suppose the subject had not been resting, but responding to some other external source of stimulation. Suppose, for example, that he had had his foot placed in a bucket of ice water. The autonomic responses to this stimulus are similar to that of the startle reflex; palmar sweat responses and peripheral vasoconstriction occur, heart rate and blood pressure go up, etc. (In fact, placing a limb in ice water is used as a "cold pressor" test for hypertension, because it can be used to detect exaggerated blood pressure rises in persons suspected of having high blood pressure.) It should be apparent that both the sudden, unexpected, and intense stimulus used in startle, and the cold stimulus used in cold pressor tests, evoke strong ANS activity.

The questions now are: What happens if the startle responses are superimposed on the cold pressor responses? Will blood pressure and heart rate, for example, increase still further? If so, will the increase be additive, i.e., the sum of the responses occurring separately? The answers may be surprising: not only is it likely that any further increase in heart rate and blood pressure will be slight, but it might even happen that the response will be a decrease!

What we are describing here is an aspect of homeostatic functioning which poses a problem for the measurement of responses. This problem was first formulated by Wilder (1957), and was called by him the law of initial values (LIV). In simplest terms, it means that an ANS response to stimulation is a function of the prestimulus level. Wilder thought that this applied to both the magnitude and the direction of the response. The higher the prestimulus level of functioning, the smaller the response to a function-increasing stimulus. And at more extreme prestimulus levels there is more tendency for no response to stimulation, and even for "paradoxical" responses—those which reverse the typical directions of responses.

Now before we consider anything else about this concept—such as whether and to what extent it is true, and if so, what to do about it—let us examine the interesting physiological implications it raises.

If the LIV is correct, we may assume that there are built-in limits to each individual's rate or amount of functioning. In heart rate, for example, if our young-man-on-a-cot has a resting average rate of 72 beats per minute, the limits to this rate may be (let us say) 47 at the lowest and 103 at the highest. If he is already at or near his maximum rate, from the cold pressor test or an injection of adrenaline, the increase normally caused by a different stimulus, such as a pistol shot, cannot occur—he has reached his limit. This "limit" is the level of functioning at which homeostatic mechanisms take over and operate to return the functioning to a more nearly normal level. It is as if the feedback from the cardiac muscles signaled the autonomic centers to change the pattern of impulses in ANS fibers going to the heart, resulting in its slowing. The feed-back would be an increase in the rate of firing of afferent fibers, and/or an increase in the number of such fibers firing. When the total number and rate of impulses reaches a given threshold in the centers of the medulla and hypothalamus concerned with cardio-vascular activity, then the "switching" effect occurs.

However, it is important to remember the "as if" quality of this explanation, because it is hypothetical. When there is no additional response to additional stimulation, or when a paradoxical de-crease in functioning occurs when we would have expected a further increase, then such a process as we have described is plau-sible, but not yet absolutely certain. That is why, when we observe such a phenomenon, we say it seems *as if* the individual has such limits, and it is as if the limits were determined in this way. Many psychophysiologists now use a term borrowed from cybernetics to describe such a homeostatic process: it is "negative feedback." This term simply means that any response away from an ideal equi-librium activates a mechanism which tends to return it to that equilibrium.

(The opposite concept of "positive feedback" means that a response will tend to perpetuate and exaggerate itself, without any inhibiting factors being called into play. Psychophysiologists have used this sort of model to describe the processes underlying psychosomatic symptoms in which it appears that there are in-adequate controls on the responses. We will return to this in Chapter X on Psychosomatic Diseases.)

A second interesting implication of Wilder's LIV is that we must take the prestimulus level of functioning into account in measuring the response to stimulation. According to Wilder, an increase of heart rate by 10 beats per minute is not just an increase of 10, because a lot more is involved. Look at it this way: if the pulse of our young-man-on-a-cot goes up from 72 to 82, that is not at all the same as if it went up from 82 to 92. The difference score in each case may be 10, but we have just seen that the closer the heart rate approaches its upper limit, the more the negative feedback is called into play to oppose the increase. To employ a crude analogy, it is like trying to depress a spring-operated plunger: you en-counter increasing resistance, and so more energy is required for

the last inch than the first. In this sense, the difference score from
82 to 92 is "worth" more than the difference from 72 to 82 because
more homeostatic activity must be overcome to achieve the 10-beat
increase at the higher levels.

You can see, too, that taking the prestimulus level into account
by a percentage score would not be satisfactory. The percentage
increase from 72 to 82 is about 14%; that from 82 to 92 is about
12%. This is because the ratios have a constant numerator of 10
compared to an increasing base rate, and so if you compute percentage increases it actually appears that there is *less* of an increase
from 82 to 92 than from 72 to 82. But we know, as we said before,
that the 10-beat increase from the higher base level was harder to
come by, and this physiological process should be more fairly
represented, statistically.

We are going to come back to this problem later in this chapter,
and describe some of the solutions which have been proposed, but
you may be reassured that we are not going to treat them in any
detail. The statistical manipulations involved may be more advanced than you have been exposed to, and we also do not want to
clutter a book on physiological principles with statistical formulas.
On the other hand, the very principles with which we are concerned
actually have statistical definitions. We saw this in the discussion of
Wenger's autonomic balance in the last chapter, it will be true of
the treatment of LIV in this one, and of the other principles in
succeeding chapters. (The recent advances in psychophysiology are
due as much to novel statistical applications as to electronic ones.)
Consequently we will have to deal with some of the concepts of
statistics, though not the techniques.

Now let us return to the beginning and examine the LIV more
closely. To what extent and under what conditions is it true that an
autonomic response is a function of the prestimulus level? Many,
many reports have appeared on this problem, and the fact of a
relationship in many instances between prestimulus level and response magnitude is quite striking. At first, only the palmar sweating variable was examined closely: it was clear that the greater the
the initial skin resistance (less sweating) the larger the drop in
resistance (sweat response) when stimulation occurred. A positive
correlation exists between the response magnitude and the pre-

stimulus level. Accordingly it would not be reasonable to consider a decrease in resistance from 250 KΩ (250,000 ohms) to 200 KΩ to be the equivalent of a drop from 150 KΩ to 100 KΩ, in the same individual or in another. This is like our discussion above on heart rate. To obtain "average" responses or to compare the magnitude of responses within or between persons, some adjustment must be made to eliminate or equate the influence of the prestimulus level on the response magnitude. A great many proposals were made: to take the logarithm of the change in conductance units; to take the logarithm of the change in resistance; to use the square root of conductance; etc. You encountered some of these in the last chapter. There are two goals in these proposed transformations: one is to have a distribution of obtained difference scores (like 10 beats per minute, or 50 KΩ), which approximates a normal distribution and so will permit the use of certain statistical tests which are based on the normal frequency curve; the other is to free the difference scores from their correlations with the prestimulus levels, so that comparisons among the difference scores can be independent of their base levels. Most of the proposed transformations achieve these results to some extent, and some work better than others, but none which have been developed for use on skin resistance are equally useful for the other physiological variables.

Another point to be made, and one which you may well have sensed and felt uncomfortable about, is that a lot of statistical juggling can cause us to lose sight of what is going on in the body, or in some way to misrepresent the physiological events. An example is the attempt to free responses from their baselines: is this fair to do? Not to take the baseline (prestimulus) levels into account may distort the accuracy of the numerical representation of the homeostatic process (Lacey, 1956).

Aside from such theoretical reasons for representing prestimulus levels in response measures, there are experimental data which also are compelling and which lend empirical support to the LIV. Let us summarize some of these studies briefly, and then go on to consider some of the attempts to deal with the problem.

Lacey (1956) reported data from several different studies, using children and adults of both sexes as subjects, and employing four different kinds of stimulation. Significant positive correlations were obtained between prestimulus and response levels in systolic blood pressure, diastolic blood pressure, palmar sweating, heart rate, and heart rate variability (measured continuously by a cardiotachometer which records beat-to-beat differences in rate.) The positive correlations, of course, mean that the response levels are a function, at least in part, of the prestimulus levels.

Hord, Johnson, and Lubin (1964) also found positive relationships between prestimulus and response levels for heart rate, respiration rate, and finger temperature (an indirect measure of peripheral vascular constriction or dilatation). However the LIV did not appear to hold for skin conductance in their data, although other investigators (e.g., Sternbach, 1960d) have found such relationships to hold for skin conductance as well.

These and other studies suggest that for nearly all ANS variables, the magnitude of a response to stimulation depends (at least in part) on the preceding level of activity. This is the essence of the law of initial values. (Of course other factors influence the response magnitude, too — the intensity of the stimulus, for one.) But there are some complications that we must consider.

One complication is that individuals differ greatly in the extent to which the LIV applies, and differ in several ways. Our young-man-on-a-cot may be the sort of person who, when plunging his foot into ice water, shows a heart rate increase from 72 to 103 every time. Or he may go from 72 to 103 one time, from 72 to 94 another time, or from 72 to 120 on a third occasion. Another possibility is that, no matter what his resting heart rate level may be, whether 60, 72, or 85 beats per minute, he may always go up to 103. In fact, some studies (Lacey and Lacey, 1962) have shown that there seems to be such a "stress level constant" value which individuals reach with a sufficiently strong stressor, no matter what the initial resting level was.

There is still another complicating factor which is due to intra-individual variability. Young-man-on-a-cot may show the constant stress level we just described in heart rate, but a variable stress level in skin conductance, and perhaps something in between for blood pressure.

Yet another complication involves inter-individual variability. Some persons may respond to any stimulus in stereotyped fashion, with a greatest response, say, in blood pressure and a lesser response in other variables. Others may respond with almost a random pattern, never showing the same kind of response hierarchy twice. (We will discuss this in detail in later chapters.)

What the LIV and its complications boil down to is this: although responses depend in part on prestimulus levels of activity, the degree of this dependence will vary from person to person, from one physiological variable to another, and from time to time. This much is the psychophysiological principle worth remembering. Now let us consider some of the statistical attempts to deal with the LIV.

You can see that if we need to take prestimulus levels into account in evaluating responses — for the theoretical and empirical reasons we described — then we need to know *how* to take them into account. And with all the complications we need to consider, you can imagine that only some fairly sophisticated techniques will be helpful. We are not going to describe them in detail, but they need to be discussed so that when we come to analyze patterns of response in later chapters, you will have some understanding of how the responses were determined.

Although a number of investigators have proposed ways of analyzing response data, only two approaches have achieved prominence, and they really have an important element in common. One is Lacey's Autonomic Lability Score (ALS), and the other is the analysis of covariance.

In the first detailed report on the implications for psychophysiology of Wilder's LIV, Lacey (1956) proposed an Autonomic Lability Score which is computed in this way (for each variable for each individual):

$$\text{ALS} = 50 + 10 \, \frac{Y_z - X_z r_{xy}}{(1 - r_{xy}^2)^{1/2}}$$

In this formula X represents the prestimulus level, and Y represents the response level; r_{xy} is the correlation term, and reflects the degree to which the response level varies with the prestimulus level. Lacey's intention was to devise a method of computing responses which would take account of the LIV and the complications we mentioned above, and which would permit

comparison of patterns of responses between individuals, or for
one person on several occasions. (See Fig. 9, which was published
by Lacey to illustrate both the ALS, and also some phenomena of
response patterning that we will be discussing in later chapters.)

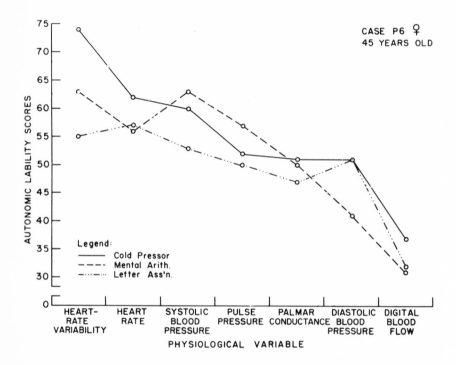

FIG. 9. Autonomic lability scores computed for responses to cold pressor, mental
arithmetic, and letter association. Any one point represents the individual's response on a specific variable to a specific stimulus, as compared to other subjects in
the group. Thus the highest point indicates that the subject responded with much
more heart rate variability on the cold pressor test than did most of the other
subjects; the lowest point indicates much less digital blood flow reactivity during
mental arithmetic than was typical for others. Notice also that the general pattern
is similar from stress to stress—a phenomenon we consider in Chapter VII. Compare also with Fig. 23. (From Lacey, 1956. Courtesy of the author and the New
York Academy of Science.)

Lacey felt that the ALS score reflects the extent of the difference (if any) between the response level (Y), and the estimated response level based on the mean responses of the other subjects who had the same prestimulus level (X). In fact he achieved two useful results with this formula. First, the $X_z r_{xy}$ term may well predict no change, or a "paradoxical" reversal, when the prestimulus level is already quite high, since it is based on the mean performance of others with the same initial level. Second, as the initial prestimulus level increases, so does the ALS, so that a heart rate change from 82 to 92 is "worth" more than one from 72 to 82 in respect to the operations of homeostatic mechanisms as we described earlier. This increase of the ALS is also due to the r_{xy} term because it takes into account the relationship between the pre- and post-levels for the entire group responding to the same stimulus as the individual being considered.

However, as Benjamin (1963) has pointed out, the conceptualization and effect of the ALS technique may actually be misleading. Instead of the LIV being utilized in the determination of the response score, it is eliminated. This is done by computing the correlation between prestimulus and response levels and then removing it (see the formula above). Thus the response scores to be compared are no longer a function of or dependent on the prestimulus levels. Therefore, the ALS does not give the adequate representation to the homeostatic process which Lacey (1956) intended; rather it reflects the individual's response to stimulation over and above the LIV effect.

The second method that we mentioned of analyzing response data is the analysis of covariance. This procedure is too complex to describe in detail so we will not present the formulas which define it, but simply describe it briefly. Covariance analysis combines the concepts of correlation and of analysis of variance (McNemar, 1955). What analysis of variance does is to allow data to be grouped in certain ways, so that responses can be compared among groups, or among successive trials, or even within subjects. Not only can responses be compared in these ways, but they can be tested for significant differences. Differences in responses among groups (for example, ulcer patients compared to hypertensives and normal subjects) are said to be significant when it is calculated that the differences could have occurred by chance only once in a hundred times (or once in a thousand, or whatever standard you choose).

The value of the covariance approach is that it combines the analysis of variance and correlation techniques in such a way that responses to stimulation among groups, or among individuals, can be analyzed for significant differences while taking the correlation between prestimulus and response levels into account. It is "taken into account" by actually computing the correlation and then removing it. Thus it turns out that this covariance analysis and Lacey's ALS are really related (Benjamin, 1963), Lacey's approach being a particular version of the covariance model. This is because both free the response scores from the initial level score. The covariance model is more general, and can be applied to analyzing differences among groups and also differences among individuals. The version of covariance used to study individual differences is actually equivalent to Lacey's ALS, which is not readily applicable to the study of group differences.

However, besides removing baseline effects and so ignoring homeostatic processes, both these approaches have a serious limitation which make them applicable only under certain conditions. The essential correlation term in both methods — the r — is based on the assumption that the measures of prestimulus and response levels are linearly related. That is, if you graph the scores, with initial values on one axis and response values on the other, the assumption is that the points thus plotted would fall along a straight line (of steep or slight slope, it does not matter) (see Fig. 10 for an example).

As a matter of fact, most reports to date on whether this linear relationship actually holds have been affirmative. However, occasionally it happens that the relationship between initial scores (X) and response scores (Y), or between initial scores (X) and difference scores $(D, = Y-X)$, are curvilinear and not linear. This means that when plotted they deviate significantly from a straight line, but not necessarily in any consistent pattern.

When this is the case, then both the covariance and the ALS techniques cannot validly be used. There are techniques for measuring curvilinear correlations, and these may be adapted to the kinds of analysis we have been discussing, but to our knowledge

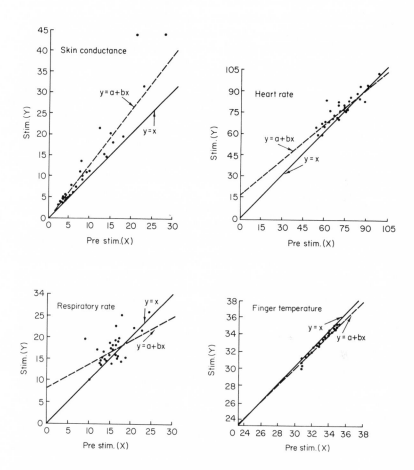

FIG. 10. Examples of linear relationships obtained (dashed lines) between pre-stimulus and "stimulus" (response) magnitudes. Solid lines indicate a theoretical one-to-one relationship between X and Y. (From Hord, Johnson, & Lubin, 1964. Official U. S. Navy photograph, courtesy of the authors and the U. S. Navy.)

this application has not yet been developed. The point of all this is that an experimenter who wants to analyze the autonomic responses he has collected will have to plot all the baseline and response scores and make sure that there is a linear relationship. If there is, he can then apply the covariance analysis or the ALS to his data. If, on occasion, a curvilinear or other relationship exists, then some other technique will have to be applied. Rarely will there be no (zero) correlation. If this were common, it would be evidence against the LIV. The great majority of studies indicate, however, that the LIV almost always applies, i.e., initial level and response are almost always related to some extent. The question we are raising here has to do with the form or shape of the relationship, whether it is straight or curved. The chances are that linearity will hold, and then the experimenter can use the covariance or ALS analysis.

Now it is time to summarize what we have covered to this point and see where we are going.

In Chapter II on the autonomic nervous system we sketched out some of the basic considerations of the structure and function of the ANS, described the dual innervation of most of the autonomic end organs, and showed how the reciprocal actions of the SNS and PNS served to maintain the ideal internal equilibrium.

This was extended, in Chapter III on autonomic balance, to show how homeostasis appears in the resting individual. It was there that we introduced the idea that statistical concepts can be usefully applied to give precise definition to physiological processes. Autonomic balance, as we saw, was an average of a distribution of scores obtained from a large number of persons and representing a selected number of appropriately weighted physiological variables. An individual thus measured, in the resting state, could be shown to demonstrate autonomic balance, or relative apparent SNS or PNS dominance, as compared to others.

Then we left the discussion of the resting individual and went on to see what happens when he is stimulated. But before we could consider patterns of autonomic responses we have had to examine — in this chapter — the relationships that exist between the resting levels of activity (which we had just previously described) and the responses to stimulation (which we are going to describe). These relationships are stated in the law of initial values, and the way in which responses are dependent on prestimulus levels of activity requires us to analyze response data in certain ways, although no method is entirely satisfactory in representing all the homeostatic implications of the LIV.

Now that we have examined the bridge between resting and reactive autonomic activity, it is time to go on and look at the responses themselves. We will start with a broad view of general responsiveness (Chapter V) and then take a closer look at the kinds of patterning of responses that may occur (in Chapters VI and VII).

V
Activation, Adaptation, and Rebound

ACTIVATION

To give you an idea of what is meant by *activation* before we consider it in detail, we can list a few synonyms that were used to label the same physiological processes before this particular term was adopted by consensus. "Arousal," "energy mobilization," and "excitation" were terms applied to changes toward apparent SNS dominance such as we described in Chapter II and which were called by Cannon the "emergency" and "fight or flight" reactions.

While physiologists were learning how the ANS responded to increasing stimulation, electroencephalographers were studying the patterns of electrical potentials of the brain's cortical cells under similar conditions. They observed that a person who was awake but resting quietly, as our young-man-on-a-cot, would typically show a pattern of regular 10-per-second waves (called the alpha rhythm) on the electroencephalogram (EEG). With stimulation, these apparently synchronized signals appeared to become desynchronized, and in fact it seemed as if a continuum of EEG patterns existed which paralleled a continuum of behavior from an extreme of deep sleep to an extreme of great excitement (see Fig. 11 for an example). Table III outlines some of the relationships found. The electroencephalographers called the EEG responses to stimulation "activation," and as this was one of the terms psychophysiologists had used to describe the phenomena they had been studying, when the two groups of investigators began comparing notes in order to understand these processes better, they settled on this word (Duffy, 1962).

If we start from a resting-yet-awake baseline, the degree of activation will be in large part a function of the nature of stimula-

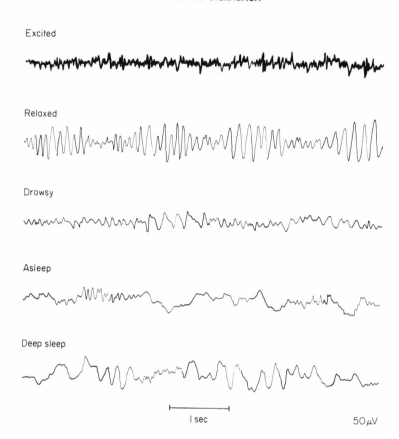

FIG. 11. Different EEG patterns in a normal subject, showing the changes from deep sleep to excitement. (From Jasper, 1941. Courtesy of the author and Charles C. Thomas Co.)

tion. (It will also depend on the degree of responsiveness of the individual, but we are putting off a discussion of individual differences in responsiveness until later.) It may be slight, as in the orienting reflex studied so intensively by the Russians (Sokolov, 1963), it may be an intense startle reflex (Sternbach, 1960a, b), or the stressor may produce a prolonged activation (Selye, 1946). Activation as a concept will be used here to refer to a generalized

TABLE III^a

TABLE III^{*a*}

PSYCHOLOGICAL STATES AND THEIR EEG,
CONSCIOUS AND BEHAVIORAL CORRELATES

Behavioral continuum	Electro-encephalogram	State of awareness	Behavioral efficiency
Strong, excited emotion (fear) (rage) (anxiety)	Desynchronized: Low to moderate amplitude; fast, mixed frequencies	Restricted awareness; divided attention; diffuse, hazy; "confusion"	Poor (lack of control, freezing-up, disorganized)
Alert attentiveness	Partially synchronized: Mainly fast, low amplitude waves	Selective attention, but may vary or shift. "Concentration" anticipation, "set"	Good (efficient, selective, quick, reactions). Organized for serial responses
Relaxed wakefulness	Synchronized: Optimal alpha rhythm	Attention wanders— not forced. Favors free association	Good (routine reactions and creative thought)
Drowsiness	Reduced alpha and occasional low amplitude slow waves	Borderline, partial awareness. Imagery and reverie. "Dream-like states"	Poor (uncoordinated, sporadic, lacking sequential timing)
Light sleep	Spindle bursts and slow waves (larger) loss of alphas	Markedly reduced consciousness (loss of consciousness). Dream state	Absent
Deep sleep	Large and very slow waves (synchrony but on slow time base), random, irregular pattern	Complete loss of awareness (no memory for stimulation or for dreams)	Absent
Coma	Isoelectric to irregular large slow waves	Complete loss of consciousness; little or no response to stimulation; amnesia	Absent
Death	Isoelectric: Gradual and permanent disappearance of all electrical activity	Complete loss of awareness as death ensues	Absent

^{*a*} From Lindsley, 1952. Courtesy of the author and the publisher.

response of the individual, independent of the nature of stimulation and of the uniqueness of the individual. As such it will be a useful topic for reviewing the autonomic functions and the nature of their responses, and it will also be helpful in providing a context for studying the more specialized kinds of response patterns due to different kinds of stimulating situations and to differences among persons.

First of all it should be clear that although we are emphasizing autonomic activity in this book, such activity is not all that is going on in the body, nor is it functioning independently of other systems. We have indicated some of the ANS-endocrine relationships (sympathico-adrenal, vago-insulin systems); and in the brief description of the startle reflex we noted that skeletal muscular responses appeared in coordination with autonomic ones. In fact, the interaction of various physiological systems has become especially clear from studies of activation responses.

The integration of bodily responses is due to the extensive network of nerve fibers and blood vessels which run to every part of the body. Nerve impulses stimulate the secretion of hormones from various endocrine glands; circulating hormones in the blood stream affect the functioning of the nervous system; the nervous system in turn regulates the flow of blood to various tissues; and within the nervous system, centers in the brain and brain stem increase or decrease the activation of peripheral fibers, while the the feedback from the periphery raises or lowers the thresholds of CNS centers.

Activation occurs not only as a result of external stimulation; central phenomena, such as exciting thoughts, can produce similar effects. Also it appears that stimuli producing changes in the classical sensory pathways (sight, sound, touch, smell) and changes in activity in various parts of the brain (especially in the cells of the outer surface, the cortex), must make use of some common activating pathway. It turns out that just such a pathway exists, and it is called the brain stem reticular formation (see Fig. 12).

Fibers from each of the sensory systems, on their way to the cortex, send off branches to the reticular formation as they pass through the brain stem. These reticulated cells project to the thalamus and to wide areas of the cortex — in contrast to the classical

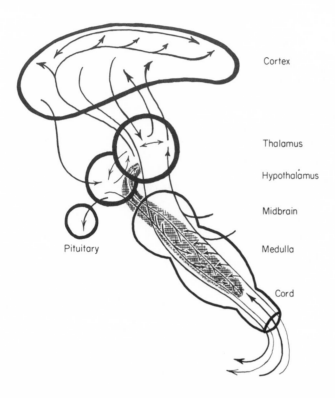

Cortex

Thalamus

Hypothalamus

Midbrain

Pituitary   Medulla

Cord

FIG. 12. Schematic representation of the interconnections of the brain stem reticular formation (crosshatched area). (Modified from Lindsley, 1951. Courtsey of the author and John Wiley & Sons, Inc.)

sensory systems which typically excite specific cortical areas. Thus there is a double effect of, say, a touch. The touched area of skin sends signals through the spinal cord, brainstem, thalamus, and to a specific cortical area, and this constitutes our perception of the touch. But on its way through the brainstem the lateral branches of this sensory system stimulate the reticular formation, which in turn excites the diffuse thalamic projection system and widespread cortical areas. The effect is a generalized cortical activation, the desynchronized activity we mentioned. Thus the reticular formation is sometimes called a "non-specific sensory system," because in some experiments it has been possible to stimulate this structure alone and produce the cortical and behavioral effects of arousal.

This reticular system in the brainstem seems quite necessary for activation. When it is damaged by accident, disease, or experiment, the individual is difficult or impossible to arouse, and is — from both EEG and behavioral evidence — in a coma, as shown in Table III.

The reticular formation handles traffic in several directions. Not only does it send upward discharges to activate the cortex, but it also stimulates hypothalamic and other autonomic centers to alter their thresholds for initiating peripheral autonomic changes. Furthermore, the reticular system can alter the thresholds of spinal motor cells so as to increase or decrease muscle tone, thereby facilitating or inhibiting muscular activity. And at the same time as it is inducing cortical, autonomic, and muscular changes, this same system can induce alterations in sensory thresholds, including the very sensory system which triggered its own activity. So, for example, that part of the body which was touched may have its threshold raised or lowered so that fewer or more impulses from the area may reach the central nervous system and either lessen or increase the process of activation.

Just as the downward discharge of the reticular formation may excite or inhibit autonomic, muscular, and sensory thresholds, so may its upward discharge excite or inhibit cortical activity. We have emphasized the activating characteristics of this system, and it is true that its stimulation usually produces cortical activation, but there also are inhibitory centers whose stimulation can reduce the thresholds of some cortical units.

The cortex, also, can stimulate the reticular formation, which in turn can produce either further cortical activity or exert an in-hibiting influence on it. It is probably by this means that ideas or thoughts (presumably cortical events) can produce autonomic changes and alterations of muscular tone — by downward discharge from cortex to reticular formation, and thence to the autonomic, motor, and sensory centers.

What may seem like possibilities for ever-increasing activity, due to stimulation of the reticular formation which produces autonomic and muscular activity which then results in greater reticular activity, is prevented by built-in mechanisms for terminating the cycle.

Homeostatic-like processes (negative feedback) operate in all such cortical-subcortical interactions.

Although we have described some of the relationships among cortex, reticular formation, and autonomic, motor, and sensory centers, we have not yet mentioned the endocrine system. You know, of course, that stimulation of the SNS will result in the secretion of adrenaline from the adrenal medulla, which in turn results in a variety of SNS-like changes. But there are still further complex interrelationships to be considered now. The brain stem reticular formation is itself sensitive to levels of adrenaline circulating in the blood stream (Bonvallet, Dell & Hiebel, 1954). In this way it is possible for cortical activity to stimulate the reticular formation, which then produces more generalized cortical arousal and increased autonomic tone, which results in the increase of circulating adrenaline, which then serves to maintain the reticular activity and thereby the cortical activation.

All this discussion about the reticular formation, which is so essential to the topic of activation, is not meant to minimize the role of the hypothalamus as the major autonomic center. It functions not only to increase and decrease SNS and PNS activity, but has also been shown to be involved in sleep-wakefulness, hunger-satiation, fear-anger, and other very complex processes. But of primary concern here is its relation to the endocrine system and to activation. The hypothalamus seems to be largely responsible for regulating the functions of its neighbor, the anterior pituitary, and it is this latter which has earned for the pituitary gland the nickname of "master gland." The anterior pituitary secretes such hormones as the thyrotropic (TTH), gonadotropic (GTH) and adrenocorticotropic (ACTH) — substances which stimulate the thyroid, gonads, and adrenal cortex, respectively.

Now the thyroid, the "pacemaker" gland, through its production of thyroxine, regulates the rate of metabolism of the entire body. The hyperthyroid individual is manifestly chronically "activated" — showing great restlessness, some weight loss, insomnia, lowered sensory thresholds apparent in his jumpiness, and quite frequently an EEG pattern of activation even while at rest. The hypothyroid person, on the other hand, is chronically sleepy and fatigued, gains weight easily, is sluggish in movements and not easily aroused — in general, "deactivated."

The gonads, in their production of testosterone, also contribute to the general activity level of the organism. Testosterone has been shown to affect not only the thresholds for sexual arousal, but also the degree of aggressive behavior and social dominance. (This is more true in lower animals, where hormonal regulation of behavior is greater than in man, for whom nervous system influences seem more important. Nevertheless, it is likely that some sensitizing or threshold-affecting influence of this hormone persists in us.)

The adrenal cortex is the layer of cells surrounding the adrenal medulla, but despite this proximity it is not directly influenced by the SNS. Instead, its relation to the autonomic system is the indirect one: hypothalamus $\longrightarrow$ anterior pituitary gland $\longrightarrow$ ACTH $\longrightarrow$ adrenal cortex. The adrenal cortex secretes a number of hormones, called the corticosteroids, and these serve to regulate water and salt balances, protein breakdown, fat and carbohydrate metabolism and, in general, to serve an essential role in enabling an organism to meet prolonged stress situations such as disease or extreme environmental threats. Much has been made of the role of these hormones in the ability of the body to mobilize for and adapt to such stressors (Selye, 1946).

These three hormones—thyroxine, testosterone, and the corticosteroids—maintain the individual in a relatively constant state of activation over periods of weeks, since normally changes in their output occur slowly and result in only gradual increases or decreases in activity. On the other hand, nervous system responses to stimulation (internal or external) are quite rapid, enabling the individual to respond to immediate needs. Where sustained activity is required for some minutes, the adrenal medulla's secretion of adrenaline supports the activation of the autonomic and central nervous system. Continuous sustained exertion results in fatigue, of course, but if there is an intermittent pattern of stress and rest, the endocrine glands and their target organs will gradually modify their functions to adapt the individual to this pattern. (We will discuss this model and some particular examples of it in Chapter X on Psychosomatic Diseases.)

What we have said so far illustrates how involved is the interaction of the various physiological systems in the process we are calling activation—and we have not by any means described it all.

The cortex, hypothalamus, reticular formation, peripheral autonomic, motor and sensory fibers, circulating hormones—all are involved, and all continuously influence each other and modify each other's and their own output. This ceaseless, interacting, modulating activity all involves varying degrees of the utilization of energy, and if you were to plot this sort of thing over time, you would probably notice (for a normal, healthy person) long slow undulations over periods of months, superimposed on which would be diurnal variations, and superimposed on these would be the briefer minute-to-minute and hour-to-hour peaks caused by responses to routine daily events.

Psychophysiologists for the most part have concentrated on these briefer periods of energy mobilization. This type of activation is far easier to control and study in the laboratory, and much of what we will be discussing comes from findings in this sort of situation. Of necessity, this means that measurements of endocrine activity are subordinated to those of the other systems. Insofar as is possible, you should keep in mind the "tidal" role of the hormones, on which the peaks and troughs of nervous and muscular activity appear. Hormonal levels may operate to raise or lower baseline activity and/or the degree of responsiveness of these other systems.

Now let us examine some of the indices frequently used to measure activation. Remember that we are talking about short-term fluctuations, or brief responses to some form of stimulation, and not the longer lasting states of activation. For the latter, tests of energy utilization such as measures of basal metabolic rate, iodine uptake, or hormonal assays, or experimental refinements of similar clinical tests might be appropriate. But for the relatively transitory responses we are considering we need indicants with relatively little lag, which are quantifiable and have good reliability, and to which, ultimately, we can point and say, These changes in these measures *are* activation. For such purposes the peripheral autonomic responses have proved useful, but so have some other indicators.

The striated (striped) skeletal muscles are under central nervous system innervations, and we usually think of having voluntary control of them. Yet it can be shown that even when we do not move, and think we are relaxed, appropriate stimulation will result in contraction of certain groups of muscles of which we are unaware. For example, though your arms may be hanging loosely by your sides, just thinking about flexing them will result in an increased number of muscle potentials being generated, and an increased blood flow to them. Furthermore, even an apparently less related mental task, like solving mental arithmetic problems, will result in an increased muscle tension of which you would probably be unaware.

The fact that contracting muscles give off muscle action potentials (electrochemical manifestation of energy utilization) makes them useful indicators of activation. Up to a point, the greater the degree of contraction, the greater the number and amplitude of potentials given off. The recording of these on a polygraph along with other physiological indicants has been shown to be an excellent aid in the study of activation. Such traces of muscle action potentials are called electromyograms (EMG). Which muscle groups will be sampled depends on the nature of the experiment. If you want to compare a "headache group" with normals, the neck muscles would be of interest; arthritic patients are likely to have more activity in joint muscles than are controls; and so on.

The electrical activity of the cerebral cortex that we mentioned earlier is not quite the same as the electrical potentials given off by the contracting striped, cardiac, or smooth muscles. The cortical activity reflects fluctuations in membrane potentials in the millions of cortical cells, and is an ongoing metabolic phenomenon, not action potentials resulting from specific stimulation. When the individual is in a relaxed waking state these shifts in resting potentials become synchronized and present the alpha rhythm we described. Upon stimulation, concentration, attention, etc., the EEG pattern of activation appears. This is described as low amplitude fast activity, and seems to represent the same electrochemical fluctuations desynchronized.

These EEG patterns reflect CNS activation. Increased muscled action potentials also reflect CNS activation, and ANS activation too, because of the vascular dilation and increased blood flow to the muscles which occurs concomitantly. Now let us take a look at some of the more purely autonomic indices.

Palmar sweat gland activity has been one of the most popular measures because, as we have said, it is easily recorded and quantified and, like the EEG and EMG, is a sensitive responder to stimuli from both external and internal sources.

Two different methods of measuring this activity are commonly used, the resistance of the skin surface to a constant current, and detection of the electrical activity of the sweat glands as potential changes. Both can reflect activation in two different ways.

A brief, mild stimulus, like a one-second tone, will usually produce a transitory EEG activation of a few seconds' duration, some increase in muscle action potentials for the same length of time, and a decrease in palmar skin resistance with a later return to the original resistance level. This latter is often called a galvanic skin response (GSR) and is shown in Fig. 13. At the same time, if sweat gland potentials were recorded, one would observe one or a few evoked skin potentials. We will call these galvanic skin potentials (GSP).

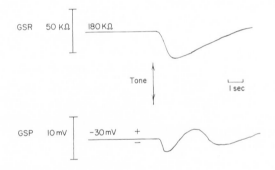

FIG. 13. A typical response (not an actual record) which could be obtained from the palms of the hands or soles of the feet. There is a transitory decrease in resistance (GSR) to a constant current, and an evoked biphasic potential (GSP) from the sweat glands.

If, instead of a brief tone we told our young-man-on-a-cot, "All right, get ready now," and he knew that this meant he was going to be plunging his bare foot in a bucketful of ice water, or that he was going to be given some mental arithmetic problems to solve which would reflect seriously on his intelligence, then we would see activation of a more persistent sort. The EEG desynchronization would last much longer, probably until the task was well over. The same would be true for the increase in EMG potentials. And the GSR would probably show a large decrease, so that the baseline for resistance would be at a lower level and also would remain there until the task was over. In addition, occasional small GSRs would probably appear at this lower level, perhaps with increasing frequency as the time for beginning the task neared. A similar phenomenon would appear in the GSP tracing: a shift in baseline level might occur but increasing numbers of GSPs would be almost certain (see Fig. 14).

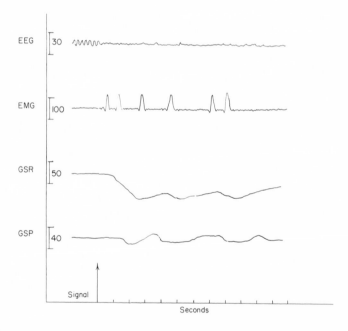

FIG. 14. Typical effects (not an actual record) of a more sustained activation. In the EEG, resting alpha (10 per second) waves disappear and are replaced by the low voltage fast activity typical of desynchronization. In the EMG, an increased number of potentials reflects an increase in muscle tonus. The GSR shows a drop in reistance which is maintained, and a number of non-specific potentials appear in the GSP.

Heart rate and blood pressure changes are also likely to occur, but the latter are difficult to assess. There is no satisfactory way of measuring both systolic and diastolic blood pressure *continuously*. There are several gadgets on the market that will intermittently inflate a cuff and record the systolic and diastolic pressures, but these are intermittent measures only, and are confounded with the responses to the inflating cuff. Some measure of blood pressure is desirable, because—as you know from our earlier discussions of the cardiovascular homeostatic mechanisms—a rise in blood pressure is often followed by a decrease in heart rate. Yet both heart rate and blood pressure increases are to be expected in activation, since activation in the autonomic system is an increase in apparent SNS activity. (In fact it is not just "apparent," or inhibition of PNS activity, because palmar sweat gland responses are entirely SNS-innervated, and so is peripheral vasoconstriction.) A number of cardiovascular measures have been used to gain additional information about the homeostatic reflexes, and these also have proved useful in studying activation.

Finger pulse volume is an indirect measure of peripheral vasoconstriction and vasodilatation and can be measured by a sealed finger cup and a closed air system, or a photoelectric cell, or a piezoelectric crystal as in a record player pickup, or any device sensitive to volume changes or magnitude of the pulse. A record of finger pulse volume (FPV) will typically show several kinds of waxing and waning, one occurring over intervals of minutes, another at about 30-second intervals, and another reflecting the breathing rate, every 3 or 4 seconds. Despite these changes, the FPV seems to be every bit as sensitive to stimulation as the GSR and GSP: a clear vasoconstriction occurs to a tone, and is followed by vasodilatation; activation due to instructions and anticipation ("anxiety") will appear as a marked and prolonged constriction.

The ballistocardiogram (BKG) provides a different kind of information about the cardiovascular system, and it is an ingenious measure too. Have you ever stood on a bathroom scale and watched the needle jiggle with each pulse? The force with which the cardiac muscles pump out blood, particularly that with which the blood strikes the aortic arch, is like a small internal shove which causes the entire body to bounce. This movement of the body is measurable by placing a tambour arrangement on the foot, or a crystal pickup, or any linear force transducer strapped to the sole of the foot. The relative size of the recorded pulse will be an index of the cardiac stroke volume, the amount of blood forced out by contraction of the cardiac muscles.

Now if we record all these cardiovascular measures (others, like skin temperature, tend to be too sluggish) during activation, the following sort of pattern emerges. Initially, the heart rate and stroke volume increase, so that greater quantities of blood are circulating and at a faster rate. At the same time, peripheral vasoconstriction occurs. These are all SNS effects, but note that each separately will tend to raise the blood pressure, which reflects the amount of force of the cardiac output and the peripheral resistance encountered; all three will result in a sudden increase in blood pressure.

But as we described earlier, the baroreceptors in the carotid sinus and aortic arch respond to this sudden increase by initiating reflexes designed to return the blood pressure to normal. This means that both the heart rate and the stroke volume will be reduced, and so will the degree of peripheral vasoconstriction. However, if the stimulus for activation persists—as in our example of anticipating a stress—so will some degree of increased heart rate, blood pressure, stroke volume, and peripheral vasoconstriction. And as "anxiety" increases with the approach of the task, so will these indices reflect the increased activation. But because of the continuous operation of the negative feedback mechanism, the observed changes will not be so clear as in the palmar sweating responses. In fact, some of the "paradoxical" reactions we mentioned might occur, so that in one or another measure an apparent PNS response or SNS inhibition may occur.

In respiration, we have another possible index of activation: we might expect it to become faster, or deeper, or both. Breathing rate is simple to record from a strain-gauge pickup around the chest or abdomen. Breathing volume is more difficult to measure without a complicated apparatus, and most psychophysiologists no longer attempt it. For some reasons that are not entirely clear, respiration rate seldom proves useful in distinguishing degrees of activation, but it serves a very important monitoring function. Changes in respiratory patterns will immediately result in changes in virtually every other physiological variable being recorded. If our young-man-on-a-cot were to sneeze, or cough, or sigh, or hiccup, or gulp, then the changes we would see in the EEG, EMG, GSR, GSP, and the cardiovascular measures would look just like (and in fact would be) activation. So respiration nowadays is often recorded primarily eliminate from the record such artifactual responses.

Now let us summarize the appearance of activation on these measures. If we are interested to see whether young-man-on-a-cot is more activated from one condition to another, or whether a group of neurotics more than controls, then the following measures are likely to prove useful: For the EEG, percent-time alpha, that is, the percentage of time in a given period in which alpha waves are present; for the EMG, the number of muscle action potentials in a given time period; for the GSR, the average skin resistance level sampled at certain intervals; for GSP, the number of non-specific potentials emitted; for FPV and BKG, the amplitude of the pulse waves at selected points; for heart rate, the average rate at certain intervals, and also the variability of the heart rate if a cardiotachometer is used (which records the rate-per-minute for each beat, from the beat-to-beat interval). And of course the blood pressure itself, at whatever intervals sampled, yields figures for systolic and diastolic pressure, and for pulse pressure, which is the simple difference between systolic and diastolic pressures.

Of course, if one is going to compare groups' responses in activation, it will make a difference in the results if the groups are not starting from the same level—and chances are they will not be. In this case allowances for initial levels must be made. That was the whole point of the last chapter, you remember.

There are several implications of activation for other aspects of human behavior, and we will describe these just briefly. First, and most obvious, activation is a process that accompanies or, rather, is a part of many emotional states. It used to be thought that by studying the physiological changes in each emotion their differences could be specified, but for a variety of reasons this has proved to be quite difficult. Nevertheless, some patterning of activation can be demonstrated, as we will describe in subsequent chapters, and this has proved useful in understanding individual differences in responsiveness. There also used to be theoretical quarrels in print as to whether emotions were adaptive or disorganizing to behavior. This is not the most fruitful sort of question to ask, since it now seems that it is not the emotions that are adaptive or disorganizing, but the activation component. In a large number of studies it has been shown that when the degree of activation is minimal, performance on any number of tasks is of mediocre quality. As activation increases to a moderate level, performance reaches an optimal point. When activation is very great, the quality of performance deteriorates to a low point again. This sort of relationship is described as the inverted-U, from the appearance of the graph when you plot degree of activation against level of performance. Of course, low, moderate, and high degrees of activation will be a function of both the individual and the task being studied (Malmo, 1959). However, in resting states, CNS and ANS measures of activation do not always correlate highly (Sternbach, 1960c).

Activation has been called the "energizer" of behavior, that which imparts intensity or force to any act. In this sense it might be subsumed under the more traditional heading of motivation. Any act or behavior may be described as to its direction, or nature, and its intensity, or energy (Lindsley, 1957). In this connection it is interesting to recall the distinction made by ethologists between appetitive and consummatory behavior. An animal with some need (hunger, sexual activity, sleep) will at first respond to its deficit with restlessness and apparently random behavior—activation has begun (appetitive behavior). As the cues from the deficit become stronger, a more patterned searching behavior becomes apparent and activation is increased. When an appropriate satisfier is found (food, partner, rest), species-specific stereotyped consummatory responses occur, and activation declines. In humans the specific consummatory responses we make to internal deficits or external cues are more likely to be the result of prior learning, yet even the best-learned habits are not likely to occur without "reason," that is, sufficient drive or activation.

A final word about activation. Despite the existence of patterning about which we will be more specific later, many different situations produce rather similar activating effects. Increased muscle tension, apparent SNS activity, and EEG desynchronization can be produced by most emotions (perhaps not depression), by mental activity, physical exercise, changes in sensations—in short, by almost any *change* in conditions. In this sense activation seems to be a set of responses in the individual alerting him for whatever may come next, in the nature of a generalized preparatory act. Such a process probably has some survival value, since it increases the probability of speedy and vigorous responses if the situation should call for them (Lindsley, 1951, 1957).

ADAPTATION

If we were to say to young-man-on-a-cot, "Get ready, now," large responses such as we described as constituting activation would occur. If there were nothing to get ready for the responses would probably still occur. But if, at regular or irregular intervals, we repeated the phrase, the responses would decrease in magnitude and eventually disappear. This diminution of responses to repetitive stimulation is called adaptation or habituation. It is somewhat like the extinction of a learned response when reinforcement is no longer given, but it is different in some ways. In Fig. 15 you can see the changes in some responses to repeated electric shocks: initial responses are large, but gradually they decrease or "adapt out." This is true despite the fact that the amount of shock delivered remains constant.

Because the intervals at which these stimuli are presented are rather long, the phenomenon of adaptation cannot be considered the same as fatigue, either in a subjective sense or in the sense in which physiologists describe fatigue of single muscle groups or nerve fibers.

It seems as if activation is a response to change, or novelty. Repetitive stimulation is quite the opposite—it is monotonous—and there is nothing to get ready for in the familiar situation. To be anthropomorphic about it, it is like a physiological version of the boy who cried wolf, or a physiological demonstration that familiarity breeds contempt. But such descriptive analogies do not explain the phenomenon.

We are not sure why adaptation occurs, although we can demonstrate it in a variety of situations. If we continue with our survival

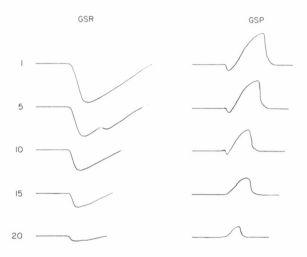

FIG. 15. The typical course of adaptation (not an actual record), showing the diminution of responses on successive trials in both GSR and GSP. Note the disappearance of the biphasic component in GSP.

model, it makes sense that in novel situations we should be prepared for any eventuality but it would be literally wasteful of energy if every situation had the same activating effect, even familiar ones. Both activation and adaptation can be seen to be useful.

It should be noted that adaptation of responses to repetitive stimulation is not always a smooth, steady decrease. Occasional responses of initial magnitude will occur in the series, and occasional non-specific responses will occur in intervals between the presentation of stimuli. It is not always clear what the reasons for this may be. The subject might have had his mind wandering and then re-attended to the stimulus, resulting in similar responses, independent of the stimulus. Both of these imply a cortical discharge to the reticular formation and consequent enhancement of the responses being recorded, but these possible explanations are only speculative.

REBOUND

If instead of repetitive stimulation we had one long or intense stimulus, such as the cold pressor test, or a single intense shock, or a pistol shot, or just the prolonged anticipatory period with no task, then we could observe a different phenomenon. Gradually all the variables we record can be seen to return to their prestimulus levels and, in many instances, to "overshoot" them. Percent-time alpha may, for a short period, be greater than just before stimulation, and so may be the amplitude of the alpha waves. Fewer muscle potentials may appear, and their amplitude may be smaller, and this applies as well to the sweat potentials. Even more frequently you can observe skin resistance rise to levels higher than the greatest resistance reached during the rest period preceding stimulation, and just as dramatic an increase in peripheral vasodilatation can be seen. Similarly there may be a slowing of the pulse, decrease in blood pressure, and decrease in stroke volume to less than the prestimulus levels, though compensatory mechanisms are likely to make these briefer and less marked.

This phenomenon has been described as "vagal rebound," or "parasympathetic overcompensation," but since it appears in purely SNS-innervated variables as well as in the dually-innervated ones, and in the CNS, we will use just the word "rebound" to refer to it.

The mechanisms of rebound are not certain. In dually-innervated organs like the heart or pupil of the eye, we can imagine that increased SNS activity and inhibition of the PNS results in a buildup of potential energy in the PNS centers, with consequent excessive PNS activity as SNS functioning decreases. This of course was the reasoning behind the terms vagal rebound and PNS overcompensation: the implication was that there would be overshooting and then undershooting and a gradually decreasing oscillation around the prestimulus level, as equilibrium was regained.

But this explanation cannot apply to, say, FPV, which is innervated by adrenergic SNS fibers. Yet of all the variables likely to be recorded on a polygraph, it is FPV which is most likely to demonstrate a waxing and waning of pulse amplitude which gradually approaches prestimulus levels. It is very similar to a bouncing ball or elastic band effect—except of course prestimulus activity also is variable, not constant.

A dramatic illustration of the effects of this sort of rebound was the report of experiments on "executive monkeys," who had to press a lever to avoid shocks (Porter *et al.*, 1958). They were put on a schedule of 6 hours work, 6 hours rest. Within a few weeks they died of perforated ulcers, while companions who received the same shocks but did not have the job of avoiding them, survived. Apparently the time schedule was essential here, because in the activated 6 hour state, gastric functions were suppressed, and then rebounded during the 6 hour rest period. This rebounding coincided with the peak of hormonal activity which was initiated during the stress period, but which because of its slower functioning showed a time lag. These hormone levels decayed slowly too, but because of the time schedule, built up again before returning to normal levels. This cumulative buildup to toxic levels, combined with the excessive gastric rebound, was sufficient to kill the animals. It has been suggested, and not unreasonably, that humans on an analogous schedule could encounter a similar fate.

Fascinating as such studies may be, they do not tell us why rebounding occurs. All we can do is describe how and under what conditions it may occur, and say something like, An excessive response in one (apparent SNS) direction is frequently followed by an excessive response in an opposite (apparent PNS) direction before returning to equilibrium. While not entirely satisfactory, it may help to think of it as a physiological expression of the principle in mechanics that every action produces an equal and opposite reaction. Allowing for homeostatic restraints which modulate the effects so that the reaction is not always equal, the phenomenon of rebounding seems very much like this.

Incidentally, rebound is subject to adaptation too, in that it will decrease with repetitive stimulation. This is not very surprising, since if the response to stimulation gets smaller you would expect the rebound to get smaller also, insofar as it is a reaction to the response. But something else seems to be involved, because there is far from a perfect relationship between response and rebound. It seems in many instances that rebound occurs only when the response exceeds a certain magnitude and then gets larger as the response magnitude increases further. During adaptation, as the response gets smaller, so does the rebound, until the rebound disappears entirely while the response continues to decrease and eventually drop out. Figure 16 shows a schematic representation of this. We have little information about the precise nature of this relationship, since to our knowledge it has not been investigated, and we have to draw on general impressions from experience. However, it seems as if rebounding has a threshold of its own (if we consider the rebound as a response, and the adequate stimulus as an original response of a certain magnitude). This might be worth investigating.

The chances are good (we have no data to draw on) that the extent to which rebound phenomena appear will depend not

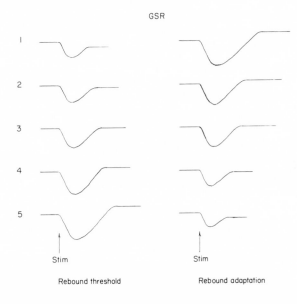

FIG. 16. Hypothetical representation of rebound phenomenon in the GSR. On the left, rebound begins to appear as the response reaches a certain threshold of magnitude. On the right, with adaptation, rebound drops out as the response decreases below a certain threshold of magnitude. The thresholds for appearance and disappearance may not be the same.

only on the response magnitude, but also on the physiological variable and the individual being recorded from. We will see in a later chapter that great differences in responsiveness exist among individuals, and this is likely to apply to rebounding as well. Meanwhile the practical application of what we do know about this phenomenon is clear: investigators who present several stimuli in succession must wait for response recovery and rebounding from previous stimuli to subside before restimulating, in order to avoid confounding responses with each other.

VI
Stimulus-Response Specificity

For many years psychophysiologists have been attempting to show that there is more to physiological responses than just activation, and that different patternings of responses occur in different situations. However, they have had a good deal of contrary evidence to overcome. In the first place, in his pioneering research W. B. Cannon (1936) had shown that the same massive SNS activity occurred in three states—fear, anger, and responses to pain. In his writings he emphasized that only the sympathetic branch responded to noxious stimulation, and that all the SNS effectors showed equal maximum activity to meet emergency situations. Secondly, the biochemical work of Hans Selye, in more recent years, has seemed to support Cannon's notion of a generalized response to threat. Despite varying the *kinds* of prolonged stressors employed (cold, exercise, fasting, injuries, and various different drugs), a similar pattern of response seemed always to occur: massive discharge of adrenal cortical steroids, destruction of the thymus gland, and bleeding stomach ulcers (Selye, 1946).

The work of Cannon and Selye tended to discourage those who would look for different patterns of physiological responses in the different emotions. It began to seem that our different *feelings* in various situations were "all in our head"—cortical activity relating perceptions of novel stimuli and familiar bodily sensations. Yet there presisted the conviction that our feelings could not be so entirely misleading: fear and anger, love and hate, joy and grief—these *feel* different, *physically* different, and no amount of argument is likely to persuade us that they do not. Even our language confirms our thinking in this. We speak of the "pallor of fear" and of growing "purple with rage," two quite different vascular responses in the face, and both different still from the "blush of shame." Stagefright gives us "butterflies in our stomachs," but the stench of a dead animal "turns our stomachs" in revulsion; and neither is quite the same as feeling our stomachs "tied in knots" when looking down a dizzying stairwell. We skip with joy, and are bowed with grief, and grim with determination.

Are these expressions only poets' fantasies? Experience and reflection tell us they are not. In fact, we tend to use physiological evidence for emotional specificity in everyday situations. Let someone in our group blush, and we are sure of his or her embarrassment. If we point out this response, the person may deny it, while blushing all the more, and we are all the more convinced of our diagnosis.

Now let us turn the problem around and look at it another way. You have probably exercised at one time or another. Do you remember your bodily reactions during a strenuous workout in calisthenics or a rough sport? You breathe faster and more deeply, and can hardly gulp enough air. You sweat "like a horse," until you are dripping (professional athletes may lose several pounds of fluid in a contest). You flush (vascular dilatation) and you can feel your heart pounding faster (increased cardiac rate and stroke volume) and your blood pressure goes up. The vascular dilatation is reflexive for temperature regulation and to keep blood pressure down, but by and large these changes represent as massive an SNS response as it is possible to have, complete with adrenal discharge, glycogen release from the liver, red cells released from the spleen, etc. But do we think of this as an emotion? Hardly. It seems like neither terror nor fury, although the same changes are occurring as are supposed to in those extreme states. Nor can we even say that it would be like those emotions except that the situational stimuli are different. At no time, as we go from mild to progressively more violent exercises, do we feel "as if" we are, or ought to be, afraid or angry, "only there's nothing there" to be afraid of or angry about. It simply does not feel the same; it does not feel the same *in our bodies.*

Now the implications here are clear. We cannot say of these

exercise responses that they are the same as fear and anger and that only the central coding of the afferents differs from state to state, as the situation changes. And the same applies to the emotions; it is simply asking too much that we should believe that the autonomic responses in fear and anger are the same, and that only cortical events make them seem different.

We are spared this demand, however, by some recent research which supports the common sense view of the matter. As we will see, there is beginning to accumulate some evidence in support of Franz Alexander's statement that "every emotional state has its own physiological syndrome" (1950, p. 68). Alexander and other psychoanalysts, such as Dunbar (1935, 1947) had long held such a position based on clinical evidence. But it is not necessary to limit our thinking to emotion-producing stimuli. In a larger sense any set of stimuli ought to evoke its own unique set of responses. And while it may not be possible to test the generality of this assumption, we can examine the extent to which responses tend to be specific to the situational stimuli which elicit them. This is the meaning of the title of this chapter; and now we can examine the experimental evidence for stimulus-response specificity.

One of the earliest and most intriguing reports was that of Wolf and Wolff (1947), who had an opportunity to make detailed observations of a patient with a gastric fistula, which permitted direct access to the digestive processes. They found that marked changes in gastric functioning accompanied emotional disturbances. There were two classes of gastric changes: the first included a depression of acid output, of vascularity, and of gastric motility, and was associated with a reaction of anxiety and a wish to flee an emotionally charged situation; the second included an acceleration of these gastric functions, often to the point of a reddening and engorgement of the mucosa frequently seen in gastritis, and was associated with feelings of anger and resentment and an unfulfilled desire to strike back. Figures 17 and 18 illustrate this differentiation of gastric responses.

Shortly after this it was discovered that a second hormone was secreted by the adrenal medulla, whose action was different from adrenaline (epinephrine). It was called noradrenaline (norepinephrine). You will recall that adrenaline causes a marked increase

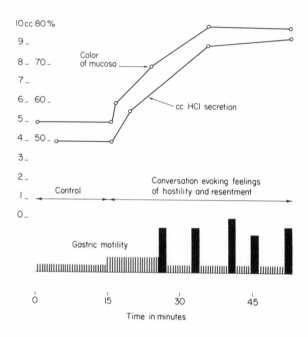

FIG. 17. Increases in gastric motility, reddening of gastric mucosa, and gastric acidity, accompanying feelings of hostility and resentment. (From Wolf & Wolff, 1947. Courtesy of the authors and Oxford Univ. Press.)

in heart rate and stroke volume, and a constriction in the superficial peripheral blood vessels. Noradrenaline, however, exerts its effect primarily on the blood vessels supplying the muscles, causing a marked vasoconstriction there, and decreases heart rate and stroke volume. The effect of both these hormones is to increase systolic blood pressure, but for different reasons: adrenaline because of the increased cardiac output, noradrenaline because of the increased peripheral vascular resistance. The latter effect also results in a markedly increased diastolic blood pressure from noradrenaline, which is quite different from the only slight decrease or increase from adrenaline (Wenger *et al.*, 1960).

Now things were beginning to look up. The stomach, an autonomically-innervated organ, clearly showed different responses in

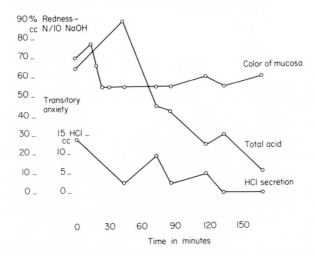

FIG. 18. Decreases in reddening of gastric mucosa and in gastric acidity, accompanying transitory anxiety. (From Wolf & Wolff, 1947. Courtesy of the authors and Oxford Univ. Press.)

different emotions, and the adrenal medulla secreted two differently acting hormones. Could it be that fine differences in response patterns could result from different ratios of secretion of adrenaline and noradrenaline? It was worth looking into, but there were some problems involved in finding out.

The first problem was not too difficult to solve. Not everyone has a gastric fistula, and it is not easy to assess autonomic functioning directly. But by this time the state of polygraphy had advanced far enough so that fine measures could be made of peripheral ANS activity, and even if all emotions involved generalized SNS discharge it would be possible to detect differences due to differing proportions of secreted adrenaline and noradrenaline.

The second problem was more difficult. How do you induce authentic emotions in the laboratory? In an experimental situation it is necessary to control events so that you can be sure that the results you obtain are attributable only to your experimental manipulations. All subjects must be treated alike if their data are to be grouped together; and if the effects of different kinds of stimulation are to be studied, then all else must be held constant or controlled in such a way that you can be sure you are studying these effects free of other contaminants. With such restraints and necessary artificiality how can genuine emotions be obtained in the laboratory?

Albert Ax (1953) hit upon an ingenious plan. He studied fear and anger responses induced by an "incompetent" polygraph operator who, in the anger situation, handled the subjects roughly and criticized and insulted them; in the fear situation, subjects received mild shocks about which the experimenter became alarmed, exclaiming about a dangerous high-voltage situation as sparks jumped near the subjects. Each of 43 subjects received both treatments, which were alternated in order among them.

Under these conditions Ax found that diastolic blood pressure increases, decreases in heart rate, increases in muscle potentials, and the number of increases in skin conductance were greater for anger than for fear. On the other hand, skin conductance and respiration rate increases and the number of muscle potential increases were greater for fear than for anger. Ax felt that the pattern in fear resembled that produced by injections of adrenaline, while that in anger were like the effect of combined adrenaline and noradrenaline. Figure 19 summarizes these very important results.

Schachter (1957) repeated this study, adding hypertensives as well as control subjects and adding pain from a cold pressor test to the fear and anger situations. He found that 35 of 48 subjects showed an adrenaline-like pattern in fear, 31 of 47 subjects showed a noradrenaline-like pattern in pain, while in the anger situation 22 showed an adrenaline-like pattern, 19 showed a noradrenaline-like pattern, and 17 showed mixed patterns. This was a clear confirmation of Ax's findings.

Now the evidence began to come in. Comparing responses in hunger and pain, Engel (1959) found that increased food deprivation led to decreases in pulse pressure primarily due to decreases in systolic blood pressure, increases in axillary (armpit) temperature and salivary output, a decrease in respiration rate, an increase in the number of rhythmic 20-second stomach contractions, and an increase in the rate of those contractions. The pain of the cold

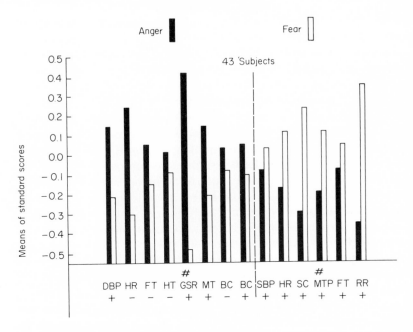

FIG. 19. Polygraph reaction patterns. The physiological differentiation of anger (black bars) and fear (white bars). Responses are plotted in standard score units to make possible the comparison of different physiological variables which employ different units of measurement. Plus signs (+) indicate increases in the variable, minus signs (−) indicate decreases. Greater average responses for anger appear in diastolic blood pressure rises (DBP+), heart rate decreases (HR−), number of galvanic skin responses (#GSR), and muscle tension increases (MT+). Greater average responses for fear appear in skin conductance increases (SC+), number of muscle tension peaks (#MTP), and increases in respiration rate (RR+). (From Ax, 1953. Courtesy of the author and Hoeber Medical Division, Harper & Row.)

pressor stimulation resulted in increases in systolic and diastolic blood pressures, increases in heart rate, decreases in finger pulse volume, and either some blocking of the stomach contractions or an increase in their rate.

Then Sternbach (1960b) reported on a comparison of responses in startle to those in response to cold pressor, exercise, and adrenaline and noradrenaline infusions. Startle responses were different in kind from cold pressor, exercise, and noradrenaline, but differ-

ent only in degree from adrenaline. This means that, for startle
and adrenaline responses, increases in systolic blood pressure and
decreases in diastolic pressure were all in the same direction, although the amount of change was not the same. So those who
consider startle a reflex which is a "prototype" of fear may, considering this and Ax's and Schachter's studies, be quite correct.

Further evidence came in a massive study reported by Wenger
and Cullen (1958) in which nine autonomic variables were measured in responses to fourteen stimulus conditions, and 14 response
patterns were obtained. Each response was compared to a baseline
obtained during sleep, and patterns were obtained for waking,
prestimulus levels, electric shock and its anticipation, insertion of
a needle, infusion of saline, adrenaline, and noradrenaline,
exercise, hyperventilation, letter association, mental arithmetic,
carbon dioxide inhalation, and cold pressor. There were some
similarities in patterns, of course. Mental arithmetic and letter
association (saying as many words as possible that begin with a
certain letter) patterns looked somewhat the same, and there was
good evidence of reliability in the similarity of patterns to two
separate needle insertions and to infusions of saline. These investigators concluded that patterns of autonomic responses seem
to vary with the kinds of stimuli which elicit them, and if the
patterns are classified into groups according to their similarities,
the group containing the greatest number of patterns suggests a
mixed adrenaline and noradrenaline effect. Davis and his colleagues (1955) similarly had demonstrated differential response
patterns to a variety of stimuli.

Now that it appeared possible to differentiate patterns of response according to the kinds of stimuli which elicit them, perhaps
it would be possible to pursue the discrimination of responses in
the subtler emotions. But unfortunately this proved more difficult
—in part because of the problem we mentioned above about the
difficulty of inducing authentic emotions in the laboratory, in part
perhaps because the subtler emotions consist of subtler ANS
changes which are either not sampled or are too small to be significant in the statistical treatment of the data.

As an example of this difficulty, Sternbach (1962) reported on
the ANS responses of children to the motion picture *Bambi*. Scenes

described by them as making them feel "saddest," "scariest," "happiest," and the "funniest" were chosen, and responses to each were compared to prestimulus levels. Although each scene apparently produced strong feelings, ANS response patterns for the whole group were not significant for the scary and funny scenes. An indirect measure of tearing—the eyeblink response—showed a significant decrease in the sad scene, and skin resistance increased, indicating a possible inhibition of SNS activity in sadness. And in the happy scene, there was a significant slowing of stomach contractions. But this was all, and not much can be made of the patterns of emotional responses obtained. Other studies have been similarly inconclusive.

But Lacey has come up with an interesting suggestion which may prove to be very productive. Rather than trying to demonstrate a separate physiological state in each separate emotion, it may be worthwhile to analyze autonomic behavior into classes of events corresponding to "psychological" (perceptual, motor, cognitive) processes.

Lacey noticed, in some studies (1959), examples of what he called "directional fractionation of response." "These are instances in which the direction of change in one physiological variable is contrary to what might be expected from the still-persistent Cannon-like view of over-all sympathetic activation by 'stress'." This directional fractionation consisted of instances in which heart rate decelerated, but skin conductance increased. The heart rate decelerations typically occurred when subjects had to pay attention to visual and auditory stimuli, such as patterns of lights, dramatic situations on tapes, etc. On the other hand, the heart rate accelerated when the subjects had to solve mental arithmetic problems, or took the cold pressor test. Lacey suggested that cardiac deceleration accompanied or facilitated "environmental intake," while cardiac acceleration accompanied or facilitated "rejection of the environment." This is illustrated in Fig. 20.

In a series of experiments Lacey extended and verified his earlier findings (Lacey et al., 1963). The stimulus conditions that produced cardiac deceleration had in common the requirement of subjects that they pay attention to the stimuli during the period of stimulation—although the conditions differed in other respects.

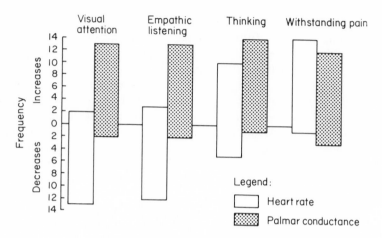

FIG. 20. The "directional fractionation of response" according to the nature of subjects' tasks. For the 15 subjects whose responses are shown here, all 4 stimulus conditions produced increases in palmar conductance, but visual attending resulted in heart rate decreases, while the other tasks involving "rejection" of input resulted in heart rate increases. (From Lacey, 1959. Courtesy of the author and Am. Psychol. Assn.)

On the other hand, the stimulus conditions which produced cardiac acceleration had in common the requirement of mental concentration (and a need to exclude disturbing stimuli), although differing in other ways. It was possible to show that the instances of heart rate decrease were not reflexive responses to increased blood pressure. And it was also shown that a task which required both attending to external stimuli *and* mental concentration resulted in an intermediate heart rate change. Skin conductance, however, always increased, no matter what kind of task was involved. Figure 21 displays these findings.

Here it is clear that stimulus-response specificity exists. Tasks emphasizing cognitive functioning are accompanied by heart rate increases; those emphasizing perceptual functioning are accompanied by heart rate decreases. Lacey draws on some neurophysiological evidence to suggest that increased heart rate serves to diminish transmission along sensory pathways and thus to decrease the effectiveness of external stimuli; the opposite effect

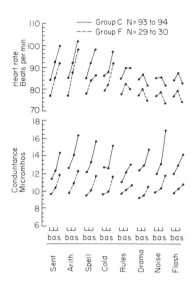

FIG. 21. Average response curves for heart rate and palmar conductance for two groups of subjects and eight stimulus situations. The situations are abbreviated at the bottom and consist of tasks involving Sentences, Arithmetic, Spelling, Cold pressor, Rules of a game, listening to a Dramatic tape, white Noise, and Flashing light. Three points are plotted in graph: "b" for base level is the average pre-stimulus resting value; "a" for alerted level is the average value during one minute of anticipation of the stimulus; and "s" for stimulus level is the average value during the task. The four conditions on the left were chosen to require exclusion of environmental input; the four conditions on the right required attending. The former result in heart rate increases, the latter in heart rate decreases, demonstrating "directional fractionation of response." (From Lacey *et al.,* 1963. Courtesy of the author and Intern. Univ. Press.)

presumably occurs with lowered heart rate. Whatever the (admittedly speculative) mechanisms involved, several important conclusions may be drawn.

First of all these studies, as the ones we described before, indicate a patterning of responses within the activated state. It is plain that there *is* such a phenomenon as activation, and that with respect to the autonomically-innervated variables it consists of a shift to relative apparent SNS dominance of activity. But it is also plain

that this non-specific response is not all there is to the matter, and
that it is no longer particularly useful to think of all emotion or
responses to stress as merely those changes which may be labeled
as "activation." As we have seen, some differentiation has been discovered among the emotions, so that fear responses look like the
changes which occur following the injection of adrenaline, and
anger responses look like changes following injection of both
adrenaline and noradrenaline. But now we see too that it may be
possible to classify the responses to stimulation in terms of their
functional significance, and to detect regularities of autonomic
patterning according to such functional groupings. This is the real
significance of Lacey's findings. Such concepts as the need to enhance stimulus input, or the need to decrease perceived stimulus
intensity, may be more useful in understanding autonomic response patterns than the traditional approach of studying the
consequences of "stress," or trying to discover the physiological
definitions of "emotions."

In this connection we may see the solution to yet another problem. You may recall that in Chapter V on Activation we described
a variety of changes that typically occur. There is a decrease in
alpha rhythm and skin resistance, increase in heart rate and blood
pressure, etc. But a question that has plagued psychophysiologists
for years has been, "Which 'index' of activation do you use"? The
great majority of experiments has shown that among all variables
sampled there are usually small positive correlations which sometimes attain significance, but which seldom are very large. This
means that the degrees of activation are variable in the different
response systems, that they are measuring different things, or that
to the extent they share certain common properties (activation)
the degree of communality is relatively small. Consequently, it was
never quite possible to really use one variable, say GSR, to represent
the degree of activation, any more than it was possible to use only
one to represent the degree of resting autonomic balance. A great
deal of debate took place over the question of which variables
"really" represented the aroused state best, and what the relatively
low intercorrelations meant.

Now we can see, from all that has been presented in this chapter,
that the reason for these relatively low inter-variable relationships

is that while from one point of view activation is a real phenomenon, from another point of view it does not actually exist. Rather
we would be more correct to think of many "activations," as many
as there are simulus conditions. The evidence is now quite convincing that there is such a thing as situational stereotypy, or stimulus-
response specificity, and as we have seen, the patterns of response
vary from situation to situation. It is in attempting to order or
make meaningful groupings of all the stimulus situation possibilities that we are beginning to think of our functioning in different ways.

Another point needs to be made here with respect to the intercorrelations among variables. In the experiment of Ax's which we
described earlier, there were consistently larger correlations among
the variables for anger than for fear. The mean of the fear correlation was .090, and for anger .157 (you see what we mean by small
intercorrelations?) The difference between these two means is
significant. Ax felt that this might indicate a greater physiological
integration during anger than during fear. He thought perhaps
that during the course of evolution a successful attack might have
required a greater organization of the individual's resources than
would a flight response. A complete lack of effective integration
might be illustrated by the paralysis of extreme fear.

This conclusion of Ax's regarding integration received strong
confirmation in the finding by Sternbach (1960a), in a study of
individual differences in speed of recovery from startle, that those
who were slowest to perform a simple motor task following the
startle simulus had shown the greatest autonomic responses to the
stimulus, as compared to the speedy recoverers. But again Lacey
(Lacey et al., 1963) introduces a complication. He found that when
subjects were told that they would hear a recording of angry ex-
changes between peers, the subjects showed a correlation between
palmar conductance and heart rate responses that was highly
significant, suggesting the "integration" Ax proposed. But when
the subjects were told they would hear a recording of a son expressing his anger toward and to his mother, the correlation was
practically zero. This indicates that aggression (anger) is not always
just aggression, but that there may be a variety of kinds of aggression. That which is directed toward peers may involve preparation

for physical assault, that directed toward Mother may include elements of guilt, making the pattern more like fear, to the extent that fear of retaliation is involved.

Some support for this comes from Funkenstein's (1956) finding of different responses in "anger out" (small, temporary reduction of blood pressure in response to mecholyl) and "anger in" (sharp response to mecholyl). Anger-out represents the usual overt expression of aggression; anger-in is supposed to be revealed as depression. But these are only speculations, and are brought up to illustrate the point that, as we said before, we may have to reorganize our usual ways of classifying experience in order to make sense out of our response patterns.

Another point comes to mind with respect to the kinds of experiments performed in psychophysiology to differentiate emotional states. As we have said before, it is difficult to induce real-life situations in the laboratory. What with wires and gadgetry, most subjects are likely to be somewhat apprehensive; those sophisticated enough not to be, are likely not to be fooled by staged situations. The Ax-type of experiment is widely cited in most elementary psychology texts, so college students, most frequently used as subjects, are likely to be aware of a faked emotional situation. For this reason experimenters have turned to other devices—hypnotic suggestion and films have been the most popular means of inducing changes. Hypnosis has problems of its own which we will consider in a later chapter. Films, as we said earlier, are seldom successful in differentiating response patterns. At best they are disappointing. Now, from Lacey's work, we have a possible explanation for this. Despite the content of the film, *i.e.*, no matter what class of responses it is supposed to elicit, it is nevertheless an audiovisual complex to which the subject must attend. As we saw from Lacey's work, *attending* is associated with a configuration of responses of its own. Even when film scenes are presented which, if actually experienced by the subject in real life, would be accompanied by a stimulus-rejection pattern, in this case the subject must continue his activity of perceiving with its concomitant stimulus-enhancement responses. Any other process evoked, such as emotions felt through "identification" or whatever mechanisms are involved, must struggle for expression against the ongoing process of attending, and when the changes are in the opposite direction, minimal or paradoxical responses may be observed. It is this sort of explanation which, in retrospect, may account for my inability to detect significant patterns in children's emotional responses to film, as well as for the disappointments of other experimenters.

Let us recapitulate briefly what we have said so far. Starting with any relaxed, resting subject, virtually any sort of stimulus will produce activation, and activation is a relative preponderance of responses in a sympathetic-like direction. But not all stimuli produce the same responses, so that really there are several kinds of activations, at least. They differ among themselves in the amount of change in the SNS direction, and in some situations some variables will show a change in the opposite (apparent PNS) direction. With continuous change possible in both directions from the prestimulus level, it is theoretically possible that a great number of specific response patterns exists. Attempts have been made to classify some patterns according to the stimulus situations which elicit them. Reliable response configurations have been found for fear, anger, startle, pain, and mental activity (problem solving), and a few other less well-replicated conditions. Only very recently has an attempt been made to classify the patterns of response according to the functions of the organism being performed at the time. This promising approach has resulted in a differentiation between a class of functions which may be called "stimulus-reducing" (e.g., responses to pain) and a class which may be termed "stimulus-enhancing" (e.g., responses to instructions). So far this differentiation applies only to the heart rate variable, but it has been shown to be quite reliable, with replication by several investigators (e.g., Obrist, 1963). The chief point to be made, however, is that patterning within the non-specific activation framework does exist, and that it takes the form of a specificity of response patterns according to the demands of the situation on the subject. But now you will see that there are even further complications in patterning due to individual differences.

VII
Individual Response-Stereotypy

One of man's favorite sports is classifying people into types, and we have been doing it for centuries, on the basis of differences in physical characteristics. The ancients had four types, based on the supposed dominance in one's system of certain body fluids: sanguinary (blood); phlegmatic (phlegm); choleric (yellow bile); and melancholic (black bile). We moderns have regressed in these skills so that we use only three types based on body builds: ectomorph (tall and thin, lonely, cerebral); endomorph (fat, jolly, visceral); and mesomorph (muscular, aggressive, dominant). The search for types still continues and so does our need of them. The reasons may be quite basic and primitive. Strangers have an unknown pattern of behavior, and are therefore potentially threatening. If, by quick visual inspection, we can place them in a category whose characteristics are known, then to some extent we will be able to predict their behavior and so be ready with our own appropriate responses.

For other than such immediately practical reasons, similar attempts have been made with respect to physiological functioning. Alfred Adler based an entire personality system on "organ weakness," and the various compensatory and overcompensatory mechanisms deriving therefrom. And you know, from Chapter III on Autonomic Balance, that a good deal has been made of "vagotonics" and "sympathicotonics." What we are going to deal with in this chapter is, in a way, a kind of typing with respect to autonomic responses. We are not doing this just for the purpose of making such types, however. Our purpose is to examine the evidence available on individual differences in order to see in what ways and to what extent people do differ. Nevertheless, because any attempt to order the data may resemble the construction of a typology, this chapter may be especially interesting to those who like such sport.

First of all we should recall that the original concept of vagotonia and sympathicotonia had to do with *responses* to stimulation by drugs. The vagotonic was the individual who showed strong responses to PNS-type stimulators or inhibitors, but little SNS reactivity. The converse held true for the sympathicotonic. This was one of the first demonstrations of the differences among individuals in autonomic responsivity.

Secondly, internists and psychiatrists have for many years pointed to the existence of certain characteristic features in patient populations. Many persons come to the doctor with complaints of certain symptoms resembling diseases, and they leave with "negative findings," but still complaining. That is, no physical or structural or organic basis for their symptoms was found—or, signs of pathological functioning are detected, but these signs may be modified easily by placebos, reassurances, or changes in the life situation. The older terminology for such cases was "cardiac neurosis," "gastric neurosis," and so on, and the assumption was that these patients had a constitutional weakness in the affected organ which predisposed them to such symptoms.

Psychosomatic disorders supply a third line of evidence for the existence of individual differences in functioning. We are going to discuss these in detail in a later chapter, so we will say here only that these diseases, representing various bodily systems, also seemed to suggest the existence of individual differences in constitutional predispositions. The word "constitutional" in these traditional explanations refers to the chronic state of the tissues on which responses to stress are superimposed. It may imply "genetic" or "hereditary," but also other factors such as may occur in intrauterine development, exposure history to the present, "conditioned" responses, and anything else that may influence or account for the present tendency to respond in a given fashion. Although "constitutional predisposition" is not much in vogue now because it is old and not specific, the fact is it is a useful term because the concept is important, and we do not have anything better. We will be returning to this later in the chapter.

As we have indicated, before there was much experimental support for individual differences in reaction patterns, clinicians had already accumulated a considerable lore in this area. Years ago Cameron (1941) could say, "There are individuals in whom the blood pressure is the major participant in the emotional reaction, in others it is the gastrointestinal tract."

The first modern psychophysiological study on this problem was that of Malmo and Shagass (1949), who examined the responses to pain stimuli of psychiatric patients with a history of cardiovascular complaints and of psychiatric patients with a history of head and neck pains. They found that heart rate, heart rate variability, and respiratory variability scores were all reliably greater for the group of patients with cardiovascular complaints, while muscle potential scores were reliably higher for the patients with complaints of head and neck pains. Malmo and Shagass concluded that patients with somatic complaints tended to show increased responsiveness in the related physiological system when exposed to stress. They thought that the increased responsiveness was specific to the system associated with the complaint, and could be demonstrated even though most of the patients were symptom-free at the time of testing. Figure 22 illustrates the differences between the groups in their muscle and cardiac responses.

This and other research on patient groups led Malmo and his associates (1950a, b) to formulate what they called the *principle of symptom-specificity*. This principle states that, for psychiatric patients with a somatic symptom, the physiological mechanism underlying the symptom is specifically responsive to activation by stressful stimuli. Now we will see an example of how clinical lore can be brought to experimental trial, and when supported, generate a principle which extends beyond the patient groups to all persons. This will be demonstrated when we consider what has become of Malmo's symptom-specificity principle.

It used to be that patients were considered a group apart, somehow qualitatively different from everyone else; in thinking, perceiving, feeling, patients were supposed to be different in kind from non-patients. Scarcely anyone thinks this way anymore. Even

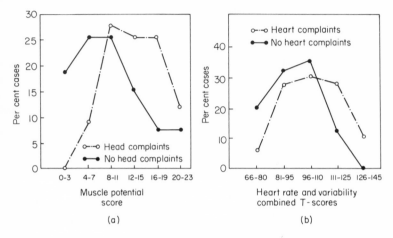

FIG. 22. Comparison of response scores from systems associated with, and free of symptoms. In (a) is shown the percentage distribution of muscle potential scores for patients with head complaints compared with those free of such complaints. In (b) is shown the percentage distribution of combined heart rate scores for patients with heart complaints compared with those free of such complaints. (From Malmo & Shagass, 1949. Courtesy of the authors and Hoeber Medical Division, Harper & Row.)

in instances in which patient groups can be shown to differ significantly from normal controls, there is usually considerable overlap among the populations. So nowadays we tend to think of patients as being quantitatively different from non-patients, as differing only in *degree* of symptomatology, in *extent* of confusion, anxiety, depression, etc.

Now if this is so, then why should not the principle of symptom-specificity apply to all? This question occurred to Lacey, and his findings—along with those of others—have been perhaps the most intriguing in recent psychophysiological research. In a series of experiments Lacey and his co-workers (1952, 1953, 1958) applied a number of stress situations to several different subject populations. Mental arithmetic, hyperventilation, word association, and the cold pressor test were the stimuli used; the groups were: 12 pregnant women; 57 boys and 53 girls aged 6 to 18; 85 male college students; and 42 adult women.

Since it was not known whether the principle of symptom-specificity could be applied to the normal case, it was reformulated as an hypothesis of relative response-specificity: "relative" because it referred the responses of each physiological variable to those of every other variable; and "response" rather than "symptom" because it would be premature to assume that response-specificity in a normal person would become his symptom-specificity if he developed a psychosomatic disease. The specific hypothesis being tested was: for a given set of autonomic measurements, individuals tend to respond with maximal activation in the same physiological function in a variety of stress situations. The variables sampled were heart rate, beat-to-beat variability of heart rate, and palmar conductance.

Trying to compare these three variables with one another is like trying to compare turtles, turnips, and turquoise; it cannot be done directly. Yet this is exactly the problem, to see whether an individual responds "more" on one variable than another. It was for this reason that Lacey (1956) developed the method of measurement using equivalent deviation units which he called the Autonomic Lability Score, and which we described in Chapter IV on the LIV. It is important to understand the reasoning underlying this method of data analysis, because the concepts arising from these studies depend on the method.

First of all, it was clearly demonstrated that individuals do tend to respond in such a way that maximal activation occurs in the same physiological function no matter what the stress. And it further appears that the entire pattern of activation may be reproduced from one stimulus situation to another. In other words, in these studies, the individual who shows a maximal response in heart rate, a moderate response in heart rate variability, and a low response in palmar conductance, when the stressor is mental arithmetic, is likely to show the same pattern in response to cold pressor. Remember that "maximum" response refers to the individual's standing in relation to the rest of the group. In this example, the individual shows more of a heart rate response than the others, and less of an increase in palmar conductance than the others — and he is likely to maintain these standings from one situation to the next. Figure 23 illustrates these findings.

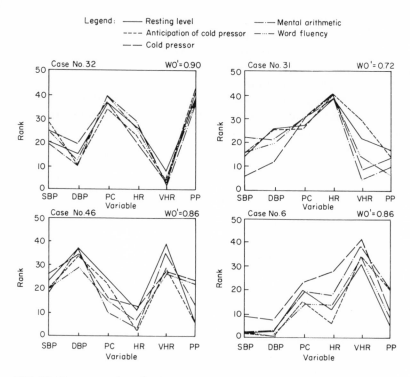

FIG. 23. Four examples of relative response-stereotypy, involving the five conditions of measurement shown at the top of the figure. On the abscissa are shown the six variables measured: systolic and diastolic blood pressure, palmar conductance, heart rate, variability of heart rate, and pulse pressure. The ordinates represent ranks, showing the relative positions of the subjects in the total group of 42. Wo' is the coefficient of concordance corrected for continuity. Note that these subjects show the same pattern of response from stimulus to stimulus. Compare also with Fig. 9. (From Lacey, 1959. Courtesy of the author and Am. Psychol. Assn.)

We are going to come back to this point shortly, with some modifications, but it is worthwhile to stop and consider what this means, and to raise an interesting question. First of all, it would seem that the phenomenon of symptom-specificity, as demonstrated by Malmo, can indeed be extended to the normal population. In terms that may be overdramatic but actually not too farfetched, it seems to be legitimate to think of some individuals as "sweating reactors," of others as "cardiac reactors," etc., *as compared to others*. And although it really is premature, as Lacey said, to assume that such individuals would develop psychosomatic complaints of the same systems when sufficiently stressed, it is certainly worth investigating this possibility. If longitudinal studies support the hypothesis that "sweat reactors" under appropriate conditions develop hyperhydrosis, that "cardiac reactors" develop "cardiac neuroses," that "stomach reactors" develop ulcers, and so on, then we shall be further along the way toward an understanding of the psychosomatic diseases.

It should be noted that a patterning of responses in a way that is unique to the individual was observed also by Ax, even though he had been studying the characteristic stimulus-response specificities of fear and anger, as we described in the last chapter. Ax noted a "marked uniqueness in physiological expression of emotion." This observation was supported by his finding a significantly larger between-subjects variance as compared with the within-subjects variance.

Now the interesting question, which must have occurred to you already, is: How can there be *both* a patterning of responses to the stimulus situation *and* a patterning unique to each individual? It would seem that if responses occurred so that activation showed one pattern for fear and another for anger, then there would be little room for variation among individuals. On the other hand, if each person showed characteristic response patterns, then there could be no responses "typical" for fear, anger, cold pressor, etc.

Before we consider *how* such double patterning can occur, we need to see whether or not it really does. In none of the studies cited so far, has any investigator specifically examined the question of whether and to what extent both stimulus (S-R) and individual (I-R) specificity of responses occurred in the same group of subjects for a given set of situations. In two papers remarkable for their sophisticated mathematical analyses, Engel (1960, 1961) addressed himself directly to the question of whether both kinds of patterning can occur simultaneously. Employing a group of 20 young nurses and student nurses, Engel presented five stimulus situations: a loud automobile horn; mental arithmetic; scrambled proverbs; cold pressor; and exercise. Each stimulus lasted 30 sec.

Improving on previous studies, Engel sampled a wider variety of autonomic functions. His response measures were: systolic and diastolic blood pressures; palmar skin resistance; finger and face temperatures; heart rate and heart rate variability; and respiration rate. Engel (1960) found that among the eight responses measured, seven showed significant differences among the subjects. His data clearly demonstrated that both stimulus-response and individual-response specificity existed for his subjects and stimuli "by all criteria."

This study was then repeated (Engel & Bickford, 1961) on twenty hypertensive women and twenty matched controls, in order to determine whether the findings could be repeated, and whether there would be greater uniformity of individual-response patterning among the hypertensives, as you might expect. The results were quite confirmatory: the frequency of occurrence of S-R specificity was not different between the groups, but the variable in which the patients most frequently responded to each stimulus was systolic pressure; this was never true of the normals. Both hypertensives and normals showed I-R specificity, but the hypertensives showed a significantly greater degree of it. And although the frequency of occurrence of I-R specificity was not different between the groups, 15 of the 20 hypertensives showed their specificity in blood pressure, as compared to only 5 of the 20 normals. An example of a stereotyped response pattern of a hypertensive subject is shown in Fig. 24.

Basic to these analyses was a covariance design, which we mentioned in the chapter on the LIV. It makes possible an examination of the data first one way, then another, while removing the influence of the other factors. The point to be made here is that both S-R and I-R patternings *do* occur simultaneously, and they are detectable only by appropriate data analysis. Which sort of pattern the investigator pays attention to will depend on his own interests and the way he chooses to look at the data.

Now, how can this double-patterning occur? In any single individual the response will be determined largely by two major factors. One is the nature of the stimulus-situation as it is *perceived by the person;* the other is the nature of his response hierarchy. As an example, let us assume that an individual is frightened in

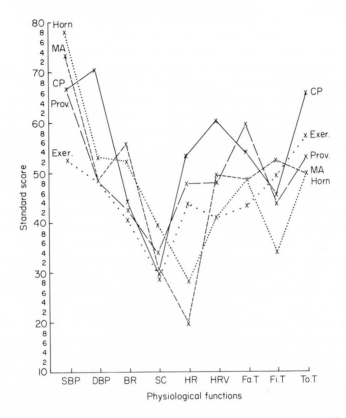

FIG. 24. An example of response-stereotypy in a hypertensive subject. The five stimulus conditions are Horn, Mental Arithmetic, Cold Pressor, Proverbs, and Exercise. The variables on the abscissa are systolic and diastolic blood pressures, breathing rate, skin conductance, heart rate and heart rate variability, and face, finger, and toe temperatures. (From Engel & Bickford, 1961. Courtesy of the authors and the Am. Med. Assoc.)

one situation, and angered in another. From the research we described earlier, we may expect that certain of the responses we can measure will be different in the two conditions. We might, for instance, observe a decrease in gastric functioning in the frightened state, and an increase in the digestive processes when he is angered.

This is likely to occur among most persons. However, the differences among individuals may occur in the *extent* to which the stomach responds. When we have converted all responses to standard scores (so that gastric motility changes, for example, can be compared to heart rate, sweating, and blood pressure changes), then we can tell whether an individual's increase or decrease in motility is greater than his other responses, or less. One person may show his largest response in both conditions with an increase in systolic blood pressure. Another person's greatest responses may be the gastric ones: in the fear situation his decreased rate of gastric motility may exceed the increases in blood pressure, heart rate, and sweating; while in the anger situation his increased gastric motility may likewise be greater than the other responses measured. In each case, remember, we are talking about magnitude of responses as compared with each other, and also as compared with those of the other individuals who have received the same treatment. It is this latter comparison which makes possible the determination of the relative magnitude of each of the individual's responses as expressed in standard scores.

Now we have to consider still another aspect of the stereotypy of individual responses. If a person responds most with a change in heart rate, will that response be the greatest one to *all* stimuli? In other words, to what extent does this kind of specificity hold up across conditions? To answer this question properly we need to take a detour and consider first several possible definitions of specificity of responses. (From one point of view it would have been better to put this discussion at the beginning of the last chapter, but it is likely to be more understandable here.) You may have noticed that when we were discussing stimulus-response specificity we sometimes described a single response system which seemed to be specific to the stimulus, and sometimes we described a patterning of responses which seemed unique to the stimulus situation. For example, if a group of subjects shows its greatest change in a blood pressure increase to the cold pressor test, then S-R specificity may be defined in just that way. Similarly, if the direction of response to a situation is always the same, then that response may be considered specific to the situation which elicited it. In this sense Lacey's description of heart rate increases accompanying stimulus exclusion *vs.* heart rate decreases accompanying the process of perceiving, may be considered an example of S-R specificity. However, if we consider a number of responses together, then our definition must be a little different. In this case we may define the specificity as a certain ranking of responses according to their magnitude. For example, the cold pressor stimulus might always produce the greatest responses in blood pressure, followed in frequency by heart rate changes, then palmar sweating, then finger pulse volume, etc.

Now the same sort of thinking may be applied to the stereotypy of an individual's responses. We may think of this stereotypy as a certain function always showing the greatest change in any group of stimulus situations. This was Malmo's principle of symptom-specificity. He showed that in the patient groups there was a clear tendency for each group to exceed the other with responses involving their symptom variable. More specifically, as Engel noted, hypertensives would show their specificity in blood pressure far more frequently than normals. Again, if we consider a number of responses, we may consider that an individual shows response stereotypy when he produces the same rank order of responses to a variety of stimuli. Both of these definitions, the one concerning maximal response of a single variable, and the other involving the relationships among responses, have been experimentally confirmed. In fact, a third definition which involves not only rankings of responses but their quantitative intercorrelations, has also been supported. This is what Engel referred to when he said that stimulus-response and individual-response specificities exist (for his subjects and stimuli) "by all criteria"; by maximum response frequencies, by rank orders, and by interresponse correlations.

However, we now have to make an interesting modification of what we have said so far. When we say that the findings "supported" or "confirmed" certain hypotheses we mean, of course, in a statistical sense. This means that the results could have occurred by chance only once in a hundred times, or whatever criterion is used. So in these studies, the number of subjects who demonstrate individual response-stereotypy is *statistically* "significant." But this is not necessarily true for *every* subject. As a matter of fact, Lacey observed that individuals vary in the extent to which they demonstrate response-stereotypy. Some exhibit almost a random pattern, showing one response hierarchy to one stimulus, another to another stimulus, and so on. At the other extreme are those individuals who seem to have almost no flexibility, reproducing the same response hierarchy in situation after situation. This latter is analogous to the information we have about the symptom specificity of psychosomatic patients, except that this lack of flexibility involves the patterning of several variables and not just maximum response in one.

In support of Lacey's observations is the finding by Johnson *et al.* (1963) that two-thirds of their subjects, and by Engel (1960) that only 8 of 20 subjects showed statistically significant stereotypy by the criteria of ranking and interresponse correlations. This again suggests a distribution of subjects ranging from those who might be called "random reactors" at one extreme to those who might be called "rigid reactors" at the other extreme. Other investigators have also reported that stereotypy is demonstrable only in some subjects. Thus individual response-stereotypy is, like our other principles, essentially a statistical concept.

Nevertheless, these findings suggest an interesting possibility. For a long time it seemed as if no clear-cut way of describing individual differences in reactivity could be found, which would be analogous to the differences in resting states described by Wenger's estimate of autonomic balance. Now it seems there may be. As the Laceys noted (Lacey & Lacey, 1958), most subjects have some tendency toward I-R specificity, but there are quantitative individual differences in this tendency.

If this could be supported, and the differences in tendency toward stereotypy were scoreable and a distribution of such scores approximated the normal one, then a description of individual differences in reactivity would be possible. The extremes of such a distribution would be the "random" and "rigid" reactors (as vagotonia and sympathicotonia were extremes of the distribution of autonomic balance scores). And one would be tempted to speculate about the clinical significance of the two extremes. But such speculations here are already far ahead of the available data.

The reason why such speculation is premature is that there is conflicting evidence about the stability of the stereotypy of re-

sponses. We need to consider to what extent this kind of patterning will hold up over time. We will come back to this point in a
moment, but first it is necessary to think about the experimental
concepts that have been implicit in our discussions of specificities
so far. When we talked about stimulus-response specificity, we
said that certain characteristic responses could be elicited by
certain appropriate stimuli. This presupposes a definite scheme
for the psychophysiological experiment: a stimulus (fear-provok-
ing) is presented to a group of subjects whose responses (heart
rate, GSR, blood pressure, etc.) are measured. You need to have
the group of subjects to make sure that the patterns of response
to the single stimulus are typical of the *stimulus,* not just typical of
one individual. On the other hand, in order to demonstrate that
individual response-stereotypy exists, you need only one subject
to whom you present a group of stimuli ("fear," "anger," "mental
concentration," etc.). The group of stimuli are necessary to show
that the patterns of response you obtain are typical for the *individual,* not just for one stimulus. Of course, in most experiments,
the experimental design just described is fleshed out for purposes
of efficiency. So, for example, in the stimulus-response specificity
study, although only one stimulus is *necessary* in order to demonstrate the point, in fact several stimuli are often presented so as
to see *how likely* such specificity is, whether it will occur in more
than one situation. In the same way, although only one individual is
necessary in order to demonstrate that response-stereotypy *can*
exist, it is usual to use a group, and in this way determine how
likely stereotypy may be, or what degrees of it we may encounter.

Now another dimension can be added to the design of our experiments, and this relates to the question of consistency over time.
Can the phenomenon of response-stereotypy be reproduced on
more than one occasion? So to the list of variables which consisted
of stimuli, subjects, and responses, we must now add *occasions.*
This question is of major importance in our speculation about the
causes of the psychosomatic diseases, and it applies to both the
concepts of stimulus and individual specificities. Because if our
assumption is that repeated exposure to certain situations (e.g.,
anger-provoking) will cause exaggerated responses leading to
tissue damage (e.g., ulcers) then we must be able to show the

reproducibility of the response pattern in anger on repeated occasions. On the other hand, if our assumption is that repeated exposure to many kinds of stressful situations will cause certain individuals (gastric reactors) to have the tissue change (ulcers) then we must be able to show the reproducibility of their response patterns on repeated occasions.

Unfortunately there is not much evidence on this matter. As we mentioned, the Laceys (1962) found that for 37 children ages 6 to 17, there was good reproducibility of response patterns obtained on two occasions, at the ages given and then 4 years later, using systolic and diastolic blood pressures, heart rate and heart rate variability, and palmar conductance. They found that the rank orders of the response magnitudes of the different physiological variables were reproduced with "greater than chance expectancy" over the 4-year period. Unfortunately, only the cold pressor test was used as a stimulus. We say "unfortunately" because as we just described it is necessary to use several stimuli in order to demonstrate stereotypy. It could be said of Lacey's study that it only shows the reproducibility of the response patterns to the cold pressor test—that is, of stimulus-response specificity. Or it may merely show that individuals are consistent in their response to this particular stimulus.

A more direct attack on the problem has been made by two groups of investigators. Oken and his colleagues (1962) measured 9 autonomic variables in 18 college students, using 3 stimulus conditions on two occasions a week apart. They found that stereotypy, whether judged by the specific variable showing maximum change, or by hierarchy of responses, did not hold up over time. Johnson *et al.* (1963) came to similar conclusions. They tested 24 Navy men with 6 stimuli on two occasions 48 hours apart, and measured 4 autonomic responses. Although significant stereotypy of responses was obtained for about two-thirds of the subjects when analysis of variance was employed, rank order tests showed that response hierarchies changed from stimulus to stimulus for more than one-half of the subjects. More importantly for our present discussion, they found that those subjects who did show stereotypy on the first day did not do so on the second day.

These findings suggest that as the number of stimulus and response variables are increased, individual response-stereotypy is harder to demonstrate over time. There is some suggestion too that if the stimuli elicit very different functions and the group of subjects is very homogeneous, then stereotypy again will be harder to demonstrate over time. We are left to conclude that response specificity does exist in varying degrees in individuals, but the specificity does not seem to hold up over several occasions of testing. It may be, as Wenger *et al.* (1961) have suggested, that we should be cautious about overgeneralizing the significance and pervasiveness of this phenomenon.

There may be several other reasons, besides those we have suggested, why specificity is not so consistently demonstrable. We will consider these possible factors in the next two chapters, which deal with what are usually thought of as "extraneous" variables.

VIII
Explicit Sets

The word *set* as we will use it here is defined by a number of synonymous phrases, such as a *readiness to respond,* a *predisposition* or *tendency* or *propensity to respond.* From another point of view, a *set* is an *expectancy* or *anticipation* of an event. The first group of phrases is primarily oriented to the production of responses, while the second group emphasizes the reception of stimuli. However, in each case the concept is that of an intervening variable. That is, *set* refers to a process which either mediates between input and output, or which modulates input and/or output, but which itself is not directly observable.

If sets cannot be directly observed, how can we know they exist? The concept was one of the very earliest in experimental psychology and was used to account for differences between "simple" and "disjunctive" reaction times. For example, it takes longer for subjects to press a key when they must do so only when one of two lights flashes, as compared with the situation in which they can press whenever either light flashes. There are a variety of other situations which make the existence of sets a reasonable inference. It is well known that not every input has a corresponding output. For instance, there are many occasions (sleep, exhaustion, "narrowed attention") when stimuli elicit no observable response, whereas they may do so on other occasions. What is different on these occasions, we are saying, is the nature or kind of set. Another, somewhat similar situation which forces us to postulate the existence of sets is this: an input at one time may result in an output which is different from that produced by an identical input at another time. For example, an odor of food may make us salivate and want to eat when we are hungry, but the identical odor may make us nauseated and turn away if we have eaten or are ill. Again, the difference is one of sets. Finally, there are times when we can observe outputs whose corresponding inputs are not specifiable. There are many kinds of behavior which we cannot squeeze into a simple stimulus-response (S-R) type of model. Not every yawn, sudden urge to see a friend, coughing at a concert, etc., can be said to follow a known stimulus. And so we must postulate processes in the organism to account for these behaviors. Sometimes these sets are known, or we can make fairly certain guesses about them, and label them "sleepiness" or "fatigue" or "hunger" and so on. On the basis of other evidence we make assumptions about the physiological state of the individual which in most instances satisfy us with their "explanatory" value. When we do so we are using the concept of sets in a causal way, and although this may be correct, we cannot always be sure. There are some cases that are very difficult to handle this way. Take the example of the new mother whose infant begins to whimper in the next room at 3:00 A.M. In an instant she is awake and hovering over the crib; but a few minutes before, or a half hour later, she may be totally oblivious to sirens outside, phone ringing, etc. To what mechanism(s) may we attribute such selective perception? We can make guesses about thresholds, but rather than try to speculate prematurely, it may be more useful to deal with the concept of set itself, and work out in some detail the ways in which it seems to mediate between input and output. This is no new idea, of course, for the field of psychology is rich with material on intervening variables. Woodworth and Schlosberg (1954) suggested always writing the formula, S-O-R (stimulus-organism-response) to keep ourselves aware of the importance of the processes in the organism that modulate both stimuli and responses. These processes are what we are calling sets, and now we need to consider the extent to which they influence the kinds of response systems which are measured in psychophysiological research.

Perhaps the best way to begin is with an illustration which demonstrates that sets do indeed influence autonomic functioning. Anyone who has recorded subjects on the polygraph over a period of days has probably noticed a phenomenon that seems to be unique to the first session. Subjects typically verbalize some anxiousness about the situation: they make feeble jokes about being "wired for sound," or "sitting in the electric chair," or "going into orbit." This "anxiousness" is our interpretation of their set which, in conjunction with the gadgetry which serve as stimuli, produces such comments. Is there any other evidence for this set? Retrospectively, *i.e.*, looking back over a series of sessions, we can see in the polygraph tracings evidence for a generalized activation at the beginning of the first session. Typically, blood pressure, heart rate, skin conductance, etc., are at considerably higher values than on subsequent occasions (excepting for responses to deliberate stimulation). Adaptation of these responses usually occurs with repetitive exposure to the situation. This is a good example also of the way the process of adaptation may be thought of as the extinction of ANS responses by non-reinforcement. In subjective terms, the anxiousness concerned anticipated pain or harm based on past experiences with electricity, or fantasies about it. But if what is expected fails to appear, then the responses diminish. On the other hand, if the experimental situation does reinforce the responses—that is, if strong and unpleasant stimuli are introduced in the session—then the adaptation does not occur, and the initial levels of autonomic activity may look the same on subsequent occasions as on the first day.

This example should make two points clear. First, there are such phenomena as sets, and they can and do affect ANS functioning. Second, there is no need to think of sets as mysterious entities or processes, because their functioning may be explained—or rather described—in terms of classical conditioning models. Whether we direct our attention to the individual's sensory processes or his response systems, fluctuations in performance, which cause us to use the concept of changing sets, will tend to observe a certain lawfulness which dispels any aura of mystery. In fact, we may deliberately manipulate sets and observe the effects of this manipulation under controlled laboratory conditions. Here is one example of just such a procedure (Sternbach, 1965).

Twelve male college students participated in a psychophysical

study of electric shock magnitudes. All subjects had been performing similar tasks in the laboratory for several weeks, and the
situation was familiar to them. Their task now was to assign numerical values to a series of shocks of different current strengths,
giving the number "10" to a shock of 6.0 milliamperes and appropriate numbers to other stimuli ranging from 2.0 to 10.0 milliamperes. There were two conditions: in one "60 cps" condition,
the subjects were told that we were using the usual 60 cycle per
second current; in the other "75 cps" condition, the same subjects had the same task and received the identical stimuli, but were
told we were now trying 75 cycle per second current which might
produce some unpleasant sensations and, perhaps, some slight
tissue damage. Half the subjects received one condition first, and
half the other. Actually, of course, nothing in the experiment
differed in the two conditions except the instructions.

You can see the results in Fig. 25. It is clear that in the "75 cps"
condition, subjects assigned greater numerical values to the shocks.
It may not be far-fetched to say that *to them,* the shocks in this con-
ditior *felt* stronger than the same shocks in the other condition.
At least, our estimate of their subjective impressions — the numerical productions — support this notion. Now, what was the difference
in instructions that accounted for this result? First, the instructions suggested that "75 cps" shocks would *feel* stronger. Second,
since we mentioned the possibility of damage, the implication was
clear that the shocks *were* stronger, in a sense, and so the subjects'
sets — their anticipation of the sensations and their readiness to produce larger numbers than they would otherwise — were modified
by these instructions. If, in addition, there was "anxiety" due to
the anticipation of pain or apprehension about damage, then this
might have served to potentiate the differences in the two conditions. If ANS measures had been recorded in this study we might
expect to find a more generalized activation in the "75 cps" as
compared to the "60 cps" condition, but such recordings which
would lead us to infer "anxiety" were not obtained. The point,
however, is that the subjects' sets — judging from their responses —
were modified in the direction you would expect from the instructions.

From the two examples we have given it appears that subjects'

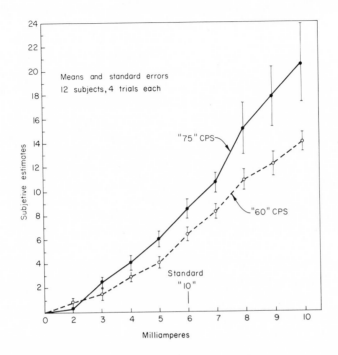

FIG. 25. Magnitude estimates of shock strengths made by experienced subjects. Although the same subjects were given the identical stimuli on two occasions, in the "75 cps" condition they were told that the nature of the shocks was different, and subjects estimated their strength as greater. (From Sternbach, 1965. Courtesy of the Univ. of Wisconsin Press and the Regents of the Univ. of Wisconsin.)

sets may influence their autonomic functioning, and that such sets may be altered or influenced by instructions. Is there any evidence to show that autonomic activity can be modified directly by instructions, or by the explicit manipulation of sets? This is the central question of this chapter, but the answers are not simple, and we will have to examine some apparently contradictory evidence.

One recent and sophisticated approach was a study by Graham, Kabler and Graham (1962) in which they attempted to change subjects' ANS responses in a specific and predicted direction. Hypnotized normal subjects were given suggestions of attitudes which had previously been found typical of patients who had hives or hypertension. The essence of the attitude in hives was that the subject felt he was being unjustly treated and could not think of anything he wanted to do about it. The essence of the hypertension attitude was that he had to be on guard against bodily assault. The stimulus for both situations was a suggested burn, or the threat of one. The predictions made were: hand skin temperatures would rise more with the suggestion of the hives attitude than with the suggestion of the hypertension attitude; diastolic blood pressure would show a greater increase with the hypertension suggestion than the hives suggestion. Although systolic blood pressure and heart and respiration rate were also measured, no prediction of changes were made for these variables.

Results confirmed the predictions. Mean change, maximal rise, and rate of change of skin temperature during the hives suggestion were significantly greater than the corresponding changes during the hypertension suggestion. Likewise, all three measures of change in diastolic blood pressure were significantly greater during the hypertension than during the hives suggestion. Furthermore, the two suggestions did not produce different effects on the other variables measured. Figure 26 shows the major results.

This report of the Grahams, along with other studies of theirs, is of particular significance for the understanding of the psychosomatic diseases, and we will consider their work in considerable detail in the chapter on that topic. Of relevance to our present discussion, however, is the fact that by inducing different sets in the subjects, differential autonomic responses were obtained.

Here you may well ask, "How do you know that different *sets* were induced by the two kinds of suggestions?"—all we really observe is two kinds of stimuli or input, and two kinds of response patterns or output. This is a reasonable question, and the answer is simply to point again to the definition of sets as unobservable intervening variables. Although it is true enough that the results suggest (and support) stimulus-response specificity, consider the nature of the stimuli. These were verbal statements abstracted from those made in psychiatric interviews by patients with the particular psychosomatic disorders mentioned. For these patients, their verbalizations represented attitudes (sets) that mediated between their stimuli (life situations) and their responses (phys-

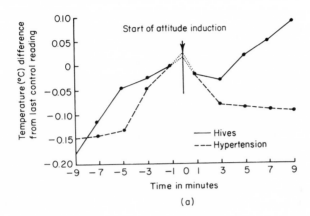

(a)

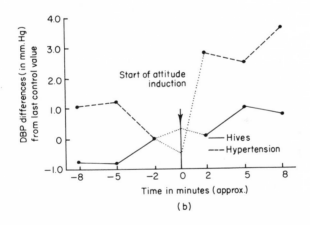

(b)

FIG. 26. The effects of different instructions given during hypnosis in responses to the suggestion of a burn. In (a) is shown the hand temperature response with the instructed attitudes of hives and hypertension patients (see text), and in (b) is shown the diastolic blood pressure response. (From Graham, Kabler & Graham, 1962. Courtesy of the authors and Hoeber Medical Division, Harper & Row.)

iological changes which became pathological). So their verbalizations are our clues to the way they perceive the world, their expectancies, or readiness to respond — their sets. Now when these same verbalizations are presented to healthy subjects, our assumption must be that, although they are stimuli as are any instructions, they are stimuli which now modify the *subjects'* sets, as they had for the patients. It is in this way that we must explain the different patterning of responses to a "burn," suggested or threatened.

Now let us take a little detour and ask, what about hypnosis? Can we really alter physiological functioning by this means? You can see immediately that although it might seem as if we are off on "another" topic, we are really still with the same one. This is still the area of explicit, instructional sets. Consequently you might expect that the effects of hypnotic instructions should indeed be influential in altering functioning just as other forms of set-changing have been shown to be. Let us, first, take a look at hypnosis itself.

In a most remarkable and important paper, Orne (1959) has reviewed and tested the major hypotheses as to just what constitutes hypnosis. While we cannot go into his findings in detail, it turns out that for all objective, behavioral criteria — such as hypnotic amnesia, paralysis, enhanced physical capacity — it is impossible to distinguish between subjects who were "really" hypnotized and those who were only "faking." Such differences as may exist between "real" and "faking" subjects seem to be purely subjective, and appear primarily as an increased tolerance for logical inconsistencies on the part of the "real" subjects.

The implications of this for our purposes is that we should not expect to find any magical effect of hypnosis on autonomic functioning. In Orne's report, instructions under hypnosis did not produce behavioral effects qualitatively or quantitatively different from those given under simulated trance. Accordingly, it would seem reasonable to suppose that the same would be true for instructions designed to influence ANS variables — that is, both hypnotic and non-hypnotic instructions would have effects, but these would not differ from each other.

Orne and his colleagues tested this hypothesis in a later study (Damaser, Shor & Orne, 1963). Two groups of subjects were used, "real" and "simulators," the latter having the task of faking hypnosis and fooling the experimenter. Four emotions were suggested: fear, calmness, happiness, and depression. Each of the four emotions was requested from each subject eight times, four times in the waking state and four times in hypnotic trance. This applied to the "simulators" as well, who had to fake it during the trance conditions. Heart rate, skin potential, and muscle potential were the variables recorded.

The obtained results are quite interesting. Not only were there consistent physiological changes, but the responses tended to fit the emotions requested. That is, the greatest changes on all variables occurred to the fear suggestion, and the least changes occurred during the suggestion of calmness, with the other emotions being intermediate. Further, a good deal of the expected individual differences occurred, so that support for both S-R and I-R specificity appears, although this was not the main intent of the study. Most important, the physiological changes which occurred in the suggested emotions were neither different nor greater in the hypnotic state than in the waking condition. Furthermore, the effects were no more frequent in the Real group than in the Simulating group, nor do the Real subjects show a greater dispersion of their responses than do the Simulators.

Graham and Kunish (1965), reanalyzing the above data, found that in fact Damaser *et al.* had obtained greater differentiation of the extreme emotions (fear and calmness) with hypnotic suggestions than with waking suggestions. In two additional experiments, Graham and Kunish found that waking suggestions could produce differential physiological responses as do hypnotic suggestions, although the effects are less pronounced.

These findings are those we said we expected. Instructions (manipulating sets explicitly) do alter psychophysiological functioning, but instructions given under hypnosis are only slightly more effective than other kinds. Similar physiological changes can be produced by those who are faking the hypnotic trance, by the real hypnotic subjects during the waking conditions, and by waking instructions.

Additional support for this conclusion comes from the work of Barber and Hahn (1962), who tested the effectiveness of hypnosis on alleviating pain due to a prolonged (3-minute) cold pressor test. Four groups of subjects were used: those who received hypnotic suggestions of analgesia; those who received waking instructions to imagine analgesia; those who received no instructions concerning analgesia, and a "control" group which was also uninstructed, but which received water at room temperature instead of 2° C. The physiological measures recorded were muscle potential, respiration irregularities, heart rate, and skin resistance.

On subjective ratings of their experiences, the hypnosis and the Waking-Imagination groups did not differ significantly in reported pain, which for both groups was significantly less than the Uninstructed group and significantly more than the Control group. Similar results were obtained for the physiological measures. The Hypnosis and Waking-Imagination groups did not differ significantly on any physiological response to the icy water. When compared to the Uninstructed group, both the Hypnosis and Waking-Imagination groups had significantly smaller increases in muscle potentials and respiratory irregularities. In fact, both kinds of instructions (Hypnotic and Waking) reduced muscle tension to the low level found in the Control condition, but this was not so effective for respiration. However, for heart rate and skin resistance, neither Hypnotic nor Waking-Imagination instructions were effective. Subjects in these two groups showed increased heart rate and decreased skin resistance that was not significantly different from the Uninstructed group, while all three of these groups differed slightly from the Control group on the two variables.

From these two independent yet similarly tightly-controlled studies, the theme of this chapter receives additional support. Instructions can modify (sets and) psychophysiological response systems, but there is no significant difference in effectiveness between hypnotic and non-hypnotic instructions. You might wonder why, in the last study, neither of the two kinds of analgesic instructions affected the heart rate or skin resistance responses to cold pressor. If instructions work, why did they not alter the autonomic responses as they did the "voluntary" (breathing and muscle) ones? We do not know the reason for this. We have shown in several studies that such changes can and do occur, but obviously we are a long way from understanding how they do, and what are the necessary and sufficient conditions for the effectiveness of explicit sets. The difference between the Orne and the Barber experiments is clear: in the Orne study, instructions were designed to induce physiological change; in the Barber study, instructions attempted to inhibit such changes. Both experiments found essentially no difference between hypnotic and non-hypnotic instructions. Yet from their results we might wish to hypothesize that it is easier to elicit autonomic responses by appropriate instructions than it is to prevent such responses to other stimuli. Let us examine some studies which bear on this question; and since we have shown that instructions are instructions, whether hypnotic or not, let us leave the area of hypnosis, which still smacks of hanky-panky for many readers, and return to the more generalized model of instructions.

In an attempt to study the effects of so-called "audioanalgesia," (diminution of pain by sound), Sternbach (1964) tested the hypothesis that any such effects would be due to suggestion (instructions, expectancies, sets). Subjects received electric shocks under conditions of loud noise and no-noise. One group was informed that noise would increase their sensitivity and shocks would feel stronger when noise was present. Another group was informed that noise served to deaden pain, and that the shocks would feel weaker when noise was introduced. A third group was told that studies indicated no effect of noise, that shocks would feel the same whether or not noise was present. Palmar skin resistance, heart rate, and finger pulse volume were the response variables measured. Conflicting results were obtained. The group which was to expect more pain under the noise condition showed only one significant difference—a bigger finger pulse volume decrease to shocks with no noise present. The "neutral" group showed a significant increase in heart rate when noise was present. Only the group which expected a diminution of shock strength when noise was present responded according to predictions. For this group both skin resistance decreases and finger pulse volume decreases were greater with no noise present.

It is hard to interpret such data. The group receiving the "analgesic" instructions conformed to predictions well enough, but the paradoxical response of the "hyperalgesic" group and the "neutral" group suggests that, for them, noise and instructions had no clear effect on responses to shock. Why this did not happen also to the "analgesic" group is not clear, nor is it clear why instructions were effective for them and not for the other groups. This "analgesic" group also showed a greater reactivity in both conditions than did the others, which may be either a sampling error or an effect of their instructions—it is not certain which. Another factor to be considered is that which we mentioned in connection with Barber's study. It may be that autonomic changes are less easily interfered with when they occur to some stimulus, but more easily induced *de novo* by instructions. This possibility was tested in the following study.

Sternbach (1964) had six students take part in a "drug" experiment consisting of three experimental sessions. A point was made of ascertaining from the subjects that they were over 21 years old because of the "drug" nature of the study. Each subject was told that he would take three different pills which had different effects on the activity of the stomach. Effects were to be of brief duration, about a half hour, with no residual or important side effects. The instructions were:

1. "Relaxant" drug (−). "This pill relaxes the stomach. You'll feel your stomach full and heavy in a few minutes, and it'll reach a peak in about fifteen minutes, at which time you'll feel bloated. Then it'll wear off gradually, and be gone in another fifteen minutes."

2. "Placebo" (0). "This pill has no effect. We use it for a control, a placebo essentially, to see the effects of just taking a pill on stomach activity. You won't feel anything."

3. "Stimulant" (+). "This pill is a stimulant to the stomach. You'll feel your stomach churning pretty strongly in a few minutes, and it'll reach a peak in about fifteen minutes, at which time you'll feel some cramps. Then it'll wear off gradually, and be gone in another fifteen minutes."

It was explained to the subjects that only the measurements of the actual physiological changes of the stomach were of interest, which was why they were being advised of the subjective sensations, so they would not become alarmed—the feelings were to be expected. Each subject took the "drugs" in a different one of the six possible orders. In each instance, *the pill swallowed was simply the small magnet* used to measure gastric peristaltic rate.

In Fig. 27 you can see the effects of these instructions on the subjects' gastric motility. For subjects 1, 2, 5, and 6 the changes are dramatically and significantly in the instructed directions. For subjects 3 and 4, the changes are not in the instructed directions and are not significant. The overall effectiveness of instructions is nevertheless statistically significant. It is interesting that the ratio of subjects who responded appropriately in this small sample — 2/3 — is about double the ratio of those in the general population who have been reported as "placebo reactors" in many other studies (Beecher, 1960). If this finding can be replicated by others, it will confirm the evidence presented here that instructions can and do influence autonomic reactivity.

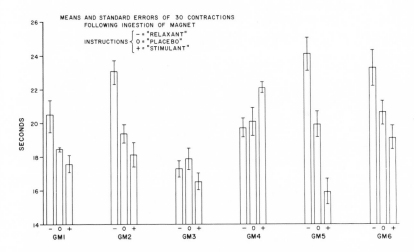

FIG. 27. Effects of different instructions (see text) on average stomach period of six subjects. Four of the subjects (1,2,5 & 6) show significant differences in rate of contractions in the directions predicted from instructions, although the "drug" taken in each instance was simply the magnet used to measure gastric motility. (From Sternbach, 1964. Courtesy of Williams & Wilkins Co.)

Now, what is the significance of this principle of explicit sets? In particular, how does it interact with the other principles we have described to determine what autonomic functioning will be like at any given moment?

If we return to our image of the young-man-on-a-cot, whom we left a few chapters back, we can summarize what we have said so far and illustrate the meanings of the various principles. We know that while he is resting undisturbed he is demonstrating homeostasis. The antagonistic functions of the sympathetic and parasympathetic branches can be seen in alternating compensatory actions as the functions we observe oscillate about some average value. This is one kind of autonomic balance, that which seems typical for the individual. Another kind of autonomic balance is one which describes his relative apparent sympathetic or para-sympathetic dominance as compared to a large normative popu-lation. Obviously both kinds of phenomena exist for any person at any time, and merely represent different ways of looking at a person's functioning. We have suggested that it is better to keep the term homeostasis for the former viewpoint, and reserve the term autonomic balance for the concept using the group was a reference.

When we study the young man's reactions to stimulation, we know that response measures are likely to be influenced by pre-response levels of functioning, and these must be accounted for. This is the point of the law of initial values. Furthermore, al-most any kind of stimulation is likely to result in a generalized shift to a dominance of sympathetic-like activity. This is activa-tion. If the stimulation does not change, but persists, functioning gradually returns to prestimulus levels, and this is adaptation. Brief, intense stimulation is likely to result in a marked sym-pathetic-like response, followed by an overcompensatory return past the baseline in the opposite direction — rebound.

Despite the general tendency of responses to be sympathetic-like, certain kinds of patterning can be detected. One is a pat-terning of responses appropriate to the stimulus situation, stim-ulus-response specificity. Another is a simultaneous patterning unique to the individual, individual-response stereotypy. Al-though neither of these is immediately obvious to any observer in the way activation can be, this double-patterning of responses is detectable by suitable analyses. In addition, there may be a distribution of individual differences in ability to demonstrate both the S-R and I-R specificities, just as there is a distribution of autonomic balance scores.

The concept of explicit sets cuts across these two kinds of patterning. Instructions can induce autonomic responses which are within the typical repertoire of the individual. In this respect instructions may serve to re-create stimulus situations which then elicit patterns of responses which are appropriate both to the situation and to the individual. Probably the mechanism involved is stimulus generalization, an aspect of classical conditioning which has been recognized for many years.

It is not so certain that instructions can modify autonomic responses to stimuli; particuarly, it has not been demonstrated that responses can be prevented or minimized, although there is some evidence that the latter may be possible. Interfering with responses by instructions is, apparently, more difficult than merely inducing them by instructions. Nevertheless, the fact that instructions have any effect at all is of considerable importance. The first and most obvious consequence is that experimenters have to be careful what they say to subjects, so as not to bias responses. But experimenters usually are careful, and that is not the major problem. Of chief concern is the fact that instructions serve to alter sets. This has been our interpretation of the results reported here, and it is a reasonably parsimonious interpretation. But the implications which follow from this are quite important. Sets can be formed and modified by a variety of experiences, quite independent of instructions. Changes in sets due to experiences outside the laboratory can greatly increase the variability of data acquired over a period of days or longer. And, we may postulate, it may be that a great deal of inter-individual differences are contributed to by differences in sets. But these are all implicit kinds of sets, those not stated explicitly, and we will turn to these now. It may be that one of the chief values of studies on explicit sets is that they alert us to the problems provided by those which are implicit.

IX
Implicit Sets

So far, we have been rather unrealistic in our view of the experimental subject. We have been talking about him as if he were little more than a squash, lying there on the cot and passively receiving and adjusting to whatever stimuli impinge upon him. The actual facts of the case are otherwise, and we now need to correct this view, and to take account of some common sense principles and see how they fit with or modify those we have already described. The point to be made here is that the subject is an active person, one who acts on the environment and interacts with others, not merely reacts to inputs. We are, in effect, saying that the S-O-R model is inadequate and needs to be modified.

Implicit sets, like all sets, are those variables in the subject which predispose him to perceive or act in a certain way. Like the explicit sets which we described in the last chapter, they are likely to influence the response variable which we are interested in measuring. Unlike those instructionally determined sets, however, implicit sets are rarely verbalized. They may be points of view the subject brings with him to the laboratory; they may be those inherent in the experimental situation and the role-playing expected of the experimenter-subject relationship; and they may be the expectations or hopes of the experimenter which he communicates to the subject in subtle, nonverbal ways. The chief point is that not only are these implicit sets unlikely to be verbalized, but they are also unlikely to be acknowledged or even to exist in the awareness of the subject or the experimenter, although it is possible to detect them nevertheless. Let us now consider some of these implicit sets, and their potential influence on the variables with which we are concerned.

Rosenthal (1964) has reviewed the evidence relating to the influence of the experimenter's orientation (hopes, expectancies, sets) on the outcome of his research. Although "experimenter bias" seems to be too strong a term because it implies dishonesty, it is clear that such bias does exist and has effects, even though it is not deliberate or "dishonest." Studies in the areas of medicine, clinical psychology, opinion surveys, and laboratory research have revealed the apparent influence of the expectations of the results on the results themselves. Even "simple" laboratory animals can respond to subtle, unconscious cues on the part of the experimenter. Rosenthal quotes the instance of rats which were able to discriminate colors, but *only* when the experimenter was in the room. Obviously, humans are also capable of detecting such cues as the experimenter may unwittingly provide, and thus their responses may be modified. A recent report by Troffer and Tart (1964) suggests that it is virtually impossible for experimenters to eliminate such cues. Eight hypnotist-experimenters administered a standardized suggestibility test to subjects under two separate experimental conditions: with and without hypnotic induction. The experimenters understood the problem of experimenter bias, knew that they were being checked, and felt that they had treated both groups alike, yet judges were able to tell under which condition the subjects were tested by listening to the tape-recorded performances of the experimenters' reading of the first item on the test. In this study, the judges could detect differences in the tones of the experimenters' voices, even though the words were the same, and even though the experimenters tried to sound the same in the two conditions and thought they had.

Orne (1962) has called the sum total of all cues which convey an experimental hypothesis to a subject "the demand characteristics of an experimental situation." These demand characteristics include a variety of cues quite apart from the communication that takes place in the experiment itself. The very act of agreeing to take part in an experiment places the subject in a well-defined relationship with the experimenter in which each implicitly acknowledges certain mutual role expectations. In particular, the subject accepts the possibility of having to perform or tolerate a great amount of tedious or unpleasant or even painful acts, and to do so without inquiring, How much? or even, Why? On his part, the experimenter accepts the responsibility of saving the subject from actual harm, and of having a good and worthwhile purpose for what he is doing.

Although there are many possible reasons for subjects' participating in experiments — pay, course requirement, time off a prison sentence, obligation of a service organization — in our culture there is often an additional hope or expectation that what the subject does will in some small way ultimately redound to the benefit of mankind. Consequently, part of the role of "being a subject" implies a working for the "success" of the experiment. He must feel as though his participation is worthwhile, that is, that the experimenter knows what he is doing and that he — the subject — is a "good" subject. It is also clear that the scientist must be unbiased and objective, and the subject will therefore expect to receive no explicit statements about the purpose of the study or the specific hypothesis being tested, since these might distort the results. Nevertheless, the subject knows quite well that the experimenter isn't doing this work for nothing — he obviously has something in mind; some hypothesis is being tested. And since the subject is anxious to be a good subject, to help validate the hypothesis or to fulfill the experimenter's expectations, he must search for cues. Now begins the elaborate ritual of the game which is called the "experimental procedure." The experimenter and subject deal with each other in objective, scientific, no-nonsense terms as befits the seriousness of the occasion and their conceptions of how an experiment ought to be conducted. But the experimenter also has an investment in a certain outcome, and is eager for the subject to show certain results. And the subject also wants his services to be useful, and is eager to live up to the experimenter's expectations. Yet neither can talk about these matters, and so such communication must take place in nonverbal ways — as in the tone of voice, the laboratory arrangement, the design of the experiment (what follows what), etc. These cues alter the subject's sets so that the more desirable behaviors are more likely to occur; yet for the sake of "honesty," the cues cannot be obvious and neither the subject nor experimenter must be aware of the communications which convey the hypothesis.

Orne (1962) described a number of procedures which allow
for control of the demand characteristics (they can never be
eliminated, but their influence can be assessed). These techniques
are not directly relevant to our discussion here, but the problems
of the demand characteristics themselves certainly are. We need
to consider the possible influence of these implicit sets on subjects'
psychophysiological functioning. Specifically, can and do such
implicit sets affect autonomic functioning?

We are not aware of any studies bearing directly on this question,
and so any evidence we adduce must be indirect. One kind of
implicit set we already mentioned—the anxiety induced in a subject by strapping and wiring him for polygraph recording. Although nothing may be said about it, the very laboratory arrangement of shielding and the act of affixing electrodes elicits fantasies
of electricity and corresponding physiological changes. This is an
example of the demand characteristics inherent in the laboratory
situation itself.

Another example has to do with the effectiveness of placebos.
This is a very complicated issue which we cannot deal with here in
detail, but some points are worth considering. Beecher (1960) has
shown that placebos are effective in relieving pain, but more
effective in relieving pathological pain (35% of cases) than experimental pain (3% of cases). Pain seems to depend on *both* the stimulation of pain receptors *and* the meaning of the sensations to the
individual (the significance of the symptom, the anxiety, the
stress). Beecher calls the latter the secondary or reactive component
to pain. Pathology alone need not cause pain, as in many instances
of battle wounds, and similarly it appears that drugs *or* placebos
are effective in relieving pain only to the extent that the reactive
component is present. Now the question arises, "Why are placebos
effective"? A great number of explanations have been offered,
including some that are analogous to the demand characteristics
we have described. The doctor gives an injection or a pill; the
patient trusts the doctor and wants the doctor to be good and
competent; the patient, on his part, will be a good and trusting
patient, anxious to cooperate; the doctor, likewise wants the patient
to feel better, and reflect credit on the doctor's ministrations. Nothing need be said about the drug, because the sets are all established

in the mutual expectations of the roles of the doctor-patient relationship. The pain, following placebo administration in this setting, is reduced. Although the experience of pain is purely subjective, its relief can be measured, either by the amount of drugs requested by the patient, or by autonomic measures. In either way, placebo effectiveness is demonstrable.

Now the essence of these demand characteristics (implicit sets) can be shown to follow a classical conditioning paradigm, just as the "first-day anxiety" we described earlier. The association between all the factors surrounding medication by "active" drugs and the resulting pain relief can result in those factors acquiring pain-relieving effects in themselves. We may wish to attribute all sorts of more human or symbolic values to the placebo phenomenon, and such may indeed by present, but it is possible to show that conditioning is the necessary and sufficient process. In fact, Herrnstein (1962) has demonstrated a placebo effect in rats, and a symbolic interpretation for his findings would seem to be superfluous.

You can see that implicit sets, like explicit ones, can modify responses by recreating, in the person of the experimenter or in the setting of the experimental situation, a set of stimuli to which previous responses have been associated, and for this reason such responses are likely to recur. How likely this is to affect autonomic functioning in any specific situation is conjectural, since experiments designed to assess the problem seem to be lacking. But you must remember that autonomic conditioning is quite common-place. Pavlov's work was with the salivary glands, an autonomic effector, and many investigators have routinely conditioned gastric functioning, pupillary responses, sweating, and the several cardio-vascular variables. Consequently it is likely that the predispositions we have been calling sets, both implicit and explicit, when revealed in changed autonomic functioning, are the result of Pavlovian conditioning.

Another type of implicit set may now be considered, in addition to those evoked by the experimenter ("demand characteristics"). These are the tendencies or predispositions that the subject brings with him to the laboratory, beyond whatever individual-response stereotypy he may possess. We would refer to these as personality characteristics, except that this term often connotes a focusing on the individual as unique and ignores his being representative of various groups (age, sex, social class, ethnic membership, etc.). So we will simply refer to this third class of events as "subjects' implicit sets," and demonstrate by example what we mean.

Years ago Bruner and Goodman (1947) tested the hypothesis that the greater the value of an object for an individual, the more likely he is to accentuate its perceptual qualities. Specifically, they were interested in testing experimentally the effect of the known value of coins on their perceived size, using the psychophysical method of average error. Ten rich children, ten poor ones, and ten controls had the task of estimating with a spot of light the sizes of a penny, a nickel, a dime, a quarter, and a half dollar, first from memory, and then with the coins present. The results were fascinating. In general, all the children significantly overestimated the sizes of the coins, the degree of overestimation increasing with the value of coins but not their real size. Furthermore, poor children overestimated more than rich ones, the difference also tending to increase with value. The implications of these results are that need-value systems affect perceptual processes. "Need-value systems," like any other intervening variable that affects perception or any other function, are a specific instance of what we have called sets, and since such socioeconomic needs and values are taken for granted and rarely verbalized (especially in 10-year-olds), we may consider them implicit sets.

We may assume that for these subjects, coin sizes *are* bigger then they are objectively, increasingly so the greater the value of the coins. And for poor children, each coin *is* bigger than the same coin seen by rich children. Whatever the nervous system processes which may be involved in this kind of perceptual event, they have been affected by the experiences inherent in the condition we call socioeconomic class. Thus there is a connection — startling as it may seem — between social events (economic) and physiological processes. However, this is only an inference when based on the results of a perceptual experiment like the Bruner and Goodman one. It is an inference because the physiological processes were not observed directly, but are only assumed to "be there" to account for the behavior involved in size judgments. To see whether such social phenomena in fact do affect physiological functioning, it is necessary to make the physiological responses the dependent variables in an experiment. The social or cultural or economic class differences would be the independent (manipulated) variables, and "values" or "meanings" or "needs" (or however you want to describe the implicit sets) the intervening variables.

Sternbach and Tursky (1965) tested the hypothesis that different ethnic groups would show differences in autonomic responses to painful stimuli (electric shocks). This hypothesis was based on an earlier report by Zborowski (1952) who found that there were differences in the behavioral expression of pain among Irish, Italian, Jewish, and Old American patients in a veterans hospital. These differences were related to orientations and values (sets) implicit in each of the subcultural groups. Before evaluating the physiological data, let us examine these ethnic attitudes briefly. The attitudes are those reported by Zborowski and were found also in systematic interviews conducted as part of the Sternbach and Tursky study. Of course, the summaries which follow are modal descriptions and do not take individual differences into account.

Old Americans (white, Anglo-Saxon, Protestant, at least three generations born and reared in this country) and Yankees specifically (New Englanders) respond to pain in a matter-of-fact way. Expressions of discomfort have only nuisance value to others and interfere with taking appropriate action. Consequently, Yankees typically report pain to a doctor in a way that is likely to be most helpful to him — where it hurts, how much, what kind of pain, etc. Moaning and crying won't help, so there is no point to it. When the pain is severe, the Yankee will express his suffering when alone, but not among others. If the pain is only mild or moderate, there is little or no expression of suffering. The Yankee expects to be a "good patient" — not a complainer, an objective observer, one who helps the doctor do the job. If nothing can be done for the pain, or if it is not severe, the Yankee will "take it in stride." It is typical of the differences among the ethnic groups that this phrase was used frequently by Yankees, but never by the others. It implies an unemotional, matter-of-fact, action-oriented individualism practically unique to this group.

Although the Irish subgroup similarly does not display expressions of suffering, the reasons seem to be rather different.

There is little of the unemotional taking things in stride, but an inhibition and tight control of anxiety concerning the pain, along with a fatalism that predicts its inevitability. "Tis a burden to be endured" is a typical phrase, and so is "You always fear the worst." Yet conflicting with these expectations is a fear of being or acting like a baby (*not* a nuisance), and a need to appear outwardly calm and in control. Needless to say, despite the attempt at control, the sense of suffering comes through to the observer.

In contrast to these two groups, the Jews and Italians have their ethnic groups' approval for the overt expression of pain responses. Although doctors and hospital staffs, typically Yankee in their orientation, think of Jewish and Italian patients as exaggerating their pains and perhaps of even having lower pain thresholds, in fact, it is only the values concerning emotional expression that are different. For both Jews and Italians, loud suffering serves to rally sympathetic responses from family and friends, and helping responses from professionals. Yet just as the undemonstrativeness of the Yankees and Irish derives from different attitudes, so does the demonstrativeness of the Jews and Italians represent different orientations.

The primary concern for the Jews is the meaning of the pain. This meaning extends in two directions. There is the meaning that refers to the pathology which the pain represents, and there is the meaning that refers to the consequences of any future impairment. The Jewish patient typically worries about what is causing the pain, and tends to be suspicious if pain is relieved: has the underlying cause of the pain been cured, or is some insidious disease still at work? In addition, he worries about the effect of pathology on his future health, his ability to work and provide for others, and is generally concerned about the implications of the present discomfort for future functioning. This is a rationalistic, future-oriented and group-directed perception which accounts for the typical behaviors, but there is one additional factor which lies behind the expressiveness. This is the ethnic belief in the value of catharsis, that it is good and important to "cry out your troubles," not to hold them in but to "get them out of your system."

The Italians, on the other hand, typically are not concerned with the meaning or implications of pain. Pain is an evil, a form of suffering to be avoided (*not* endured). It represents the workings of a capricious fate which cannot be understood and which is therefore meaningless. Consequently the expressions of distress are primarily directed toward the elimination of the pain itself. Whereas the Jewish patients attempt to elicit sympathetic concern and help in achieving a cure, the Italians attempt to elicit sympathetic understanding and help in relieving suffering. There is less emphasis on the value of emotional catharsis, and consequently the expression of suffering is more limited to the immediate goal of gaining support and pain relief. There is more of a hedonistic quality to this ethnic orientation than in the other groups.

From these brief descriptions of the implicit cultural sets, it is possible to make some predictions of what would happen if members of these ethnic groups were subjected to experimental pain. Now experimental pain, in some ways, is not at all like the pain which comes with injury, disease or surgery. The situation in the laboratory is sufficiently different from the natural setting so that the anxieties concerning impairment—the factors especially emphasized in the Jewish ethnic group—are minimal. Furthermore, the morality associated with experimentation precludes any serious tissue damage. The implicit role-playing sets we described earlier in the chapter make it clear that between subject and experimenter there is an (often unacknowledged) agreement that the subject will be protected from harm. From these considerations, we would expect Jewish subjects not to be especially aroused, since the laboratory situation is reassuring with respect to their long-range concerns. Irish subjects, who would suffer in silence, would also have little to respond to or suffer about, since the noxious stimuli presented, electric shocks, could not be terribly painful in an experiment. On the other hand, the Italian subjects, oriented to the avoidance of discomfort under any circumstances, would be expected to find it more difficult than the other groups to accept the more intense shocks. The Yankees, if indeed they "take things in stride," might be expected to show more and faster adaptation to discomfort, as compared to the others.

You can see, in Table IV and Fig. 28, that there is some evidence to support these expectations. In Table IV it is clear that the upper thresholds of electric shock differentiate among the four ethnic

TABLE IV[a]

MEAN THRESHOLDS (IN MILLIAMPERES)
FOR ELECTRIC SHOCK FOR FOUR ETHNIC GROUPS

Response	Yankee (14)[b]	Irish (15)	Jewish (14)	Italian (13)
First lower threshold	2.06	2.12	2.01	1.82
Average lower threshold	2.19	2.31	2.20	1.97
Unmotivated upper threshold	9.74	8.68	8.83	6.12
Motivated upper threshold	10.23	9.35	10.16	7.11

[a] From Sternbach & Tursky, 1965. Courtesy of William & Wilkins Co.
[b] Figures in parentheses represent numbers of subjects.

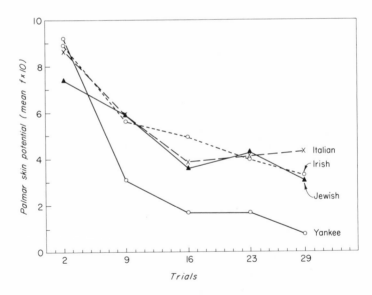

FIG. 28. The average frequency over trials of biphasic palmar skin potentials produced in response to electric shocks. The Italian, Irish, and Jewish subjects' curves are not significantly different from each other, but the overall difference among the groups is significant due to the faster and more complete adaptation of the response by the Yankee ethnic group. This difference is associated with a difference in set toward pain, as described in the text. (From Sternbach & Tursky, 1965. Courtesy of Williams & Wilkins Co.)

groups. This is because of the lower values obtained by the Italian subjects as compared with the others. Their "unmotivated upper threshold" (voluntarily stopping the increase in shock intensity) is lower, and so is their "motivated upper threshold" (highest shock intensity accepted with coaxing). Perhaps even more interesting is the difference (suggestive, but not statistically significant) in the number of subjects in each group to require coaxing to go beyond a 7 milliampere shock level: 4 of 14 Yankees, 6 of 15 Irish, 8 of 14 Jews, and 9 of 13 Italians. This certainly seems to support the hypotheses derived from interviews that the Yankees would be the most likely to accept the situation, and the Italians least likely to do so.

In Fig. 28 you can see further evidence of this sort. The skin potential response to sudden strong stimulation is usually a diphasic one; with repetitive stimulation, adaptation takes the form of a shift to a monophasic potential, and then a gradual diminution and disappearance of any discernible responses. Figure 28 shows the average number of diphasic responses for the groups, for a series of repetitive shocks. Clearly, the Yankees show a more rapid and complete adaptation than do the others (and the Italians somewhat less than the other groups). Again, this seems to be a clear physiological confirmation of the attitude expressed by the Yankees that they "take it in stride."

We have gone into this study in some detail only because there seem to be no others which assess the relationship between implicit sets of any sort and physiological responsivity. From what we have seen, it appears that implicit sets, as well as explicit ones, may indeed influence psychophysiological functioning, and do so in ways which the experimenter may not be able to predict without independently assessing such sets.

Now we should summarize the several notions which we have dealt with in this chapter. Under the heading of implicit sets we have subsumed all those nonverbal factors which predispose individuals to perceive or respond in certain ways, except for the individual-response stereotypies which we have considered separately. (Explicit sets are arbitrarily considered to be those predisposing influences which are verbalized.) Although such a definition of implicit sets is very broad, we have considered in some detail only three subclasses of such sets: experimenter bias, demand characteristics of the experiment, and subjects' implicit sets. The evidence that these subclasses influence autonomic functioning is very meager. We have cited some studies in other areas to indicate that experimenter bias and demand characteristics can alter other response systems. We infer that since these results can be explained by a simple conditioning model, and since the ANS is peculiarly susceptible to classical conditioning procedures, there is every reason to expect our psychophysiological measures to be similarly influenced. With respect to the third of the subclasses, subjects' implicit sets, the evidence is more direct, and suggests that such factors as ethnic membership can and do influence some autonomic functions in certain situations.

It should be obvious that this is an area greatly in need of further experimental work. The purpose of this and the previous chapter has been to alert you to the kinds of extraneous variables which often distort or subtly influence results in this field, without the experimenter's awareness.

X
Psychosomatic Diseases

If the principles presented in the previous chapters are to have any more than intrinsic interest or value, they should be helpful in understanding the psychosomatic diseases. To make an analogy, psychophysiology is to the psychosomatic diseases what physiology is to pathology. That is, both psychophysiology and psychosomatic disorders are special ways of thinking about general physiology and general pathology. What is special is that the roles of ideas and feelings are placed in some relationship to physiological function and dysfunction.

Now we must hasten to point out that there are several kinds of models for thinking about the psychosomatic diseases, and in addition there are a great many definitions of the term. There has also been a good deal of argument about which diseases are psychosomatic, and the extent to which any particular disease is psychosomatic. Without presenting all the arguments or evidence concerning these issues, let us at least clarify what we mean by the term and how we conceptualize the problems involved.

The terms "psychosomatic disease" and "psychosomatic medicine" were originally coined to impress on the users that mind (psyche) and body (soma) are interacting processes, not separate entities. This was necessary because, as philosophers continually point out, ever since Descartes we have tended to be dualistic in our thinking about human functions — they are *either* mental *or* physical. The word "psychosomatic" should remind us that all functioning and all diseases are both mental and physical, because both mental and physiological processes are going on continuously. Unfortunately, many persons persist in making the dualistic dichotomy even while acknowledging mental-physical interactions. "Sure, emotions are involved in ulcers, but do they *cause* the ulcers?" Although most workers in this field no longer ask such questions (partly because they are not answerable, and partly because they beg the question), the dualistic approach is so built into our way of thinking and into our language that it is difficult to avoid. Even the most ardent monist is likely at times to lapse into speculating about how certain fantasies *result* in allergic reactions, or what role is played by the emotions in *causing* tuberculosis. It is very difficult to maintain a holistic-organismic approach. But, it is also very difficult to take seriously those who maintain that all feelings are only by-products (epiphenomena) of physiological events, or that the opposite is true—all physiological responses are only the results of our feelings. Both extremes seem hard to justify.

Although there are emotions involved in all diseases, the attempt to show a cause-and-effect relationship between an emotion and the pathology is very difficult. This is because, when determining cause, it is necessary to show that A is always followed by B before being able to say that A is a cause or part of the cause of B. If B occurs once in a while without A, then A becomes only a sufficient or partly sufficient cause of B, but not a necessary one. Since it is difficult to determine how much emotion preceded the onset of a given disease, let alone to determine which emotion, with what frequency, etc., the extent of emotions as causative factors in pathology is not clear.

However, over the years it has appeared that, in certain illnesses, emotional antecedents were more frequent or striking than in other diseases. These illnesses have come to comprise a list which is identified as psychosomatic. The list is different from writer to writer, and is continually expanding. What makes these "traditionally" psychosomatic diseases different from others is that specific emotions have been noted frequently to occur at some time prior to the onset of symptoms, whereas this is not so clear in the other diseases. In some illnesses, specific emotions have been found to accompany or to follow symptoms (diabetes, tuberculosis), but many are reluctant to call any illness psychosomatic until there is good evidence for emotional participation that is antecedent, and therefore possibly causative.

This is too bad, in a way, because it tends to foster the impression many people (both professional and non-professional) seem to have, that, if an illness is psychosomatic, it is therefore "all in the head," and so either imaginary, or a sign of malingering, or due to a defect in character. But it is easy to show that even the most traditional psychosomatic illnesses (such as ulcers) are not like that. An ulcer is not imaginary, it is a real hole in the stomach. And the person who has one is usually quite the opposite of a malingerer. In fact, it is thought by some that ulcer patients are those who (among other things) work too hard without letup, and have, if anything, too much "character."

The point of view we are proposing here is that all illness and all normal functioning is psychosomatic. Walking down the street is psychosomatic and so is falling down and breaking a leg. This is because all responses have both physiological and ·mental or emotional aspects. If, however, we want to consider certain diseases as having more clear emotional or "psychological" aspects than others, that is all right, provided we remember that at no point can we say with any certainty that an emotion "caused" this psychosomatic disease, or that other diseases do not have their emotional components. The problem lies in the tendency to confuse emotional correlates with causes; not every concomitant of a response can be its cause.

Now with this lengthy and cautionary introduction, let us turn to the main problem. Granted that certain diseases are usually considered psychosomatic, and that they are so considered because of frequently identified emotional antecedents, how can emotions cause or contribute to the cause of tissue pathology? Several explanations have been offered. One class of explanations concerns itself with the adaptive or maladaptive nature of emotions. The reasoning goes something like this.

In the course of evolution, emotions served to mobilize energy in such a way as to insure man's survival. Strong arousal led to fight-or-flight responses which would enable an individual to overcome or flee a threatening situation, and thus he would be more likely to survive and produce offspring than one who could not be so mobilized. Therefore a selection would have taken place in primitive times to create a population of emotional responders, simply because these strong emotions were adaptive. Now, however, such violent physical responses are no longer adaptive in our complex civilization. The individual who is angered by his boss, or frightened by a crowd, cannot strike or flee. Such responses are incompatible with survival in the sense that our society imposes physical restraints on the person who acts that way. Consequently, although the individual may experience the emotions and have the accompanying intense physiological changes, he is unable to discharge the increased energy which has been mobilized by taking appropriate action. Therefore the organic changes persist and result in pathology.

This interpretation obviously combines the views of Darwin and Cannon, and in a sense lays the "blame" for psychosomatic diseases on the mores of a society which does not allow the appropriate expression of once adaptive emotional responses. A similar approach which has a different emphasis is one which considers emotions as maladaptive. Emotions are thought of as vestigial responses which may once have had survival value, but which no longer do so, and the individual who has such fight-or-flight reactions frequently is responding to inadequate stimuli, and thus is responding inappropriately.

Another psychosomatic model emphasizes failures of adaptation, rather than adaptiveness. In this view, a psychosomatic disorder results whenever any physiological response in an emotion is too much or too little. That is, mechanisms of homeostatic control fail to keep the functioning within optimal limits, resulting in excessive responses (as in too much gastric acid) or inadequate ones (as in too little blood supply). This sort of model can apply to all diseases, of course, including those whose major components may be infection or injury. What is different about the psychosomatic diseases is that infections or injuries are not readily discernible antecedent events; the failure in feedback control seems to occur as an extreme at one or another end of a continuum of normal functioning, and frequently does so in conjunction with strong emotions. This model may be used to stress either innate (constitutional) defects, or failures of control which are acquired. Familial dysautonomia is an example of the former (the Riley-Day syndrome: inherited defects in several autonomic functions, often associated with mental retardation); and conditioned autonomic responses are examples of the latter. You will see to what extent both may participate in pathology in the sections which follow.

The general framework of the adaptation model is the one which fits our approach, in that it is compatible with the principles we have described. But before we go into these in any detail, let us just mention briefly one other class of explanations which has been offered, the psychoanalytic ones. Despite some variations, these approaches in general have stressed the subjective aspects of psychosomatic diseases. The patient is often seen as having regressed to an earlier developmental stage, and primitive emotions or fantasies associated with unfulfilled and unconscious childhood wishes are thought to be causative antecedents of symptoms. Consequently, pathology results from the continued presence of provoking situations, or because the individual is of a personality type which responds to any situation with archaic emotions. Except for the stress on the psychic phenomena *causing* the tissue damage, this model is quite similar to one which would propose a stimulus-response specificity or individual response-stereotypy as an explanation. Indeed, the latter principles can be thought of as up-to-date refinements of the psychoanalytic theories, although they were arrived at by different procedures.

Now let us examine the psychosomatic diseases. There are many, and as we said the lists vary, but here are those about which there seems to be frequent agreement: metabolic edema; hypertension; regional enteritis; Raynaud's disease; hives; anorexia nervosa; acne; hyperthyroidism; psoriasis; asthma; eczema; constipation; colitis; backache; migraine; duodenal ulcer; rheumatoid arthritis. We cannot discuss all of these, but let us use three as examples in the following discussions: duodenal ulcers, hypertension, and hives. Ulcers, as you know, are erosions in the gastric lining; hypertension is high blood pressure, usually defined as a diastolic pressure of at least 90; and hives are a reddening, swelling, and itching of the skin.

From what we have said of the psychophysiological principles, how can we understand the formation of these pathologies? Let us begin with individual response-stereotypy. We can safely assume that a patient who has ulcers, hypertension, or hives is a gastric, blood pressure, or skin "reactor," respectively, and not only by definition. We saw in the earlier chapters that there is real evidence to support the view that, regardless of the nature of the stimuli, psychosomatic patients show their greatest physiological responses in the systems in which they have their symptoms; as compared with normals, they display a far greater degree of "physiological rigidity," in the sense that there is a greater invariance in the hierarchies of response magnitudes of the systems measured. (It complicates the picture somewhat, but is not inconsistent with the schemes we are presenting, to point out that there are individuals who display two or more kinds of psychosomatic disorders.)

Thus the first postulate which can be made is that the appearance of psychosomatic symptoms requires an organ system which is maximally responsive to most situational stimuli, as compared with the other physiological systems. For gastric symptoms to appear, it is necessary that the individual's stomach be the viscus which shows the greatest responses to various inputs; similarly for the blood pressure and skin disorders—they must consistently be the most reactive systems. Now when we say that it is "necessary," or that this kind of response hierarchy "must occur," it should be clear that we are referring to the statistical correlations which we discussed earlier. An individual is more likely to develop an ulcer, for example, if he shows response-stereotypy with gastric activity as the maximally reactive system. It may be that it is also necessary, in a causative sense, that an ulcer patient always respond maximally with gastric hypersecretions or hypermotility and that other responses (blood pressure, skin temperature) follow in order of magnitude, but we do not know this for certain. We are really only describing a statistical association. This response-stereotypy, then, constitutes a predisposing condition, and as such it is a necessary but not a sufficient cause.

We must admit that it is not clear what causes the stereotypy in the first place. Certainly in some instances this is a genetic matter. In many patients with hypertension, for example, it is possible to show that the disease runs in the family and is associated with a defect in the control of a substance called renin. Yet autonomic responses are easily conditioned, as we have noted, and so it seems to us unreasonable to assume that in any given instance of stereotypy the patterning of responses (or the predisposition) is *either* inherited *or* acquired. Probably both factors are always involved, but we would have difficulty in knowing to what extent. The problems of separating genetic transmission from early conditioning in a family are considerable. For the present time we must simply begin with the fact of response stereotypy as a given.

Now let us turn to the principle of stimulus-response specificity. We have seen that there is a good deal of evidence that certain response systems tend to be activated more in certain emotions (stimuli-situations) than in others. In anger, for example, there is greater gastric activity than in fear, which tends to inhibit gastric functions. The same is true for hypertensive symptoms—anger regularly is associated with a greater diastolic blood pressure increase than is fear. On the other hand, we are all aware that certain emotions are easily observed in vascular responses of the skin: flusing with anger or blushing in embarrassment are two of the most common. It is interesting that anger is the emotion that most frequently is associated with psychosomatic types of responses. Actually this may be partly an artifact of the limited number of emotions that have been examined successfully in the laboratory. Partly, too, it may be because we have directed our attention to the emotions whose immediate effects are similar to those observed in the psychosomatic diseases. But you will remember from our discussion on rebound phenomena that there are other possibilities in the production of symptoms. For example, the inhibition of gastric activity in fear or anxiety may be followed by a hyperactivity which is indistinguishable from that directly associated with anger or resentment.

Accordingly we may postulate as a second "necessary" (but not necessarily sufficient) condition for psychosomatic symptoms, the exposure of the individual to certain emotion-arousing situations. From the limited experimental information we have, we may assume that anger and fear are the two kinds of emotions most likely to be associated with the appearance of symptoms. Anger perhaps is most frequently involved, but fear may be also, both in its own right and as a prelude to rebound. All of us experience these emotion-provoking situations, of course, yet we do not all experience symptoms. Therefore we would have to assume that the emotions must be of sufficient intensity and duration to produce changes. That is, the physiological responses must be great enough, and occur with sufficient frequency, to produce the tissue damage which is given a disease label. This would require, therefore, that the individual continually receive exposure to such activating situations.

Now you can see that, if an individual with marked response-stereotypy were involved in situations which regularly provoked emotional responses, this may be sufficient to result in the production of symptoms. But another principle is involved here, that concerning homeostasis. If a person with marked response-stereotypy is continually exposed to stressful situations, he may nevertheless avoid having psychosomatic symptoms if his autonomic feedback and control mechanisms operate efficiently. The individual's own autonomic balance (homeostasis) may be kept within the limits of normal functioning by the reflex mechanisms we have discussed, which prevent either responses or rebounds from being of such magnitude that tissue damage occurs. Thus even though he may have "physiological rigidity" in the sense that one organ system always shows greater responses than the others, and even though these responses are continually and frequently activated by intensely provoking situations, reflexive control of the response systems may make it possible to avoid the appearance of symptoms.

Therefore we must add a third condition as necessary for psychosomatic disorders—the inadequacy of homeostatic restraints on the response systems. These three conditions may be put in the form of a logical If-Then proposition:

$$\text{If} \left\{ \begin{array}{l} \text{Individual} \\ \text{Response} \\ \text{Stereotypy} \end{array} \right\} \text{and} \left\{ \begin{array}{l} \text{Inadequate} \\ \text{Homeostatic} \\ \text{Restraints} \end{array} \right\} \text{and} \left\{ \begin{array}{l} \text{Exposure to} \\ \text{Activating} \\ \text{Situations} \end{array} \right\} \text{Then} \left\{ \begin{array}{l} \text{Psychosomatic} \\ \text{Episodes} \end{array} \right\}$$

In this scheme of conditions leading to psychosomatic episodes what we are attempting to do is to account for individual differences. We are essentially asking, Why does this person and not that one show symptoms? and, Why does he have this symptom and not those others? and, Why now and not another time? The outline suggests some possible answers. In the first place, an individual at any given time must have a "constitutional predisposition," as evidenced by the response hierarchy we have called stereotypy. This stereotypy may be present at birth or may be due to exposure to situations in the past in which responses were differentially reinforced, or some combination of these. But together with homeostatic failure, the stereotypy can account for the reason why this person has this symptom. On the other hand, the exposure to the activating situations is necessary for the responses to occur, and can account for the time of symptom formation. In addition, if the stimulus-situation is one which will maximally activate a certain organ system (stimulus-response specificity), and this coincides with the individual's response specificity and homeostatic weakness, then the likelihood of a psychosomatic episode is greatly increased.

At this point psychotherapists may point out that psychosomatic patients show other attributes that seem to make them unique. Inasmuch as our knowledge of these disorders is very far from complete, we should consider such data suggested by clinical experience, and see how they fit with the other information we have. Many clinical descriptions concern the unconscious fantasies of the patients which are associated with the specific diseases. Without going into each of them, we can say that in general these fantasies seem to be related to the psychoanalytic concepts of the various stages of psychosexual development. Clinicians working with patients are frequently able to predict the appearance of symptoms on the basis of certain fantasy material (and the emotions associated with them). More commonly, it is possible retrospectively to draw parallels between productions offered by a patient in therapy and the appearance and disappearance of symptoms.

It is for this reason that the psychoanalytically-oriented have assumed, as we mentioned earlier, that the fantasies stand in a causative relationship to the symptoms, using as a model the somatization of psychic energy. Assuming the validity of these clinical observations (and there seems every reason to do so), we may be able to use an explanatory model that is more parsimonious than the concepts of "somatization" and "psychic energy," one which is perhaps better related to the psychophysiological ap-

proach we have been following. ("Parsimony" in this sense refers
to theoretical or explanatory economy. It is not ncessarily a more
accurate or valid representation of the true—but not yet known—
state of affairs.)

It is possible to conceive of unconscious fantasies, to the extent
that we know what they are or can obtain evidence of them, as
particular instances of sets. In recalling what we have said of sets,
you will remember that they are defined as predispositions to perceive or respond in certain ways. In the sense in which we have used
the term, fantasies may parallel in subjective experience the physiological responses (stereotypy!) which constitute an important
condition of psychosomatic symptoms.

Although this may seem like psychophysical parallelism, we are
not suggesting this philosophical view. We do not know, nor can
we, whether fantasy material is merely an epiphenomenon of
physiological events, or the reverse, or whether the two are independent but "parallel." What we are saying is that the same kinds
of lawfulness of behavior may apply to both psychic and physiological processes, and that the concept of sets may be useful in
describing some of these events that seem to occur in both. We
want to avoid, where possible, lapsing into a dualistic discussion
such as we have just been doing, and we may avoid this by translating the clinical concepts into the psychophysiological terminology.

Accordingly we may think of fantasy productions as evidence of
predispositions to perceive and think in certain ways. And if
perceptual and thought processes are thought of as responses,
then the fantasies are signs of predispositions to make certain responses, just as autonomic response hierarchies are evidence of
such predispositions. This is what we have called sets—those
tendencies to respond in certain ways which may be inferred as
intervening variables from examining the relationships between
inputs and outputs. When psychosomatic patients show a relationship between the appearance of certain (perhaps unconscious)
ideas or feelings and the appearance of their symptoms, we may
consider this as evidence of a common set to perceive and respond
to the world in a certain way. In this sense the concept of sets cuts
across the other necessary conditions we postulated for psycho-

somatic episodes, just as earlier we saw it cut across the other psychophysiological principles. Given stereotypy and homeostatic inadequacy, the existence of an appropriate set can trigger the appearance of a symptom even when there is no real life stimulating situation to do so. This is because the set is such (due to previous exposures) that the patient perceives otherwise innocuous stimuli in a distorted way. It is this set which results in physiological responses to situations *as if* they were appropriate stressors; it is this set which results in emotions which are inappropriate to the situation in which they occur; and it is this set which leads therapists to the conviction that unconscious fantasies *cause* the symptoms. Actually, as we have noted, the unconscious fantasies and the physiological responses may be different aspects of the same sets.

Is there any advantage, other than conceptual, in making this sort of translation? There is, if it results in data which supply new information about the psychosomatic disorders. This approach leads to different kinds of questions, which can be examined experimentally. For example, what are the sets associated with the various psychosomatic symptoms? Fortunately, there have been studies of this problem, and data are available which support the point of view which we have been presenting. Up to now our discussion has been theoretical. Let us turn to some of the evidence concerning the psychosomatic disorders.

The Grahams and their colleagues have conducted a series of studies on the specific relationships between attitudes and physiological responses. The attitudes were obtained in interviews with psychosomatic patients. The hypothesis they investigated was that there exists a specific relation between the attitude toward a stressful stimulus and the disease which occurs in response to the stimulus. Three different kinds of studies were employed: judgments and ratings of interviews with the patients; selections by patients of cartoon illustrations representing attitudes; and suggestions of these attitudes to normal subjects. This is a step-by-step zeroing-in on the role of those intervening variables we have called sets. Therefore let us examine their findings in some detail.

The attitudes arose first in a clinical study of 128 patients with 12 different psychosomatic diseases or symptoms (Grace & Graham, 1952). It was found that patients with the same disease used similar words to describe their attitudes toward events which occurred just before the appearance or exacerbation of symptoms. Attitudes were defined as the way the patient felt about what happened to him in the situation, and what he wanted to do about it. Further studies of patients using similar interviewing techniques resulted in a list of 18 diseases and attitudes. It was from these interviews that the investigators proposed the hypothesis that there is a relationship between the attitude of a person toward a stressful event, and the physiological changes which occur in response to the event.

The first step in testing the hypothesis was to make sure that the attitudes which had been obtained were not due to either observer or sampling bias. Therefore two interview studies were carried out (Graham *et al.*, 1962), the first using 16 patients with eight different diseases and the second using 20 patients with ten different diseases. Patients were not specially selected for emotional problems, but taken from a hospital medical ward in a prearranged order. The possibility of bias in conducting the interviews was controlled by using, for half the patients in each of the two studies, a psychologist interviewer, who was unfamiliar with the predictions about the relationships between the attitudes and the diseases; his interviews are referred to below as "blind," in the sense that he was "blind" to the details of the hypothesis, while the other interviews, conducted by Graham, are called "nonblind." All interviews were recorded, and then edited to remove references to symptoms before being evaluated by judges. Control of biases by judges was obtained by using four judges, of whom two were not medically trained, and who had no extensive experience with either the attitude hypothesis or with other psychodynamic approaches. The task of the judges was to select from the list of 18 attitude descriptions the three which were most similar to those expressed by the patient in the interview; and also to rank all 18 attitudes in the order in which they applied to the patient.

The percentage of correctly predicted choices was significantly greater than that expected by chance in both studies, and in both the blind and the nonblind interviews. The average of correctly predicted choices in the two studies were 28% and 45% for the blind interviews, and 38% and 62% for the nonblind interviews.

Three judges chose the predicted attitudes significantly often from the interviews conducted blind, and all four judges did so from the nonblind interviews. The judges showed significant agreement with each other, and the nonmedical judges did as well as the medical ones. It was also found that a particular attitude was judged more applicable to a patient when he had the disease predicted to be associated with it than when he had another disease. The ranks for predicted attitude-disease associations were significantly more applicable in the blind interviews of the second study and in the nonblind interviews of both studies.

From these results the investigators concluded that different psychosomatic diseases were indeed associated with different attitudes, and that the association could be demonstrated even when a naive interviewer and naive judges were used. Now let us look at the 18 diseases and the attitudes which had been correctly predicted to be associated with them.

1. *Hives.* Feels he is taking a beating and is helpless to do anything about it.
2. *Ulcers.* Feels deprived of what is due him and wants to get even.
3. *Hypertension.* Feels threatened with harm and has to be ready for anything.
4. *Asthma.* Feels left out in the cold and wants to shut the person or situation out.
5. *Colitis.* Feels he is being injured or degraded and wishes he could get rid of the responsible agent.
6. *Eczema.* Feels he is being frustrated and can do nothing about it except take it out on himself.
7. *Acne.* Feels he is being picked on or at and wants to be let alone.
8. *Psoriasis.* Feels there is a constant gnawing at him and that he has to put up with it.
9. *Hyperthyroidism.* Feels he might lose somebody or something he loves and takes care of, and tries to prevent the loss.
10. *Vomiting.* Feels something wrong has happened, usually for which he feels responsible, and he wishes it hadn't happened.
11. *Constipation.* Feels in a situation from which nothing good could come but keep on with it grimly.

12. *Migraine.* Feels something has to be achieved and then relaxes after the effort.
13. *Multiple Sclerosis.* Feels forced to undertake some kind of physical activity, usually hard work, and wants not to.
14. *Metabolic Edema.* Feels he is carrying a heavy load and wants somebody else to carry all or part of it.
15. *Rheumatoid Arthritis.* Feels tied down and wants to get free.
16. *Raynaud's Disease.* Wants to take hostile physical action.
17. *Regional Enteritis.* Feels he has received something harmful and wants to get rid of it.
18. *Low Backache.* Wants to run away.

The important point to note about these attitudes is that those which were predicted (from earlier interviews) to be associated with the diseases were significantly more applicable to patients having the disease in question than to patients who did not have the disease, and that these findings obtained for the naive interviewer and the naive judges.

In a second type of study (Graham, 1962) cartoons were prepared to illustrate the attitudes, and these were presented to hospitalized patients having one or another of the relevant diseases. Figure 29 shows some sample cartoons. The hypothesis was that a patient with a disease related to a cartoon would respond to that cartoon differently from patients with other diseases. The psychophysical method of paired comparisons was used in which cartoons were presented two at a time and the patients had to compare every cartoon with every other one. Their instructions were to choose, in every pair, the one which reminded them the most of a situation they had been in and their feelings at the time. The choices made by each patient were scored by ranking the 18 cartoons according to the frequency with which they had been chosen. For each patient there was only one relevant cartoon, the one corresponding to his disease, and so the cartoon's rank by all the other patients served as a control. Then it was determined whether the rank given the cartoon by the patient with the related disease fell into the top, middle, or bottom quartiles of its control distribution. However, it was noticed that some patients seemed to treat their relevant cartoon differently by choosing it much less often than would be expected. When the patients were divided into

FIG. 29. Sample cartoons, illustrating attitudes expressed by patients having certain psychosomatic diseases. (a) Hives: This person feels he is taking a beating (being unfairly treated or mistreated), and is helpless to do anything about it. (b) Raynaud's disease: This person wishes to take hostile action, such as hitting or strangling. (c) Essential hypertension: This person feels that he is threatened with harm and has to be on guard. (d) Duodenal ulcer: This person feels deprived of what is due him and wants to get even. These attitudes were those expressed by the patients about a situation or incident which occurred prior to the onset or exacerbation of their symptoms. (From Graham, 1962. Courtesy of the author and Univ. of Wisconsin Press and the Regents of the Univ. of Wisconsin.)

groups above and below the median score on the WAIS Vocabulary Scale, it turned out that the more intelligent half chose their relevant cartoon significantly more often. These results support a phenomenon long known to clinicians, that is, that denial as a defense mechanism appears more frequently among the less intelligent. The results also support the original hypothesis, when this grouping by intelligence is used, that whether selection or rejection is the response, patients respond to the cartoon relevant to their disease in a way which is different from patients with different diseases which are not relevant to that cartoon.

Thus far, the results of the two kinds of studies support the hypothesis that specific attitudes are related to specific symptoms, but the studies have used only patients as controls for other patients. A more compelling study would be one in which normal subjects were used, and the nature of the relationship between attitudes and physiological responses could be specified. From the above studies, it is really not clear that the attitudes are responses to pre-symptomatic stressful situations; they could well be, wholly or in part, responses to the symptoms themselves. Consequently, a third type of study has been performed, in which the attitudes of selected diseases are suggested to normal subjects, while physiological responses are being measured.

In the first of these studies (Graham *et al.*, 1958) normal subjects were hypnotized and told to assume the attitudes associated with hives and Raynaud's disease. Since a rise in skin temperature is related to the development of hives and a fall of skin temperature is part of Raynaud's disease (severe peripheral vasoconstriction, usually of the fingers), it was predicted that skin temperature would rise with the hives suggestion and fall with Raynaud's suggestion. Evaluating 22 experimental sessions with 8 subjects and 41 separate attitude suggestions, these predictions were confirmed. Furthermore, the difference between the temperature responses to the two suggestions was statistically significant and for each suggestion, temperature changes reached a point significantly different from the last previous control temperature. These results clearly support the hypothesis. Figure 30 illustrates the findings.

In a second study (Stern *et al.*, 1961), 28 hypnotic sessions were

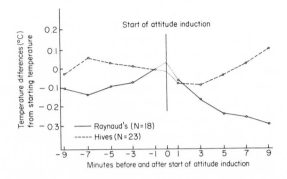

FIG. 30. Mean differences in hand temperatures during the induction of attitudes specific for hives and Raynaud's disease. Compare with Fig. 26. (From Graham, Stern & Winokur, 1958. Courtesy of the authors and Hoeber Medical Division, Harper & Row.)

analyzed, in which 18 normal subjects were given the attitude suggestions of hives, Raynaud's disease, and hypertension. The specific predictions made were that diastolic blood pressure should rise under the hypertension attitude, and as before, skin temperature should rise with the hives suggestion and fall with the Raynaud's suggestion. Although systolic blood pressure, heart rate and respiration rate were also recorded, no predictions were made concerning them. Results were generally confirmatory. With the hypertension attitude, there was a rise in diastolic blood pressure greater than the one in Raynaud's and significantly greater than with the hives attitude. Although there was a drop in skin temperature during the first four minutes of the attitude period for all attitudes, during the last six minutes of the attitude period the skin temperature rose for hives and remained low for Raynaud's and were significantly different. There were no significant differences among attitudes in systolic blood pressure, heart rate or respiration. Consequently, these findings replicate and extend the previous one, and further support the hypothesis.

In a third experiment (Graham, Kabler, & Graham, 1962) similar procedures were followed, using an improved experimental design, to compare hives and hypertension responses. Once again predictions were confirmed. Mean change, maximal rise, and rate of change of skin temperature during the hives suggestion were significantly greater than the corresponding changes during the hypertension suggestion. All three measures of change in diastolic blood pressure were significantly greater during the hypertension than during the hives suggestion. And there were no differential effects of the two attitude suggestions on systolic blood pressure, heart rate, or respiratory rate. These results were illustrated in Fig. 26, Chapter VIII.

The reason why just these three diseases have received experimental test so far is, of course, the ease of measuring the physiological responses related to the symptoms. It is much more difficult, technically speaking, to measure in a laboratory the responses relevant to the other diseases, or to find relevant response systems that change rapidly enough for experimental manipulation. Nevertheless, it is clear from the work of these investigators that certain attitudes are specifically related to certain psychosomatic symptoms; and that when these attitudes are adopted by normals, a set is induced such that physiological responses occur which are analogous to the symptom formation.

Now let us restate the formula. We begin with a person who has response-stereotypy to the extent that whatever the nature of the activating stimulus, one response system always or usually shows the greatest magnitudes of change as compared to his other response systems. This person also has a deficiency in feedback control so that either in initial responsiveness, or in rebound, some limit is exceeded by this maximally reactive system which results in some tissue damage or symptom appearance. This event will occur either when a stressful situation arises which is specifically stimulating to the response system in which the individual is also maximally reactive, or when any stressful situation occurs which is of sufficient intensity and/or frequency to result in maximum and/or frequent reactivity. In the absence of objective real-life stressors, this condition may be met by the individual whose set is such that he perceives ordinary events as if they were those stressors, and who will reveal the existence of that set both by the appearance of symptoms and by verbal expressions of attitudes (or fantasies).

This explanatory scheme for the psychosomatic disorders has the advantage of using only the psychophysiological principles we have described earlier. As additional research is performed the principles will be modified, and so too will this scheme. It is now in such a form that hypotheses may be derived for testing, either in respect to the psychosomatic disorders themselves, or directly concerning the underlying principles. The author will be pleased if this book helps to stimulate research in any area of psychophysiology.

REFERENCES

Alexander, F. *Psychosomatic Medicine, Its Principles and Applications.* New York: W. W. Norton & Co., 1950.

Ax, A. F. The physiological differentiation between fear and anger in humans. *Psychosom. Med.,* 1953, **15,** 433–442.

Barber, T. X., and Hahn, K. W., Jr. Physiological and subjective responses to pain-producing stimulation under hypnotically-suggested and waking-imagined "analgesia." *J. abn. soc. Psychol.,* 1962, **65,** 411–418.

Beecher, H. K. Increased stress and effectiveness of placebos and "active" drugs. *Science,* 1960, **132,** 91–92.

Benjamin, L. S. Statistical treatment of the law of initial values (LIV) in autonomic research: A review and recommendation. *Psychosom. Med.,* 1963, **25,** 556–566.

Bonvallet, M., Dell, P., and Hiebel, G. Tonus sympathique et activite' electrique corticale. *EEG clin. Neurophysiol.,* 1954, **6,** 119–144.

Bruner, J. S., and Goodman, C. C. Value and need as organizing factors in perception. *J. abn. soc. Psychol.,* 1947, **42,** 33–44.

Cameron, D. E. *Objective and Experimental Psychiatry.* (2nd ed.) New York: Macmillan, 1941.

Cannon, W. B. The mechanism of emotional disturbance of bodily functions. *New Eng. J. Med.,* 1928, **198,** 877–884.

Cannon, W. B. *Bodily changes in pain, hunger, fear and rage.* (2nd ed.) New York: Appelton-Century, 1936.

Damaser, E. C., Shor, R. E., and Orne, M. T. Physiological effects during hypnotically requested emotions. *Psychosom. Med.,* 1963, **25,** 334–343.

Davis, R. C., Buchwald, A. M. and Frankmann, R. W. Autonomic and muscular responses, and their relation to simple stimuli. *Psychol. Monogr.,* 1955 (No. 20), **69,** 1–71 (whole No. 405).

Duffy, E. *Activation and Behavior.* New York: John Wiley & Sons, 1962.

Dunbar, H. F. *Emotions and Bodily Changes.* New York: Columbia Univ. Press, 1935.

Dunbar, H. F. *Mind and Body: Psychosomatic Medicine.* New York: Random House, 1947.

Engel, B. T. Some physiological correlates of hunger and pain. *J. exp. Psychol.,* 1959, **57,** 389–396.

Engel, B. T. Stimulus-response and individual-response specificity. *Arch. gen. Psychiat.,* 1960, **2,** 305–313.

Engel, B. T., and Bickford, A. F. Response-specificity: Stimulus-response and individual-response specificity in essential hypertensives. *Arch. gen. Psychiat.,* 1961, **5,** 478–489.

Eppinger, H., and Hess, L. *Vagotonia.* Ment. nerv. Dis. Monogr. No. 20. New York: Nerv. & Ment. Dis. Publ. Co., 1915.

Eysenck, H. J. *The Structure of Human Personality.* New York: John Wiley, 1953.

Funkenstein, D. H. Nor-epinephrine-like and epinephrine-like substances in relation to human behavior. *J. nerv. ment. Dis.,* 1956, **124,** 58–67.

Gellhorn, E., Cortell, L., and Feldman, J. The effect of emotion, sham rage and hypothalamic stimulation on the vago-insulin system. *Am. J. Physiol.*, 1941, **133**, 532–541.

Gellhorn, E., and Loofbourrow, G. N. *Emotions and Emotional Disorders*. New York: Hoeber Medical Division, Harper & Row, 1963.

Grace, W. J., and Graham, D. T. Relationship of specific attitudes and emotions to certain bodily diseases. *Psychosom. Med.*, 1952, **14**, 243–251.

Graham, D. T. Some research on psychophysiologic specificity and its relation to psychosomatic disease. In R. Roessler & N. S. Greenfield (eds.), *Physiological Correlates of Psychological Disorder*. Madison: Univ. of Wisconsin Press, 1962.

Graham, D. T., Kabler, J. D., and Graham, F. K. Physiological response to the suggestion of attitudes specific for hives and hypertension. *Psychosom. Med.*, 1962, **24**, 159–169.

Graham, D. T., Lundy, R. M., Benjamin, L. S., Kabler, J. D., Lewis, W. C., Kunish, N. O., and Graham, F. K. Specific attitudes in initial interviews with patients having different "psychosomatic" diseases. *Psychosom. Med.*, 1962, **24**, 257–266.

Graham, D. T., Stern, J. A., and Winokur, G. Experimental investigation of the specificity of attitude hypothesis in psychosomatic disease. *Psychosom. Med.*, 1958, **20**, 446–457.

Graham, F. K., and Kunish, N. O. Physiological responses of unhypnotized subjects to attitude suggestions. *Psychosom. Med.*, 1965, **27**, 317–329.

Gunderson, E. Autonomic balance in schizophrenia. Unpublished doctoral dissertation, University of California, Los Angeles, 1953.

Herrnstein, R. J. Placebo effect in the rat. *Science*, 1962, **138**, 677–678.

Hord, D. J., Johnson, L. C., and Lubin, A. Differential effect of the law of initial value (LIV) on autonomic variables. *Psychophysiol.*, 1964, **1**, 79–87.

Jasper, H. H. Electroencephalography. In W. Penfield and T. C. Erickson, *Epilepsy and Cerebral Localization*. Springfield: Charles C. Thomas, 1941.

Johnson, L. C., Hord, D. J., and Lubin, A. Response specificity for difference scores and autonomic lability scores. *USN Med. NP Res. Unit Rep. 63-12*, Aug., 1963.

Kuntz, A. *The Autonomic Nervous System*. Philadelphia: Lea & Febiger, 1953.

Lacey, J. I. The evaluation of autonomic responses: Toward a general solution. *Ann. N.Y. Acad. Sci.*, 1956, **67**, 123–164.

Lacey, J. I. Psychophysiological approaches to the evaluation of psychotherapeutic process and outcome. In E. A. Rubinstein and M. B. Parloff (eds.), *Research in Psychotherapy*. Washington, D.C.: Am. Psychol. Assn., 1959.

Lacey, J. I. Bateman, D. E., and VanLehn, R. Autonomic response specificity and Rorschach color responses. *Psychosom. Med.*, 1952, **14**, 256–260.

Lacey, J. I., Bateman, D. E., and VanLehn, R. Autonomic response specificity: An experimental study. *Psychosom. Med.*, 1953, **15**, 8–21.

Lacey, J. I., and Lacey, B. C. Verification and extension of the principle of autonomic response-stereotypy. *Am. J. Psychol.*, 1958, **71**, 50–73.

Lacey, J. I., and Lacey, B. C. The law of initial value in the longitudinal study of autonomic constitution: Reproducibility of autonomic responses and response patterns over a four-year interval. *Ann. N.Y. Acad. Sci.*, 1962, **98**, 1257–1290; 1322–1326.

Lacey, J. I., Kagan, J., Lacey, B. C., and Moss, H. A. The visceral level: Situational determinants and behavioral correlates of autonomic response patterns. In P. H. Knapp (ed.), *Expression of the Emotions in Man.* New York: International Univ. Press, 1963.

Lindsley, D. B. Emotion. In S. S. Stevens (ed.), *Handbook of Experimental Psychology.* New York: John Wiley & Sons, 1951, 473–516.

Lindsley, D. B. Psychological phenomena and the electroencephalogram. *EEG clin. Neurophysiol.*, 1952, **4**, 443–456.

Lindsley, D. B. Psychophysiology and motivation. In M. R. Jones (ed.), *Nebraska Symposium on Motivation.* Lincoln: Univ. Nebraska Press, 1957, 44–105.

Malmo, R. B. Activation: A neuropsychological dimension. *Psychol. Rev.*, 1959, **66**, 367–386.

Malmo, R. B., and Shagass, C. Physiologic study of symptom mechanisms in psychiatric patients under stress. *Psychosom. Med.*, 1949, **11**, 25–29.

Malmo, R. B., Shagass, C., and Davis, F. H. Symptom specificity and bodily reactions during psychiatric interview. *Psychosom. Med.*, 1950, **12**, 362–376. (a)

Malmo, R. B., Shagass, C., and Davis, F. H. Specificity of bodily reactions under stress: A physiological study of somatic mechanisms in psychiatric patients. *Res. Publ. Ass. Res. nerv. ment. Dis.*, 1950, **29**, 231–261. (b)

Markwell, E. D., Jr. An investigation of autonomic balance in tuberculous patients. *Psychosom. Med.*, 1961, **23**, 392–399.

Markwell, E. D., Jr. Autonomic nervous system measures and factor correlates with personality indices in a tuberculous population. *J. consult. Psychol.*, 1962, **26**, 194.

McNemar, Q. *Psychological Statistics.* New York: John Wiley & Sons, 1955.

Obrist, P. A. Cardiovascular differentiation of sensory stimuli. *Psychosom. Med.*, 1963, **25**, 450–459.

Oken, D., Grinker, R. R., Heath, H. A., Hertz, M., Korchin, S. J., Sabshin, M., and Schwartz, N. B. Relation of physiological response to affect expression. *Arch. gen. Psychiat.*, 1962, **6**, 336–351.

Orne, M. T. The nature of hypnosis: Artifact and essence. *J. abn. soc. Psychol.*, 1959, **58**, 277–299.

Orne, M. T. On the social psychology of the psychological experiment: With particular reference to demand characteristics and their implications. *Amer. Psychologist*, 1962, **17**, 776–783.

Porter, R. W., Brady, J. V., Conrad, D., Mason, J. W., Galambos, R., and Rioch, D. McK. Some experimental observations on gastrointestinal lesions in behaviorally conditioned monkeys. *Psychosom. Med.*, 1958, **20**, 379–394.

Rosenthal, R. Experimenter outcome-orientation and the results of the psychological experiment. *Psychol. Bull.*, 1964, **61**, 405–412.

Schachter, J. Pain, fear, and anger in hypertensives and normotensives. *Psychosom. Med.*, 1957, **19**, 17–29.

Selye, H. The general adaptation syndrome and diseases of adaptation. *J. clin. Endocrin.*, 1946, **6**, 217–230.

Sokolov, E. N. Higher nervous functions: The orienting reflex. *Ann. Rev. Physiol.,* 1963, **25,** 545–580.

Stern, J. A. Toward a definition of psychophysiology. *Psychophysiol.,* 1964, **1,** 90–91.

Stern, J. A., Winokur, G., Graham, D. T., and Graham, F. K. Alterations in physiological measures during experimentally induced attitudes. *J. psychosom. Res.,* 1961, **5,** 73–82.

Sternbach, R. A. Correlates of differences in time to recover from startle. *Psychosom. Med.,* 1960, **22,** 143–148. (a)

Sternbach, R. A. A comparative analysis of autonomic responses in startle. *Psychosom. Med.,* 1960, **22,** 204–210. (b)

Sternbach, R. A. Two independent indices of activation. *EEG clin. Neurophysiol.,* 1960, **12,** 609–611. (c)

Sternbach, R. A. Some relationships among various "dimensions" of autonomic activity. *Psychosom. Med.,* 1960, **22,** 430–434. (d)

Sternbach, R. A. Assessing differential autonomic patterns in emotions. *J. psychosom. Res.,* 1962, **6,** 87–91.

Sternbach, R. A. The effects of instructional sets on autonomic responsivity. *Psychophysiology,* 1964, **1,** 67–72.

Sternbach, R. A. Autonomic responsivity and the concept of sets. In N. S. Greenfield & W. C. Lewis (eds.), *Psychoanalysis and Current Biological Thought.* Madison: Univ. Of Wisconsin Press, 1965.

Sternbach, R. A., and Tursky, B. Ethnic differences among housewives in psychophysical and skin potential responses to electric shock. *Psychophysiology,* 1965, **1,** 241–246.

Troffer, S. A., and Tart, C. T. Experimenter bias in hypnotist performance. *Science,* 1964, **145,** 1330–1331.

Wenger, M. A. The measurement of individual differences in autonomic balance. *Psychosom. Med.,* 1941, **3,** 427–434.

Wenger, M. A. The stability of measurement of autonomic balance. *Psychosom. Med.,* 1942, **4,** 94–95.

Wenger, M. A. Preliminary study of the significance of measures of autonomic balance. *Psychosom. Med.,* 1947, **9,** 301–309.

Wenger, M. A. Studies of autonomic balance in Army Air Forces personnel. *Comp. Psychol. Monogr.,* Vol. 19, No. 4, Berkeley: Univ. of Calif. Press, 1948.

Wenger, M. A., Clemens, T. L., Coleman, D. R., Cullen, T. D., and Engel, B. T. Autonomic response specificity. *Psychosom. Med.,* 1961, **23,** 185–193.

Wenger, M. A., Clemens, T. L., and Cullen, T. D. Autonomic functions in patients with gastrointestinal and dermatological disorders. *Psychosom. Med.,* 1962, **24,** 267–273.

Wenger, M. A., Clemens, T. L., Darsie, M. L., Engel, B. T., Estess, F. M. and Sonnenschein, R. R. Autonomic response patterns during intravenous infusion of epinephrine and nor-epinephrine. *Psychosom. Med.,* 1960, **22,** 294–307.

Wenger, M. A., and Cullen, T. D. ANS response patterns to fourteen stimuli. *Amer. Psychol.,* 1958, **13,** 423 (abstract).

Wenger, M. A., and Ellington, M. The measurement of autonomic balance in children: Method and normative data. *Psychosom. Med.,* 1943, **5,** 241–253.

Wenger, M. A., Jones, F. N., and Jones, M. H. *Physiological Psychology.* New York: Henry Holt & Co., 1956.

Wilder, J. The law of initial values in neurology and psychiatry. Facts and problems. *J. nerv. ment. Dis.,* 1957, **125,** 73–86.

Wolf, S., and Wolff, H. G. *Human Gastric Function* (2nd ed.). New York: Oxford Univ. Press, 1947.

Woodworth, R. S., and Schlosberg, H. *Experimental Psychology.* (Rev. ed.). New York: Henry Holt & Co., 1954.

Zborowski, M. Cultural components in responses to pain. *J. soc. Issues,* 1952, **8,** 16–30.

Appendix:
Some Important Readings in Psychophysiology

Notes on the Readings

These are the rules by which the following papers were chosen: the selections should show some of the historical roots of the field, but emphasize the recent developments; the older papers should be "classic" in importance, yet not easily accessible to the average reader; the newer papers should not be the same as those discussed in detail in the text, but should be relevant to the topics covered. Altogether, the papers should be fairly representative of psychophysiology.

The first paper, by Cannon, summarizes the knowledge in the field in 1928. That state of knowledge was largely due to Cannon's own research, for he more than any other pioneered in investigating the relationships between physiological and behavioral events. He demonstrated the role of the ANS in homeostasis, the functioning of the sympathico-adrenal system in "emotions" (activation), and postulated a "thalamic" (hypothalamic) mechanism for the regulation of emotional behavior.

As Cannon did for the sympathico-adrenal system, Gellhorn has done for the vago-insulin system, demonstrating its anabolic role in the dynamics of homeostasis. He also has greatly extended our knowledge of the hypothalamic mechanisms in emotions, emotional disorders and homeostasis.

When beginners have asked more experienced psychophysiologists for sources, in order to get acquainted with the field, the single work most frequently cited is the paper here by Darrow. It summarizes so well the problems of measuring ANS functions that

163

it is almost as timely today as when it was written. Darrow was one of the first to use the polygraph to record ANS activity, one of the few who routinely recorded EEG and ANS activity simultaneously, and he contributed greatly to our understanding of cortical and peripheral autonomic relationships. The appearance of this paper marked a turning point between the classical and modern stages in the history of psychophysiology.

As Darrow investigated EEG-ANS relationships, Davis investigated those between motor and autonomic functions, pioneering in the simultaneous recording of EMG and ANS activity. He was one of the first to demonstrate the existence of patternings in responses, thus helping to correct the all-or-none view of activation which had persisted since Cannon's work.

In a remarkable paper, Schnore studied the relationships among S-R and I-R specificities and activation. This much-cited work helped to establish the fact of their coexistence, following the earlier reports by Malmo and Lacey.

Much has been made of the relative influence of adrenaline and noradrenaline in the various emotions, and of their effects on physiological functioning. In perhaps the most thorough and carefully controlled study of its kind, Wenger and his co-workers detailed the ANS patterns resulting from infusion of these hormones. Although best known for his work on autonomic balance, Wenger's contribution here is equally important.

The last three papers represent some of the current research in the field. McDonald, Johnson and Hord study the orienting response (much investigated by Soviet workers) and show its relationship to two of our principles, activation and adaptation. Williams and Krasnoff examine two psychosomatic disorders not considered in detail in the text, and find support for the relevant psychophysiological principles. And Ax, who first differentiated fear and anger responses in humans, and who was a major organizer of the Society for Psychophysiological Research and a founder of the journal *Psychophysiology*, contributes a thorough and thoughtful analysis of the goals and methods of psychophysiology.

The New England
Journal of Medicine

VOLUME 198   JUNE 14, 1928   NUMBER 17

The Massachusetts Medical Society

THE MECHANISM OF EMOTIONAL DISTURBANCE OF BODILY FUNCTIONS*

BY W. B. CANNON, M.D.†

IN 1896, when I was a first-year medical student, Professor Henry P. Bowditch, whose memory his former students delight to recall, invited me to make use of the then newly discovered Röentgen rays in a study of the activities of the alimentary canal. In December of that year we demonstrated to the members of the American Physiological Society the passage down the esophagus of a swallowed mass made opaque to the rays by adding subnitrate of bismuth. After that beginning we studied the mechanical functions of the stomach and intestines, and the various conditions affecting the rate of passage of food through the digestive tract. Almost from the start of these investigations an outstanding fact appeared. The smooth-running recurrent waves of peristalsis coursing over the stomach, and the rapidly shifting segmentation of the food masses in the small intestine were promptly abolished whenever the subject showed signs of anxiety, distress or rage. It was evident that these alimentary functions were extremely sensitive to emotional disturbances. My interest in effects of excitement, which was thus initiated, led to studies of the services of the sympathetic nervous system, by itself and in coöperation with glands of internal secretion, and that in turn to an examination of the parts of the central nervous system which govern these fundamental reactions of the organism. You will pardon these references to personal experience, I trust, for they account for the selection of the title of this discourse. Since you have asked a physiologist to address you, you will permit him, I feel sure, to come and bring his contribution to medical thought and counsel. It has seemed to me, therefore, that we might profitably consider together the ways in which strong emotional states may endanger bodily welfare.

I think that we must admit that, although physicians have not infrequent occasions to observe instances of functional disturbance due to emotional excitement, there is an inclination to minimize or to slight that influence, or even to

deny that it is part of a physician's service to his patient to concern himself with such troubles. Let the patient go to the clergyman for comfort and consolation and for the resolution of his deep anxieties. A too common unwillingness among physicians to regard seriously the emotional elements in disease seems to me to be due perhaps to the subtle influence of two extreme attitudes and disciplines. On the one hand is the powerful impress of morphological pathology. So triumphantly and so generally has it demonstrated under the microscope the structural alterations which accompany altered functions that any state which has no distinct "pathology" appears to be unreal or of minor significance. Fears, worries and states of rage and resentment leave no clear traces in the brain. What, then, have we physicians to do with them? On the other hand, these mysterious and dominant feelings which surge up within us from unknown sources—are they not pure perturbations of the "psyche"? In that case, what, again, have we physicians to do with them? If we show this indifference, however, is it surprising that men and women, beset by emotional stresses, turn from us and go for help to faith healers, to Christian Scientists and to others who recognize the reality of these disturbing states?

An escape from the insistent demands of the pathologist for morphological evidence of disease, and also from the vagueness and mysticism of the psychological healers, can be found, I am convinced, in an understanding of the physiological processes which accompany profound emotional experience. As a physiologist I have the reasonable right to consider what goes on in the nerve paths of the brain as not associated with any demonstrable structural change. Indeed, very pronounced and disastrous consequences may result in the organism because of habit reactions, which may be regarded as not different in quality from any of our ordinary ways of behaving. Also as a physiologist I have the reasonable right to regard suddenly altered functions of organs innervated from the central nervous system as occurring in consequence of nerve impulses discharged from that system.

*The Annual Discourse delivered before the Massachusetts Medical Society, at Worcester, June 6, 1928.

†For record and address of author see "This Week's Issue," page 920.

Using the physiological point of view, therefore, I propose to consider emotions in terms of nerve impulses, much as I might consider the nerve impulses from the "motor area" of the cerebral cortex as they govern the movements of skeletal muscles. Although I shall use words with psychological implications, such as "fear," "rage," "feelings," and others, let me state at the outset that I use them solely as convenient short terms for complex activities in the brain. I shall be discussing, throughout, the *physiological* aspects of emotional excitement—the nervous mechanisms which are operating.

First, what is an emotion? From the physiological point of view it is a typical reaction pattern. Let us consider rage as an example. In its extreme form the signs of rage include the crouching body, the moist or frowning brow, the firm lips, the clenched or grinding teeth, the growled threats or imprecations, and the tightened fists or the seized weapon ready for attack. This is a complex attitude which we do not have to learn—its occurrence is a part of our native inheritance. It occurs promptly when the stimulus is appropriate. It is a constant and uniform type of behavior, having features which are common in widely scattered races of men and even in lower animals, so that the nature of the attitude is at once understood without the necessity of words. It is a permanent mode of reaction; throughout an individual's life the characteristic display of the rage response may be suddenly evoked in all its elaborateness and, whether in childhood or old age, it differs only in minor details. Further, it is a response to a fairly definite stimulus—any hampering or checking of activity, or opposition to one or another primary impulse brings it out. Threaten the free motion of a dog or a man and the teeth will be uncovered. Again, the rage response may be interpreted as being useful. Elsewhere[1] I have called attention to the wide range of bodily adjustments which occur when one is enraged—the more rapid heart-beat, the redistribution of the blood, the increase of red blood corpuscles in the circulation, the larger ventilation of the lungs, the dilatation of the bronchioles, the liberation of sugar from the liver, the secretion of adrenin with its favorable action on fatigued muscles—all of which may properly be regarded as rendering the organism more efficient in struggle, in such struggle as may be required to overwhelm the opposition and to allow the natural impulse to prevail. As we survey the characteristics of the outburst of rage as a typical emotion—the inborn, prompt, constant, uniform, permanent and useful nature of the response to a definite kind of stimulus—we note that these are the characteristics of a simple reflex, such as sneezing or coughing. They differ not in quality but in complexity.

Man is superior to the lower animals mainly because of the extensive development of the cerebral hemispheres. Comparative anatomy shows that these structures have been superposed on a brain stem which differs relatively little in the higher vertebrates. And physiological investigation has proved that whereas the reactions which involve the cerebral cortex may be delayed, unpredictable, short-lived, and readily modifiable, those which involve the lower levels of the brain and spinal cord are prompt, uniform and stereotyped. Hence the difference between the complex behavior of the normal human being and the relatively simple behavior of the idiot. It is of interest, therefore, to learn where the nervous mechanisms lie which operate the various emotional displays. Do these mechanisms have their seat in the newly developed cerebral cortex or in the more ancient parts of the brain?

In the brain stem are centers which, in the lower vertebrates, lacking a cerebral cortex, carry on the primitive functions of maintaining existence, such as seizing their prey and escaping from their enemies. These are activities which in man are associated with attack or with flight from danger and are attended by the emotions of rage or fear. In higher forms the centers for these functions, though normally held in check by the dominant cortex, are capable of energetic response when conditions require urgent and insistent action. It seemed reasonable to expect that the centers in the brain-stem would manifest their typical activity if the cerebral cortex was removed. Removal of the cortex would destroy the possibility of sensation and, therefore, a depressing or disturbing anesthetic could be dispensed with. Accordingly Britton and I[2], using cats as subjects, undertook an investigation of some of the immediate effects of a decortication which left intact almost all of the gray masses at the base of the brain. As soon as recovery from anesthesia was complete a remarkable group of activities appeared, such as are usually seen in an enfuriated animal—a sort of sham rage. These quasi-emotional phenomena, which appeared to result from the restraint, included lashing of the tail, arching of the trunk, thrusting and jerking of the restrained limbs, display of the claws and clawing motions, snarling and attempts to bite. These were all actions due to skeletal muscles. Besides these, and more typical and more permanent, were effects on the viscera, produced by impulses discharged over the sympathetic nerve fibres. They included erection of the tail hairs, sweating of the toe pads, dilatation of the pupils, micturition, a high blood pressure, a very rapid heart beat, an abundant outpouring of adrenin, and an increase of blood sugar up to five times the normal concentration[3]. This display of a "pseudaffective" state or sham rage might continue for two or three hours.

As stated above, Britton and I left untouched almost all of the basal gray matter of the anterior brain-stem. Where among these basal ganglia does the neurone pattern for the rage response reside? The answer to this question was obtained by Bard[4] who, after removing under ether the cerebral cortex and various amounts of the brain-stem, studied the behavior of the preparation. He found that typical sham rage, accompanied by vigorous discharge of sympathetic impulses, occurs when both hemispheres, the corpora striata and the anterior half of the diencephalon have been completely isolated (i. e., the crosshatched parts in figure 1).

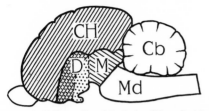

FIGURE 1. Median section of the brain. CH, cerebral hemispheres; D, diencephalon (indicated by dots); M, mesencephalon; Cb, cerebellum; Md, medulla. The crosshatching, from right downward to left, marks the portion of the brain which can be removed without interfering with the emotional expression of rage.

The additional extirpation of the posterior half of the diencephalon promptly abolishes the spontaneous activity. Further tests proved that the center lies in a small brain mass in the ventral part of this region, i.e., in the subthalamus.

Here is a fundamental fact which I wish to emphasize—that the nervous organization for the display of rage, both in bodily attitudes and in visceral changes, is located in an ancient portion of the brain, the optic thalamus which is a part of the diencephalon. This region is not like the cerebral cortex where new adjustments with the outer world are constantly being made or modified. Instead, it is like the spinal cord, a place where the simpler mechanism for orderly motions reside and where stimulation evokes fixed and uniform reflex responses. The typical postures and visceral changes which result from action of the thalamus are more complicated than the knee jerk or other spinal reflexes, but they are not essentially different.

I have laid stress on the locus of the physiological mechanism for the reflex figure of rage because it may serve as a model for other primitive emotional responses. The expressions of fear, joy and grief are similar to it in character. In their essential features they are not learned (i. e., they are inborn) and they are prompt, constant, uniform and permanently established patterns of reaction to appropriate stimuli. In other words they are like the simple reflexes and not like the complicated adjustments managed by the cortex. There is good evidence that the central control for the expression of these emotions, like that for rage, lies in the thalamic region. For example, Bechterev[5] has reported that in an animal freshly deprived of its cerebral hemispheres, petting may call forth signs of pleasure, e. g., purring in the cat and tail wagging in the dog.

The evidence which I have adduced to show that the neural arrangement for emotional display is near the optic thalamus has been based wholly on experiments on lower animals. That evidence, however, is consistent with indications that in man also emotional expression is managed by parts of the brain below the cortex and specifically by centers in or near the optic thalamus. Thus when in human beings the cortical processes are abolished by anesthesia, emotional display may be most remarkable. During the excitement stage of anesthesia, for example, the patient may sob as in grief, or laugh as in joy, or make the energetic aggressive actions of rage. While the patient is struggling, shouting and muttering the surgeon may open the chest or perform other operations of equal gravity; a few minutes later, when conscious, the patient will testify that he has been wholly unaware of what has happened. It is when "laughing gas" or alcohol has set aside the cortical functions (i. e., has functionally decorticated the individual), that he laughs or weeps. In all these conditions the drug acts first as a depressant on the highly sensitive cells of the cortex and thus lessens or temporarily destroys their control of lower centers; then the lower centers, released from the dominance of the cortex as in surgical-

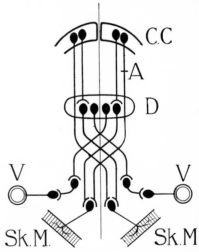

FIGURE 2. Diagram of possible relations of the nerve cells of the cerebral cortex (C.C.) and of the thalamic portion of the diencephalon (D.) to the viscera (V.) and to skeletal muscles (Sk.M.). The cortico-thalamic fibre is regarded as inhibitory. Sensory fibres are not represented. Damage to the cortico-spinal tract at A interrupts cortical control of certain skeletal muscles on one side, but it does not prevent control of these muscles on both sides by the centers in the diencephalon. Unilateral injury of centers in the diencephalon may leave bilateral control from the cortex.

ly decorticated animals, show forth their functions in free play.

In harmony with the experimental evidence from lower animals and the just described pharmacological evidence from man is that derived from pathological studies of human cases. In certain forms of hemiplegia patients are incapable of moving the face on the paralyzed side; but if an emotional (i. e., a sorrowful or joyous) situation develops, the muscles which were unresponsive to voluntary (i. e., cortical) control flash into action and give *both* sides of the face the expression of sadness or gaiety[6]. These are cases of subcortical interruption of the motor tract (e. g., at A. figure 2), and presence of an intact optic thalamus. The converse of this condition is seen in unilateral injury of the thalamic neurones (figure 2); then the patient moves symmetrically both sides of the face at will, but when he laughs or weeps the emotional expression is unilateral. Cases of pseudo-bulbar palsy also bring interesting testimony. In this disease there is usually a bilateral facial paralysis, with one side somewhat more involved than the other. Voluntary pursing of the lips as in whistling, or wrinkling of the forehead, or making a grimace, may be impossible. And yet the apparently paralyzed muscles function quite normally in laughing or crying, scowling or frowning. Indeed patients may have prolonged and uncontrollable fits of laughing or weeping. According to Brissaud[7] the pathological condition in this disease is a lesion of a part of the cortico-thalamic tract which frees a portion of the thalamus from the cortical check. All these observations, experimental and clinical, consistently point to the optic thalamus as the region in which resides the neural organization for the different emotional expressions.

The thalamic region is not only the seat of the neural patterns for the various emotional displays. It appears to be also the source of the peculiar feelings which contribute glow and color or to otherwise drab sensations. The evidence for this inference is mainly clinical. Head[8] has cited numerous cases of unilateral lesions in the thalamic region in which stimuli which evoke feelings have an excessive effect—pin pricks, painful pressure, pronounced heat or cold all produce much more distress on the damaged side than on the normal side of the body. Agreeable stimuli likewise are felt keenly on the damaged side; a warm test tube, for example, may give rise to intense pleasure, attended by signs of enjoyment on the face and by exclamations of delight. Again, the playing of music and the singing of hymns may arouse such increased emotional feeling, which is referred by the patient to the damaged side, that they may be intolerable. Imagined or remembered situations associated with past emotional experiences have an influence on the damaged side similar to the disturbing stimuli from the sense organs. This excessive influence of affective stimuli, whether from the body surface or from the cortex, Head attributed to the release of the thalamus from cortical control. When freed from check it overacts. And since in these cases the feelings are magnified on the damaged side, Head has concluded that the thalamus is occupied with the emotional aspect of sensation and that the uni-

lateral overaction there is the cause of the unilateral magnification of feeling.

We have reviewed the evidence that the neurones of the thalamic region discharge outward and downward to muscles and viscera to produce the typical bodily changes of emotional excitement, and that they discharge upward to the cortex to add richness and warmth to the simple sensations. Two other important points I wish now to emphasize.

The first of these is concerned with the relations of the cortical and the thalamic control of bodily processes. It is clear that *skeletal muscles are governed at both levels, cortical and thalamic* (see figure 2); for example, we may laugh spontaneously because of a ludicrous situation (thalamic laughter) or we may laugh as a voluntary act (cortical laughter). It is quite as clear that the *viscera*, on the other hand, are *only under thalamic government;* we cannot by direct act of will increase the blood sugar, accelerate the heart, or stop digestion. When there is double control the cortical neurones, to be sure, are ordinarily dominant and may not release the excited neurones of the thalamus (though we sometimes cry or laugh "in spite of ourselves"). Then there is conflict between the higher and lower controls of the bodily functions—there are opposing influences with accompanying confusion. The cortex, however, can check only those bodily functions which are normally under voluntary control. That point I would emphasize. Just as the cortex cannot cause, so likewise it cannot prevent those stormy processes of the thalamus that increase the blood sugar, accelerate the heart, stop digestion, or produce the other disturbances characteristic of great excitement. When an emotion is repressed, therefore, it is repressed only in its external manifestations. There is evidence, to be sure, that when the external manifestations are maximal, the internal turmoil is also maximal[2]; and it is probable that cortical control of the outward display of excitement results in less internal disturbance than would accompany free expression. Nevertheless in a conflict between the cortical government and the activities of the thalamic centers the ungovernable internal manifestations might be intense.

The second point is related to evidence that states of consciousness are associated only with the cortical neurones. Certainly we are unaware of the numerous and complicated reflexes which determine bodily posture or the size of the pupil, for example, although these reflexes are regulated in the brain-stem. It follows that the neural mechanisms for the primitive emotions, active in the basal ganglia, are likewise probably not directly associated with consciousness. This consideration explains, I conceive, some of the most characteristic features of emotional experience. The disturbance in extraconscious parts boils up into the realm of the conscious. Therefore, we have emotional "seizures"; we may laugh, weep or rage "uncontrollably"; we feel as if "possessed"; what we do in the stress of excitement is "surprising" or "shocking"—something "surges up within us" and our actions seem no longer our own. These common bywords are explicable in terms of a sudden and powerful dominance of the bodily forces by subcortical neurones, i. e., neurones whose activity is not immediately attended by conscious states. Under favoring circumstances, with only a momentary lifting of the normal inhibitory check, these lower neurones capture the machinery of action and drive it violently into one or another of its variegated patterns.

I have now reviewed the evidence that the thalamic region, when freed from cortical control, is capable of elaborate independent activity of a stereotyped character; that when it acts it produces the typical reaction patterns in posture, expression and visceral responses that characterize various strong emotions; and that the activity of the thalamus occasions the feelings of excitement or depression which we experience during an emotional disturbance. Now the question arises, how are these considerations related to practical affairs? How do the processes going on deep down in the old part of the brain affect the workings of the body? To show how events in the thalamus can profoundly disarrange the nice adjustments of the normal organism, I shall cite some illustrative cases. I am sure that they will not seem unusual or improbable to many of you.

First, with regard to digestive functions. As stated earlier, my interest in the effects of emotions in the organism began with observations on the abolition of gastric peristalsis during excitement. Elsewhere[9] I have described instances of total stoppage not only of the mechanical action of the canal, but also of the work of the digestive glands, in consequence of emotional stresses. An evening's meal may remain undigested all night in the stomach if there is persistent worry during the period. The saliva, the gastric and the pancreatic juices all may be stopped by fear. The whole digestive process, which is subject to check by the sympathetic system, may be profoundly disarranged by anxiety and distress—the minor aspects of fear. McLester[10] has estimated that one-third of patients with disorders of the alimentary tract are suffering because of lack of emotional balance. Alvarez[11] cites a case of persistent vomiting which started when an income tax collector threatened punishment if a discrepancy in the tax statement was not explained, and which ceased as soon as Alvarez himself went to the collector, as a therapeutic measure, and straightened out the difficulty. The natural processes of the alimentary canal are fundamental to all other functions of the body. Any disturbance of normal peristalsis, segmentation, and secretion of the digestive fluids may have widespread ill effects in the organism. Cabot[12] has recorded

an instance of fracture of the leg which failed to unite. Investigation showed that the patient was fearful lest his family was suffering while he was absent at the hospital, i. e., the anxiety resulted in loss of desire for food (absence of hunger contractions of the stomach), that resulted in impaired nutrition, and that in turn led to such impairment of the reparative processes that the bone fragments were not welded together. Assurance that his family was well and happy, and being cared for, quickly altered the patient's condition; he ceased worrying, thereupon began to eat heartily and gain in nutrition, and then his broken bones began to knit.

The cardiovascular system, like the digestive system, is under the influence of the sympathetic nerves, but instead of being depressed or inhibited, it is stimulated by them. The excitement which stops gastric digestion makes the heart beat more rapidly and raises blood pressure by contracting the blood vessels. During the War there appeared not infrequently cases of "disorderly action of the heart" or, as it was sometimes called, "soldier's heart." The slightest excitement or perturbation would send the pulse bounding at a high rate (130 to 150 beats per minute). The general physical and nervous condition of the victims of this disturbance—their anxious faces, their troubled eyes, the drawn lines about the mouth, their trembling—was such as to make reasonable the view that the stresses of the war had become intolerable and had resulted in such sensitizing of the sympathetic control of the heart that even mild stimulation produced extreme effects[13]. The mechanism by which emotion may bring about such sensitizing is illustrated in a case reported by Foster[14]:—

A wife, who was free from any cardiac disorder, saw her husband walking arm in arm with a strange woman and acting in such a way as to rouse jealousy and suspicion. Profoundly stirred by the incident the wife hastened home and remained there several days. She then began to fear going out lest she might meet her husband with her rival. After days of wretchedness she was persuaded by a friend to venture forth, "probably in a state of abject terror," as Foster remarks, but she had not gone far when she ran back to her home. Then she noted that her heart was thumping hard, that she had a sense of oppression in her chest and a choking sensation. Later attempts to go outdoors produced the same alarming symptoms. She began to feel that she might die on the street if she went out. There was no organic disease of the heart, and yet slight effort as she moved from her home brought on acute distress.

The influence of excitement on arterial blood pressure may also be noted. The pressure is produced by the energy of the inflow of blood into the arteries and the resistance to the outflow from them. The sympathetic impulses, by speeding the heart rate and constricting the arterioles, raise the pressure by affecting positively both factors. Gallavardin and Haour[15] have reported after a study of 100 cases that the first time the blood pressure is taken, and the subjects are, therefore, excited, the systolic level may be 25 to 35 millimeters higher than it is later. And Schrumpf[16] relates an instance in which fear of a serious diagnosis raised the pressure 33 per cent., with prompt return to normal when reassurance was given. In extreme cases of pleasure, anger or fright a rise of 90 millimeters of mercury may occur. It is clear that patients suffering from hypertension and senile impairment of the circulatory system should avoid conditions and obligations which are likely to cause excitement.

Another effect readily produced by sympathetic impulses is the increase of blood sugar. The influence of emotional disturbance in bringing about a hyperglycemia in men subjected to the intense stresses of competitive sports or critical examinations I have pointed out elsewhere[1]. The same phenomenon has been observed in diabetic patients, probably because the sugar excretion is watched more closely in such persons. Woodyatt[17] cites the following from among many similar experiences in his practice:—

A man of 65 years, a diabetic, was in the hospital on a quantitative diet and with a small dose of insulin daily was passing a sugar-free urine. Suddenly one day, without any change in regimen, he secreted 43 grams of sugar. And on another day he secreted 76 grams and developed a mild acidosis; the glycosuria, therefore, could not have been due merely to the taking of extra food. A careful checking of all the circumstances and tests proved that there was no error of technique; nor did examination reveal any evidence of intercurrent physical disease. It was found, however, that the patient had received news which led him to fear that the corporation in which he had been an officer for more than 20 years had taken steps to retire him. That was the occasion for his disturbed sugar metabolism.

As Woodyatt remarks, "It is interesting to be able to measure the power of emotion in terms so tangible as ounces of sugar. *The power of emotions to produce physical alterations of the body* does not seem unreal under these conditions."

There is evidence that violent emotional disturbance can produce profound effects on the organism through influences on the thyroid gland. Marañon[18] has collected an extensive series of cases of hyperthyroidism brought on by stressful experiences during the Great War. Recently Emerson[19] has reported some striking instances of hyperthyroidism which followed intensely affective scenes in the lives of the patients.

One was a married woman who had had two illegitimate children and whose husband committed suicide in her presence as a rebuke to her manner of living. Thereupon she dropped to the floor and exhausted herself in shrieking. At once she had a sense of constriction of her throat and was troubled with difficulty in swallowing; the thyroid gland enlarged and six weeks after the incident she had a metabolism 65 per cent. above normal. Later troubles of an exacting character were associated with the development of high blood sugar and a high arterial pressure.

Another case. A man of twenty years had a quarrel with his fiancée. She, pretending to commit suicide, had in his presence swallowed some pills and fallen down screaming. The man departed hastily. Within a week he was suffering from swelling of the neck and nervousness. When he appeared at the hospital four months later he had lost weight, he presented a large goitre over which a definite thrill could be felt, and his basal metabolism was up 24 per cent. above the normal level.

A third case was that of a married woman who had seen her husband kill his two brothers. The husband bitterly reproached her for not coming to his defense at the trial. A week after the trial a goitre became evident and reached a large size in seven days. When she came to the hospital a few months later, the goitre was huge, it pulsated visibly, had a palpable thrill and was causing an oppressive sense of suffocation. There was pronounced exophthalmus with marked tremor and restlessness. The basal metabolism varied from +40 to +117 per cent.

There are other emotional effects on bodily functions which might be mentioned, such as disorders of menstruation[20], emptying of the bladder[21], secretion of milk[22], discharge of adrenin[23], altered coagulability of the blood[24], increase in the number of red corpuscles[25], and others. Enough instances have been given, however, to show that there are effects wrought on the organs innervated by the sympathetic nervous system—glands both of external and internal secretion and parts supplied with smooth muscle—that are just as real as the effects which are produced when the biceps is used to lift a weight. A remarkable difference lies in the level of the nervous control of these two effects. Whereas the biceps is usually managed from the cortex, the viscera are managed from the diencephalon. Whereas the biceps is under "voluntary" control, the viscera are not under that control, but are influenced favorably or unfavorably by processes associated with feelings and emotions. Although the neural center for emotional expression is subcortical indeed, is low in the brain-stem—yet cortical processes are involved in the total reaction to a situation which evokes strong feelings. We might be frightened by a real bear, but not by a stuffed bear. The discrimination between the two is made by the cortex. How may this relation between cortex and thalamus be interpreted in physiological terms?

Earlier I have pointed out that an emotional reaction has many of the characteristics of a reflex response. To evoke a reflex an appropriate stimulus must be applied; an irritant in the larynx produces coughing, food in the mouth calls forth a flow of saliva. Similarly with emotional expressions. Watson[26] has studied new-born babies and has found that from the beginning loud sounds and also indications of loss of support are the natural stimuli for the reaction of fear. Limitation or hampering of the freedom of bodily movement is from the beginning the natural stimulus for rage.

Agents other than the natural stimuli, however, can easily be made to set a reflex in action if only they are closely associated with the natural stimuli. Thus if a red light is flashed repeatedly at the same time that food is placed in the mouth, the red light will itself, alone, become as effective as the food in causing a salivary discharge. The indifferent stimulus, the red light, is then called the conditioned stimulus and the reflex salivary secretion, under the circumstances, a conditioned reflex. All sorts of ordinarily indifferent external agents—not only a light, but a sound, a shape, a contact, an odor, indeed *anything* that will influence a sense organ—may be made into an effective stimulus by close association in time with the normally effective stimulus. Thus objects and events in the world about us are constantly acquiring new significance for our reactions. All the processes of conditioning are carried on in the cerebral cortex. These facts, which have been studied in great detail and most instructively by the Russian physiologist, Pavlov[27], have pertinence for the explanation of emotional behavior.

Our emotional reflexes, like the salivary reflex, become complicated by the conditioning of indifferent stimuli. A white rat shown to a baby causes the baby to reach for it and to play with it; there is no fear. Then the rat is presented repeatedly but at the same time a loud sound is made by striking a steel bar. The rat thus becomes a conditioned stimulus for the fear reaction produced by the loud sound, and thereafter, when the rat is shown, the baby cries and turns away. He is now afraid of the rat not because it is a rat but because it has become the signal and symbol of something fearful—the loud sound. In such ways as this the indifferent circumstances of an emotional disturbance become conditioned stimuli or signals for renewal of the disturbance. The wife who saw her husband paying attention to a strange woman on the street had an intense emotional experience which was renewed, not by seeing again the errant husband and his distressing companion, but by going into the street! Thus by extended associations emotional responses become subjected to more and more involved conditioned stimuli, until great complexity and intricacy of affective behavior result.

In the foregoing discussion I have purposely emphasized the physiological mechanisms of emotional disturbances, and for two main reasons. First, I wished to show that these remarkable perturbations could be described in terms of neurone processes. And again, I wished to persuade you that these interesting phenomena should not be set aside as mystical events occurring in the realm of the "psyche,"

but rather should be regarded as movements and inhibitions and disturbances in the body which properly fall within the province of the physician.

Probably a physiologist is venturing too far if he attempts to suggest practical modes of treatment. And yet in what I have presented to you there are physiological implications which have practical bearings on the care of patients who have been or are being profoundly disturbed by emotional experience.

First, there is the importance of early treatment. We are all acquainted with the readiness with which habits are established in the nervous system by frequently repeating an act. Every time the nerve impulses traverse a given course they make easier the passage of later impulses. Thus habitual emotional expressions, both in the facies and in the viscera, may become fixed and deep-set in the neural organization, just as the complicated adjustments of swimming, skating or bicycle riding become inwrought during our later years by repeated practice. It is clear that so far as possible emotional habit-reactions should be prevented by prompt treatment.

As we have seen, the cortex has no direct control over the functions of the viscera. It is useless, therefore, to try to check a racing heart or to lower a high blood pressure, or to renew the activities of an inhibited digestive system by a coldly reasoned demand for different behavior. The man whose broken bone failed to knit because he was fearful about his family's welfare could not be *argued* out of his fear; the fear left him when he learned that his family was actually comfortable. The cortex, which is concerned with analysis of the outer world, should not, therefore, be the sole means by which treatment is attempted; the *occasion* for worries, anxieties, conflicts, hatreds, resentments, and other forms of fear and anger, which affect the thalamic centers, must be removed. In short, the factors in the whole situation which are the source of strong feeling must be discovered and either explained away or eliminated.

Although the cortex has no direct control over the viscera, it has indirect control—we can walk into danger and have a thrill, though we cannot have a thrill by merely resolving to have one. Similarly we can often avoid the circumstances which rouse fear or rage or disgust and their attendant visceral turmoil—we need not go near the agitating spot.

Again, when the reason for the perturbation is not clear, it can sometimes be found by careful enquiry or analysis. It is an interesting fact that a full explanation of the way in which the trouble has been caused will not infrequently suffice to remove the trouble, promptly and completely.

Finally, a word of warning may not be out of place. If an objective cause for a patient's complaint is not found, nothing is easier than to attribute the difficulty to nervous factors. There is danger, when one emphasizes the importance of nervous factors as disturbers of the bodily peace, that one may be understood as minimizing the need of search for a gross pathology. Nothing could be farther from my intention. The assumption that emotional agencies are causing mischief in the organism should be a last resort—an explanation which is offered only after every effort has been made to find another explanation. And even when the cause is ascribed to fear or rage or some other strong feeling, proof for that conclusion should be carefully sought both at the source of the trouble and in the effect of appropriate therapy. Nor should the possibility be overlooked that along with profound emotional disturbance there will be discovered a demonstrable lesion. The two conditions, the altered structure of some organ and the altered function of the nervous system, may be causally related, and may have to be treated as a single disorder. Certain it is that only when they are both regarded as the perturbations of a single unity, the organism, will they be properly conceived and effectively treated.

I have tried to indicate the ways in which the functions of the body may be upset by the neural processes which are associated with emotions. I hope that I have convinced you that interest in this realm of medicine should not be relegated to cults, mental healers and the clergy. The doctor is properly concerned with the workings of the body and their disturbances, and he should have, therefore, a natural interest in the effects of emotional stress and in the modes of relieving it. The field has not been well cultivated. Much work still needs to be done in it. It offers to all kinds of medical practitioners many opportunities for useful studies. There is no more fascinating realm of medicine in which to conduct investigation. I heartily commend it to you.

BIBLIOGRAPHY

1 Cannon: Bodily Changes in Pain, Hunger, Fear and Rage, New York, 1915.
2 Cannon and Britton: Am. Journ. Physiol., 1925, lxxii, 283.
3 Bulatao and Cannon: Ibid., 295.
4 Bard: Ibid., 1928, lxxxiv, 490.
5 Bechterev: Virchow's Arch., 1887, cx, 345.
6 Roussy: La Couche Optique, Paris, 1907, p. 31.
7 Brissaud: Leçons cliniques, 1894.
8 Head: Studies in Neurology, London, 1920, ii, 620.
9 Cannon: The Mechanical Factors of Digestion, London, 1911.
10 McLester: Journ. Am. Med. Assn., 1927, lxxxix, 1019.
11 Alvarez: Personal communication.
12 Cabot: Harvard Alumni Bulletin, 1925, xxviii, 384.
13 Cohn: Am. Journ. Med. Sci., 1919, clviii, 453.
14 Foster: Journ. Am. Med. Assn., 1927, lxxxix, 1018.
15 Gallavardin and Haour: Arch. de Mal du Coeur, 1912, v, 81.
16 Schrumpf: Deutsch. med. Wochenschr., 1910, xxxvi, 2385.
17 Woodyatt: Journ. Am. Med. Assn., 1927, lxxxix, 1013.
18 Maranon: Annal. de Med., 1921, ix, 81.
19 Emerson: Trans. Assn. Am. Phys., 1927, xlii, 346.
20 Mayer: Schwarz's Psychogenese und Psychotherapie körperlicher Symptome, Vienna, 1925, p. 298.
21 Schwarz: Ibid., p. 273.
22 Greving: Müller's Die Lebensnerven, Berlin, 1924, p. 226.
23 Cannon, Britton, Lewis and Groeneveld: Am. Journ. Physiol., 1927, lxxix, 433.
24 Cannon and Mendenhall: Ibid., 1914, xxxiv, 251.
25 Izquierdo and Cannon: Ibid., 1928, lxxxiv, 545.
26 Watson: Lectures on Behaviorism, New York, 1925, 114.
27 Pavlov: Conditioned Reflexes, Oxford, 1927.

Reprinted from *American Journal of Physiology*
Vol. 132, 532–541 (1941).

THE EFFECT OF EMOTION, SHAM RAGE AND HYPOTHALAMIC STIMULATION ON THE VAGO-INSULIN SYSTEM[1]

E. GELLHORN, R. CORTELL AND J. FELDMAN[2]

*From the Departments of Physiology and Psychiatry, College of Medicine,
University of Illinois, Chicago*

Accepted for publication April 6, 1941

Through the important studies of Cannon we are well informed about the excitation of the sympathetico-adrenal system under conditions of emotion. The fact that severe emotional disturbances (fear, terror) may be accompanied by excitation of certain branches of the parasympathetic system as well as sympathetico-adrenal discharges, was not unknown to Cannon, but he assumed that it represented a pathological phenomenon in which the reciprocal relationship between sympathetic and parasympathetic innervation is disturbed rather than the expression of a physiological mechanism characteristic of the emotional process. It cannot be doubted on the basis of clinical experience that parasympathetic discharges may occur even in relatively mild states of emotional excitement. For example, weeping is brought about as a result of parasympathetic excitation (Lund). Excited emotion may cause increased gastric secretion (Wittkower) or may precipitate a biliary colic (Bergmann). Increased peristalsis and more frequent urge to urinate are common signs of increased parasympathetic activity during emotional excitement. Startle may produce a marked fall in pulse rate (Tomaszewski). These findings seem to indicate that the emotional process is characterized by discharges affecting both branches of the autonomic nervous system at the same time.

The results of electrical stimulation of the hypothalamus also lend support to this idea, since in contrast to older observations of Ranson, Kabat and Magoun, signs of parasympathetic excitation may be elicited from the whole hypothalamic area provided that weak stimuli or stimuli of low frequencies are used (Masserman and Haertig; Hare and Geohagan). Our own experiences (Carlson, Gellhorn and Darrow) indicate that hypothalamic stimulation may lead to excitation of the parasympathetic and the sympathetic, and also to an inhibition of the parasympathetic, and that excitation of both systems may result from the stimulation of the

[1] Preliminary report: Science **92**: 288, 1940.
[2] Aided by a grant from the John and Mary R. Markle Foundation and W.P.A. Project 30278.

532

same part of the hypothalamus.   On the basis of these experiments it is not impossible that hypothalamic stimulation induced either by electrical stimulation or under conditions of emotion can lead to both parasympathetic and sympathetic discharges.

Feldman, Cortell and Gellhorn (1940) were able to show recently that chemical stimulation of autonomic centers leads to a simultaneous discharge over both the sympathetico-adrenal and the vago-insulin systems. It was deemed of interest to investigate whether the processes of sham rage as induced by hypothalamic stimulation or of rage and other forms of emotion in the waking animal may also involve the vago-insulin system.

METHODS.   The experiments which were carried out on cats may be divided into three groups.   In the first group the animals were anesthetized with chloralosane (100 mgm./kgm. subcutaneously).   The adrenals were removed and the liver denervated in order to eliminate the effect of hypothalamic stimulation on part of the sympathetico-adrenal system.   The hypothalamus was stimulated with faradic currents and a typical sham rage reaction was produced.   The Horsley-Clarke apparatus was used to place the electrode into the hypothalamus.   In order to evaluate the effect of sham rage on the vago-insulin system, blood samples were taken before and after bilateral vagotomy at various intervals and analyzed for sugar by the Somogyi modification of the Shaeffer-Hartman method.

In the second group of experiments the spinal cord was sectioned at the sixth cervical segment and the thyroid and parathyroid glands were removed under ether.   Eighteen hours later the animals were lightly anesthetized with chloralosane (35 mgm./kgm. intravenously) and the hypothalamus was stimulated as in the first group.

In a third group the cervical cord was sectioned as in the second group and 18 hours later the cat was confronted with a barking dog in an attempt to elicit a rage response.   This experiment was repeated after the vagi had been cut subdiaphragmatically without the use of narcosis.

Another group of experiments was performed on rats which were divided into three groups (normals, adreno-demedullated rats and adreno-demedullated rats which had been vagotomized below the diaphragm). These rats were subjected to "emotional excitement" by exposing them to the noise of fire-crackers, which has been found to stimulate the sympathetico-adrenal system in normal rats (Harris and Ingle).   Furthermore, the influence of struggle resulting from tying the animals to a board and from the application of slight faradic shocks was also studied on the vago-insulin system (Lumley and Nice).

RESULTS.   Figure 1 illustrates two experiments typical for the first group in which the effect of a hypothalamic stimulation on the blood sugar was studied in animals deprived of the adrenals, the thyroid and parathyroid glands and in which the liver had been denervated.   In the first experiment (1) the blood sugar was constant at a very low level. Stimulation of the hypothalamus immediately posterior to the mammillary body elicited a marked sham rage response with arching of the back, extension of the forelimbs and an excellent pilomotor response. The blood sugar was slightly decreased during the half-hour which followed the period of excitation. Hereafter the vagi were cut and the period of stimulation was repeated, giving rise to a response qualitatively and quantitively similar to that observed prior to vagotomy. But the blood sugar response is entirely different. Instead of observing a fall in blood sugar a temporary

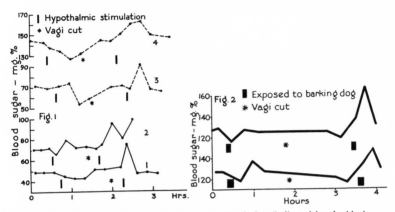

Fig. 1. The effect of hypothalamic faradic stimulation (indicated by the black rectangle) on the blood sugar of cats before and after vagotomy. Vagi were cut at *. In the experiments of graphs 1 and 2 the adrenals were removed and the liver denervated. In graphs 3 and 4 the cervical spinal cord of the cats had been sectioned at the 6th cervical segment 18 hours prior to the experiment.

Fig. 2. The effect of rage on the blood sugar of cats whose spinal cord had been sectioned at the 6th cervical segment before and after vagotomy.

rise occurred. The second experiment, in which the mammillary body was stimulated, showed no marked alteration in blood sugar following the sham rage reaction in spite of distinct signs of pilomotor reactions. It is found that the blood sugar decreased slightly at first and then showed a small rise. However, after the vagi had been cut the blood sugar rose distinctly and for a long time.

All experiments of this group have one feature in common, i.e., that the rise in blood sugar after vagotomy is much more marked in these animals with inactivated adrenals than it is when the vagi are intact. The nature of this blood sugar rise is not fully understood. It is probable that in this group of experiments sympathin plays a rôle. It is also conceivable that the liver was not completely denervated in every instance and that some effect of stimulation of sympathetic fibers leading to the liver was not eliminated. However, this interpretation is not very likely since Britton found no or only a very slight influence on glycogenolysis of the sympathetic fibers innervating the liver under conditions of emotional excitement (Cannon). It seems to us of greater importance to show that the vagotomy invariably altered the blood sugar response to hypothalamic stimulation, and that the effects indicate that hypothalamic stimulation leading to the characteristic syndrome of sham rage produces hypoglycemia via the vagi which may or may not be overshadowed by the simultaneous liberation of sympathin.

In the second group the sympathetico-adrenal system was eliminated by sectioning the cord at the sixth cervical level. In addition, the thyroid and parathyroid glands had been removed. The effects of sham rage on the blood sugar were quite similar to the first group. Graph 3 of figure 1 shows that stimulation of the lateral hypothalamic area leading to a mild sham rage reaction characterized by spreading of the claws and pupillary dilatation caused a fall in blood sugar when the vagi were intact. This effect was completely reversible. If, however, the stimulation was repeated after vagotomy, the only effect was a temporary rise in blood sugar. Graph 4 represents a similar experiment in which the lateral hypothalamic area was stimulated. The blood sugar level was high but remained constant over many hours. Following the first period of hypothalamic stimulation in which the vagi were intact a distinct fall in blood sugar was observed. Eighty minutes after the period of stimulation the blood sugar had returned to the original level. The experiment was then repeated after bilateral vagotomy and led now to a distinct rise in blood sugar. Another experiment was also characterized by a relatively high blood sugar level but this level was maintained throughout the experiment quite satisfactorily. The electrode was inserted close to the red nucleus. A marked rage reaction was observed, with dilatation of the pupil, increased respiration, upward movements of the forelimbs and swallowing. The stimulation produced a distinct fall in blood sugar which was reversible within 15 minutes. After vagotomy a similar period of stimulation producing a rage reaction closely akin to the reaction observed during the first test resulted in a distinct and reversible rise in blood sugar.

All the experiments show convincingly that hypothalamic stimulation leading to the syndrome of sham rage produces in cordotomized and thyroidectomized animals a fall in blood sugar which is mediated by the vagi. After these nerves have been divided, a slight rise results from the hypothalamic stimulation.

It seems to be of interest to discuss briefly an apparent exception to this rule. In an experiment in which the animal was prepared as in the last group and in which the mammillary peduncle was stimulated, the blood sugar fell 34.4 mgm. per cent as a result of hypothalamic stimulation. Because the animal was used for another experiment involving the nictitating membrane, the vagi were then cut but the sympathetic, which can easily be separated from the vagi in the cat, was left intact. In this experiment it was observed that after vagotomy a less but still distinct fall in blood sugar (22.6 mgm. per cent) was observed. It seems likely in the light of the other experiments discussed in this paper, in which such hypoglycemic effects after transection of the vago-sympathetic were not observed, that the "sympathetic" may contain some vagal fibers sufficient to increase insulin secretion.

The last group of experiments on cats comprises those experiments which were performed on cordotomized cats without anesthesia. The animals were confronted with a barking dog and in some instances in which they did not react satisfactorily to the dog they were teased for several minutes. The effect of the rage thus elicited was studied on the blood sugar before and after the vagi had been cut below the diaphragm as illustrated in figure 2. The upper graph of this figure shows a relatively high blood sugar level at the beginning of the experiment. The rage reaction induced a fall in blood sugar which was to a large extent reversible. Abdominal vagotomy was performed and several hours later a second rage reaction was elicited. The effect was quite different from that observed in the first test since now a marked rise in the blood sugar resulted. The experiment illustrated in the lower graph of figure 2 shows only a slight variation in blood sugar after the rage reaction but a marked rise resulted when the experiment was repeated after division of the vagi below the diaphragm.

The experiments seem to show that sham rage produced by hypothalamic stimulation and rage elicited in the cat by confronting it with a barking dog result in a hypoglycemic effect which is due to excitation of abdominal branches of the vagi. This interpretation is strengthened by the experiments of Britton and La Barre, who showed that stimulation of abdominal vagal fibers leads to hypoglycemia by increasing the rate of secretion of insulin.

Rats subjected to the noise of fire-crackers for three minutes show typical motor responses suggesting fear. The effect on the autonomic centers is similar to that resulting from the injection of metrazol as reported by Feldman, Cortell and Gellhorn. Normal rats respond to the stimulus with a considerable hyperglycemia whereas adreno-demedullated rats show a temporary fall in blood sugar averaging 20 mgm. per cent. Fifteen minutes later the sugar level has returned to approximately the control value. Rats in which in addition to the demedullation of the adrenals the vagi have been cut below the diaphragm show a rise in blood sugar of a few milligrams per cent which in spite of its statistical significance is hardly significant physiologically (table 1).

TABLE 1

Effect of fear* on blood sugar

RAT NO.	BLOOD SUGAR (MGM. PER CENT)		
	Control	Time after stimulation	
		1-5 min.	15-20 min.
A. Normal rats			
1	70.9	96.8	81.1
2	73.1	97.8	86.0
3	74.1	102.1	86.0
4	73.1	98.9	91.3
5	75.2	102.1	97.8
6	70.9	94.6	86.0
Mean....................	72.9	98.7	88.0
Standard dev.............	1.6	2.8	5.3
P.......................		<0.01	<0.01
B. Adrenalectomized rats			
1	65.5	43.0	64.5
2	66.6	40.8	65.5
3	63.4	51.6	64.5
4	65.5	43.0	59.1
5	64.5	49.4	60.2
6	67.7	46.2	56.9
Mean....................	65.5	45.7	61.8
Standard dev.............	1.4	3.8	3.2
P.......................		<0.01	0.034
C. Adrenalectomized-vagotomized rats			
1	68.8	68.8	76.3
2	65.5	70.9	73.1
3	67.7	70.9	77.4
4	66.6	69.8	73.1
5	66.6	68.8	82.7
6	68.8	70.9	75.2
Mean....................	67.3	70.0	76.3
Standard dev.............	1.2	0.9	3.3
P.......................		<0.01	<0.01

* The rats were exposed to the noise of fire-crackers for 3 minutes.

A final series of experiments was conducted on rats which struggled because they were tied to a board. The struggle was reinforced by application of painful stimuli (faradic shock) to the toes. The results reproduced in table 2 are similar to those obtained in experiments involving fear reactions.

In both sets of experiments it was found that rats subjected to emotional

TABLE 2

Effect of struggle* on blood sugar

	BLOOD SUGAR (MGM. PER CENT)		
RAT NO.	Control	Time after completion of stimulus	
		3 min.	15 min.
A. Normal rats			
1	74.1	95.6	79.5
2	77.4	97.8	84.9
3	75.2	99.9	79.5
4	72.0	89.2	75.2
Mean	74.7	95.6	79.8
St. dev.	1.9	4.0	3.4
P		<0.01	0.044
B. Adrenalectomized rats			
1	65.5	51.6	64.5
2	67.7	48.3	60.2
3	63.4	47.3	64.5
4	63.4	54.8	58.0
Mean	65.0	50.5	61.8
St. dev.	1.8	2.9	2.8
P		<0.01	0.104
C. Adrenalectomized-vagotomized rats			
1	64.5	70.2	74.1
2	66.6	68.8	70.2
3	64.5	68.8	68.8
4	66.6	70.2	68.8
Mean	65.6	69.5	70.5
St. dev.	1.1	0.7	2.2
P		<0.01	<0.01

* The rats were tied to a board for 10 min.

excitement react with a marked hyperglycemia when the adrenals are intact and with a conspicuous hypoglycemia after demedullation of the adrenals. Since the latter reaction disappears after the additional sectioning of the vagi below the diaphragm it is evident that the hypoglycemic reaction elicited by emotional excitement in adreno-demedullated animals is due to an increase in the rate of insulin secretion brought about by central stimulation of the vagus.

DISCUSSION. The experiments reported in this paper show clearly that hypothalamic stimulation leading to the sham rage syndrome is accompanied by a fall in blood sugar in animals in which the secretion of adrenalin by sympathetic excitation is eliminated. This fall seems to be due to impulses reaching the pancreas via the vagi since the reaction is abolished when the vagi are cut and the experiment is repeated with the same outward success. The fall in blood sugar is slight and occasionally absent, but the comparison of the blood sugar reaction obtained in the normal and the vagotomized animal invariably indicates a greater hyperglycemic effect of the sham rage reaction in the latter. Since it is well known that hypothalamic stimulation (Magoun and collaborators) as well as emotional excitation (Bodo and Benaglia; Partington) may lead to the contraction of the denervated nictitating membrane in adrenalectomized animals, it is highly probable that the rise in blood sugar observed in adrenalectomized and vagotomized animals is due to sympathin. The fact that these results were obtained in animals with the thyroid and parathyroid removed clearly proves that any alteration in thyroid secretion is not responsible for changes in the blood sugar level.

Since the identity of the autonomic changes accompanying sham rage and rage reactions may be questioned, it is of great importance to decide whether the results obtained in experiments on sham rage are applicable to the natural emotional process. The rage reaction elicited in the cat by a barking dog was chosen for the study of the autonomic changes in emotion. This reaction is known to produce marked sympathetico-adrenal discharges (Cannon). When the effect on the sympathetico-adrenal system had been eliminated by the sectioning of the spinal cord at the sixth cervical level, it was found that rage produced a hypoglycemic reaction mediated by the vagi but such reaction was absent after the vagi had been sectioned below the diaphragm.

This work was confirmed and extended by experiments on rats involving struggle and, in another group, "emotional excitement" by exposure to loud noises. Since in the rat experiments the sympathin response is apparently very small, the effect on the vago-insulin system as shown by the hypoglycemic response to excitement is still more distinct than in our experiments on cats.

It is interesting to note that the hypoglycemic response to noise of adrenalectomized rats was observed by Harris and Ingle. Lumley and Nice found in the majority of their adrenalectomized rats a hypoglycemic response to struggle and Britton found the rage reaction to cause a fall in blood sugar in adreno-demedullated cats. However, these authors failed to see the significance of their findings and did not study the effect of abdominal vagotomy which disclosed the nature of the hypoglycemic reaction.

Our experiments explain also an apparent paradox observed by Bodo and Benaglia. These authors found that both stimulation of the accelerator nerves and emotional excitement cause a similar contraction of the denervated nictitating membrane in cats with inactivated adrenals. However, the blood sugar rose 100 to 200 mgm. per cent in the case of the accelerator nerve stimulation whereas in conditions of emotional excitement the rise in blood sugar was very slight. On the basis of our experiments it must be assumed that emotional excitement caused the liberation of insulin as well as sympathin. The effect on the blood sugar is consequently less than it is in the case of stimulation of the accelerator nerves although the amount of sympathin liberated and tested by the nictitating membrane may be similar in both instances.

The experiments show also that various forms of emotional excitement (fear, rage) although calling forth different cerebrospinal responses (motor patterns) act in a similar manner on the vago-insulin and the sympathetico-adrenal systems.

Cannon has repeatedly emphasized the great physiological significance of the increased blood sugar level for conditions of fighting which accompany emotional excitement. If we consider the blood sugar level alone, the activation of both vago-insulin and sympathetico-adrenal systems might be looked upon as a disadvantageous reaction, since the insulin secretion must have a tendency to counteract the rise in blood sugar. It must be remembered, however, that the utilization of glucose depends not only on the blood sugar level but also on the amount of insulin present (Soskin). Consequently a hyperglycemic reaction combined with increased insulin secretion creates optimal conditions for the utilization of glucose. The vago-insulin and the sympathetico-adrenal system act as synergists as far as utilization of glucose is concerned. This synergistic action is made possible by the greater reactivity of the sympathetico-adrenal system which causes and maintains a hyperglycemia in spite of the increased secretion of insulin under conditions of emotional excitement. It is interesting to note that this relationship is preserved under various conditions leading to a central excitation of the autonomic centers, since similar results are obtained in anoxia, after metrazol (Feldman, Cortell and Gellhorn), and electrically induced convulsions (Kessler and Gellhorn), and under the influence of cocaine and bulbocapnine (Feldman, Cortell and Gellhorn).

SUMMARY

If the effect of central excitation on the adrenal system is eliminated (denervation of adrenals, sectioning of the spinal cord), it is found that sham rage produced by faradic excitation of the hypothalamus is accompanied by a fall in blood sugar. Since this effect is abolished by subdiaphragmatic vagotomy it is assumed that the hypoglycemia is a result of excitation of the vago-insulin system.

The rage reaction causes a fall in blood sugar in cats in which the cervical spinal cord has been sectioned. After vagotomy, rage produces in such animals a slight hyperglycemia which is probably due to the action of sympathin.

Fear and struggle cause hypoglycemia in adreno-demedullated rats and no change or a slight rise in the blood sugar (sympathin) in adreno-demedullated-vagotomized rats. Since in normal animals emotional excitation (fear, rage) and sham rage cause hyperglycemia it follows that emotion as well as sham rage causes a discharge over both vago-insulin and sympathetico-adrenal systems with a predominance of the latter. The significance of this phenomenon is discussed.

REFERENCES

BERGMANN, G.   Funktionelle Pathologie (2nd ed.).   Berlin, 1936.
BODO, R. C. AND A. E. BENAGLIA.   This Journal **121:** 738, 1938.
BRITTON, S. W.   This Journal **74:** 291, 1925.
        This Journal **86:** 340, 1928.
CANNON, W. B.   Bodily changes in pain, hunger, fear and rage.   New York, 1929.
        The wisdom of the body.   New York, 1932.
        Bull. N. Y. Acad. Med. **16:** 3, 1940.
CARLSON, H. B., E. GELLHORN AND C. W. DARROW.   Arch. Neurol. Psychiat. **45:** 105, 1941.
FELDMAN, J., R. CORTELL AND E. GELLHORN.   This Journal **131:** 281, 1940.   Proc. Soc. exper. Biol. and Med.   In press.
GELLHORN, E., R. CORTELL AND J. FELDMAN.   Science **92:** 288, 1940.
HARE, K. AND W. A. GEOHAGAN.   This Journal **126:** 524, 1939.
HARRIS, R. E. AND D. J. INGLE.   This Journal **120:** 420, 1937.
KESSLER, M. AND E. GELLHORN.   Proc. Soc. exper. Biol. and Med.   In press.
LA BARRE, J. AND O. VESSELOVSKY.   Arch. int. Physiol. **37:** 188, 1933.
LUMLEY, F. H. AND L. B. NICE.   This Journal **93:** 152, 1930.
LUND, F. H.   J. Soc. Psychol. **1:** 136, 1930.
MAGOUN, H. W., S. W. RANSON AND A. HETHERINGTON.   This Journal **119:** 615, 1937.
MASSERMAN, J. H. AND E. W. HAERTIG.   J. Neurophysiol. **1:** 350, 1938.
PARTINGTON, P. P.   This Journal **117:** 55, 1936.
RANSON, S. W., H. KABAT AND H. W. MAGOUN.   Arch. Neurol. Psychiat. **33:** 467, 1935.
SOSKIN, S. AND R. LEVINE.   This Journal **120:** 761, 1937.
TOMASZEWSKI, W.   Ztschr. Kreislforsch. **29:** 745, 1937.
WITTKOWER, E.   Klin. Wchnschr. **7:** 2193, 1928; **10:** 1811, 1931.
WITTKOWER, E. AND W. PILZ.   Klin. Wchnschr. **11:** 718, 1932.

PHYSIOLOGICAL REVIEWS

VOL. 23   JANUARY, 1942̸3̸   No. 1

PHYSIOLOGICAL AND CLINICAL TESTS OF AUTONOMIC FUNCTION
AND AUTONOMIC BALANCE

CHESTER W. DARROW

*Institute for Juvenile Research and Department of Physiology, University of Illinois, College
of Medicine, Chicago*

To attain significance a test of autonomic function must circumvent the mutually antagonistic action of the two branches of the autonomic nervous system so that it may be clear whether an observed peripheral event is due to increase of activity in one branch of the autonomic system or to decrease of activity in the other. There must be no question, for example, whether an observed pupillary dilatation is due to sympathetic excitation or to inhibition of the parasympathetically determined irido-constrictor tone. The problem is literally to determine the weight on either side of a "balance" when that on neither side is known. The mere knowledge that the balance has been upset by a given condition, as afforded by many so-called tests of autonomic function, may be physiologically or clinically of little value except as indication that something has been disturbed. It does not necessarily define the foregoing events in the neural and neurohumoral systems, and in consequence may even be misleading in determining proper corrective procedures. Furthermore, peripheral autonomic events which now may bear one relation and now another to initiating processes in the nervous system need have no consistent relation to those manifestations of nervous system function known as "behavior." This may explain the sterility which, with few exceptions, has beset attempts to correlate measurements of peripheral autonomic changes with human "behavior."

Circumvention of the difficulties in the pathway to interpretation of peripherally observed autonomic effects in terms of events in the neurohumoral system has been attempted in several ways: 1, by recording changes in those exceptional mechanisms having only a single autonomic innervation, e.g., in the nictitating membranes; 2, by elimination of one of the opposing dual innervations surgically, e.g., by cutting the sympathetic supply to the pupils; 3, by assaying *in vitro* or *in vivo* the output of the respective neurohumoral mediators, adrenalin or sympathin, and acetylcholine: 4, by blocking one of the opposed neurohumoral mechanisms pharmacologically, e.g., by administration of atropine or ergotoxin; 5, by deriving the activity of the autonomic system from the respective effects on differentially sensitive autonomic effectors; 6, by recording the electric activity of the respective autonomic nerves. The main methods of autonomic measurement will be considered in the above order.

The interpretation of findings so obtained is further beset by difficulties imposed by homeostasis, since the rôle of the autonomic system is not merely to produce adaptive changes, but to maintain the internal milieu. Medullary, hypothalamic, hypophyseal, aortic and carotid sinus *feed back* "buffer" or "moderator" mechanisms are as important for neurohumoral control as are the

1

buffers for controlling pH in the blood.   So sensitive are they that the intervention incidental to a given test procedure may actually produce results in certain effectors exactly the opposite of the expected peripheral change.   Under 7 we shall consider the mechanisms of maintaining "balance" or *dynamic equilibrium*.

The criteria by which we may determine the sympathetic (orthosympathetic) as opposed to the parasympathetic character of a given mechanism are varied and not always consistent with one another.   The following will be tentatively accepted as indicators of sympathetic (orthosympathetic) as opposed to parasympathetic activity pending specific exceptions which may later be referred to: 1, thoraco-lumbar as opposed to cranio-sacral innervation; 2, postganglionic as opposed to preganglionic peripheral innervation, and 3, adrenergic as opposed to cholinergic humoral transmission of impulses to the effector.   The possible rôles of the ions potassium vs. calcium, catabolic vs. anabolic metabolism, dehydration vs. hydration, etc., may be given weight in specific instances.

I. *Tests based on autonomic mechanisms having a single innervation.*   A. *The nictitating membrane.*   The most definite indications of normal autonomic function are perhaps obtained in the case of those effectors having an innervation from only one of the opposed branches of the autonomic system.   The autonomic innervation of the nictitating membrane of the cat, as shown by Rosenblueth and Bard (1932) is purely sympathetic[1] and, barring certain antagonistic effects from the skeletal external rectus muscle, eliminated by curare or deep anesthesia, it provides an ideal sympathetic indicator.   It is pharmacologically adrenergic, being maximally sensitive to excitatory (E) sympathin (Rosenblueth and Cannon, 1932).   That the reaction to adrenalin may be enhanced by eserin and decreased by atropine (Rosenblueth, 1932; Secker, 1937) and that the N.M. may react to large doses of acetylcholine in the animal sensitized by denervation (Morrison and Acheson, 1938) does not seriously detract from its usefulness as a sympathetic indicator under normal conditions.   It has been utilized as such an indicator of sympathetic activity, among others, by Acheson, Rosenblueth and Partington (1936), Bargeton (1938), Rosenblueth and Schwartz (1935), Brooks (1933), Brown (1934), Gellhorn and Darrow (1939).

As a sympathetic indicator the N.M. may provide an index not only of sympathetic excitation, but also of a decrease or inhibition of sympathetic tone. Such effects from stimulation of the viscera (bladder and rectum) have been reported by Watkins (1938).   Gellhorn and Darrow (unpublished) have observed the effect following traction on the intestines.   Rosenblueth and Schwartz (1935) show relaxation of the N.M. following vagal (depressor nerve?) stimulation.   Relaxation of the N.M. or decrease of response in the presence of a rise in the blood pressure as reported by these latter authors and by Gellhorn, Darrow and Yesinick (1940) and the exaggeration of N.M. response reported by Rosenblueth and Schwartz following vagotomy and carotid sinus denervation does not detract from the value of the N.M. as an indicator of sympathetic function.   Rather, such responses provide examples of the application of this mechanism as an indicator of sympathetic regulation by the moderator nerves.

---

[1] Bucy (1927) raises question as to a sympathetic innervation of N.M. in the rabbit.

B. *Sweat glands.* Another group of mechanisms having a single innervation and widely used as indicators of intact sympathetic nerve supply are the sweat glands. Lesions of the postganglionic nerves to the periphery produce local anhydrosis of the skin which may be registered as an extreme rise in the electrical resistance (Richter, 1927) with no return of spontaneous activity (Tower and Richter, 1932). After preganglionic section in the cat the rise in resistance was less than after postganglionic section, restoration of function being registered electrically in 28 days (Tower and Richter, 1931; see also Hinsey, Phillips and Hare, 1939).

Another test of sweating is provided by applying to the skin bits of filter paper dried after soaking in a solution of cobalt chloride which changes from red to blue when dry (Wetherell, 1905). Graded series of color changes have been obtained by the writer by adding as hygroscopic agent varying percentages of glycerine to the cobalt chloride solution. For photographic mapping of sweat distribution in neurologic cases the method of Minor (1928) has had wide and successful application (Guttman, 1931; List and Peet, 1938–1939; Richter and Woodruff, 1942; Hyndman and Wolkin, 1941a, b). A solution of iodine and castor oil is sprayed over the patient, after which he is dusted with fine starch powder which turns blue-black in the presence of moisture from the sweat glands. Richter and Woodruff (1941–42) have correlated the iodine-starch with the electrical resistance methods of mapping, demonstrating their correspondence.

Sweating and the concomitant (Darrow, 1927, 1932, 1934) electrical changes of the skin, especially of the palms of the hands, is not only dependent upon an intact sympathetic supply (Richter, 1927) but is extremely susceptible to alterations affecting the level of activity of the central nervous system such as narcosis and sleep (Richter, 1926), and attention or alertness (Darrow, review 1936). While it must be conceded that from sleep to alert attention sympathetic tone is altered more or less in parallel with the activity manifested by the sweat glands, it may still be questioned whether measurements of palmar sweating provide an uncomplicated measure of sympathetic activity. In the first place the sweat glands themselves are dependent upon cholinergic transmission at the effector (Dale and Feldberg, 1934) and conditions altering such cholinergic activity, whether by the amount of available acetycholine, the concentration of cholinesterase, or the presence of adrenalin (Billigheimer, 1920; Langley and Uyeno, 1922; Darrow and Gellhorn, 1939; Darrow review, 1937) limit the level of secretory activity and the magnitude of response to stimulation. The apparent adrenergic limitation of sweating at the effector should be taken into consideration (see sec. V) when sweat measurements are the basis for deductions regarding the activity in the autonomic nervous system.

Furthermore, reflex palmar sweating in response to peripheral stimuli is in great part determined by centers located in the forebrain (Langworthy and Richter, 1930; Wang and Lu, 1930; Schwartz, 1936) and ease of elicitation of the response is dependent to a very great extent upon the state of the higher levels of the brain. As pointed out by others and as we have had repeated occasion to observe (Carlson, Gellhorn and Darrow, 1941) light anesthesia, too moderate to interfere with sympathetic activity as indicated by nictitating membranes or other sympathetic mechanisms, decreases or may eliminate reactions in the footpads of the cat. Palmar or foot pad sweating, most commonly measured as the "galvanic skin reflex," is not, despite its single sympathetic innervation, an uncomplicated indicator of sympathetic function.

C. *Adrenal medulla*. That the adrenal medulla is another example of mechanisms having a purely sympathetic innervation (Elliott, 1912, 1913; Hollinshead, 1936; McFarland and Davenport, 1941) offers better justification for the utilization of circulating adrenalin as an index of sympathetic activity than the fact that it is a "sympathomimetic hormone," for whereas the production of adrenalin is by sympathetic excitation, the action of adrenalin is both excitatory and inhibitory. Aside from the fact 1, that the peripheral transmission of impulses to the adrenal glands is cholinergic and determined by conditions affecting cholinergic activity (Feldberg and Tsudjemura, 1934), and the fact 2, to be considered in more detail later, that the action of inhibitory (I) adrenalin is the inhibition of parasympathetic or cholinergic mechanisms rather than an effect on sympathetic ones, and the fact 3, that adrenalin by sensitizing the moderator nerves (Heymans, 1929) produces a degree of reflex inhibition of general sympathetic activity, circulating adrenalin (plus undifferentiated sympathin) may be considered an index of general sympathetic function. The assay of humoral mediators is considered in section III.

Other mechanisms alleged to have but a single autonomic innervation such as the pilomotors, the spleen and the uterus have been variously used as autonomic indicators. Those subject to adrenergic inhibition such as the uterus are discussed in section III.

II. *Tests based on the elimination of the nerve supply from one of the opposing branches of the autonomic innervation.* This method has had wide application in the delimitation of responses from dually innervated mechanisms, as witness the use of vagotomy in the attempt to reduce the parasympathetic factors in circulatory changes. The method should be confined to acute experiments in order to exclude the possibility of sensitization of the humoral mechanisms whose neural counterpart it is desired to eliminate. Although maximum sensitization occurs only after nerve degeneration, even within the period of an acute experiment there appears the possibility of a degree of sensitization as suggested by the observations of Darrow and Gellhorn (1939) in the case of the pupil.

A. *The pupil.* One of the most useful applications of this method of control is that of cutting the cervical sympathetic supply to the pupil on one side to permit study of reactions determined by a purely parasympathetic innervation. The difference between the reactions of the parasympathetically innervated pupil and those of the dually innervated structure of the opposite side gives indication also of the concomitant sympathetic activity. In corresponding manner the parasympathetic supply from the third nerve has been severed (Anderson, 1904; Ury and Gellhorn, 1939) to provide a pupil having only a sympathetic innervation. This method of experimental control provides striking experimental confirmation of the fact that it is the inhibition of parasympathetic tone rather than sympathetic excitation which is the predominating factor in the dilatation of the iris of the cat and rabbit following painful stimuli. The sympathetic supply unquestionably also contributes to the pupillary response after emotional stimuli affecting the hypothalamus (Wang, Lu and Lau, 1932; Carlson, Gellhorn and Darrow, 1941; Hodes and Magoun, 1941) and perhaps also when the inhibitory effects of adrenalin have been eliminated (Darrow and Gellhorn, 1939). The neural mechanisms of the response have been worked out by Karplus and Kreidl (1911), Lieben and Kahn (1930), Bain, Irving and McSwiney (1935), Harper, McSwiney and Suffolk (1935), Harper and McSwiney (1937), McSwiney and Suffolk (1938). The evidence that inhibition of parasympathetic tone plays an important, if not a predominating rôle (possibly different in the monkey, (Bender, 1938; Bender and Siegal, 1940) in a response which has often been referred to uncritically as indicating "sympathetic" activity may well lead to a re-examination of the evidence behind similar interpretations in the case of other dually innervated mechanisms.

B. *Blood pressure.* Perhaps nowhere is such a re-examination more appropriate than in the case of blood pressure. Too often it is uncritically assumed that a sympathetic-like rise in blood pressure in the intact animal is an indication of sympathetic activity, and that a parasympathetic-like fall in pressure indicates parasympathetic activity. That the rise may actually be due to decrease of parasympathetic tone and that a fall may be the result of inhibition of sympathetic tone, as for example by action of the carotid sinus, is often disregarded. The same workers sometimes committing this oversight may take great pains at other times to eliminate the ambiguity of blood pressure interpretation by vagotomy, carotid sinus denervation, atropinization, sympathectomy, and so on. The prevailing lack of correspondence between blood pressure changes and changes in valid sympathetic indicators such as the nictitating membranes, as shown by studies of Acheson, Rosenblueth, and Partington (1936), Rosenblueth and Schwartz (1935), and Watkins (1938) among investigators already mentioned in this paper is proof of the ambiguous significance of blood pressure, assuming of course that the sympathetic system discharges as a whole (Cannon, 1915, 1920; Bard, 1928, 1929). Even after hypothalamic stimulation it was shown by Carlson, Gellhorn and Darrow (1941) that some of the sympathetic-like effects commonly associated with rise in blood pressure may be due to inhibition of parasympathetic tone. On the other hand the fact that Bronk, Pitts and Larrabee (1940) have demonstrated an inhibition of sympathetic impulses in the nerve to the heart following increase of blood pressure in the carotid sinus, and the fact that section of the nerves to the carotid sinus and other moderator mechanisms results in a chronic hypertension of varying duration as shown by Heymans and Bouckaert (1931, 1935), Bacq, Brouha and Heymans (1932, 1934), which can be prevented by prior complete sympathectomy (Heymans and Bouckaert, 1935; Grimson, 1940) points to carotid sinus inhibitory control of the sympathetic system as a factor in blood pressure.

Autonomic control of factors in blood pressure such as heart rate and stroke volume, venous and pulmonary return, and vasoconstriction and dilatation should receive separate consideration. Two will be discussed.

C. *Pulse rate.* The indiscriminate use of pulse rate as an index of sympathetic function in the intact animal is perhaps more to be deprecated than the uncritical employment of blood pressure for that purpose. Not only is pulse rate, like blood pressure, a function of the balance or "resultant" of sympathetic and parasympathetic influences (Rosenblueth and Simeone, 1934; Brown and Eccles, 1934 a, b) but by action of the aortic, carotid sinus, and other moderator nerves upon sympathetic and vagus centers, there tends to be a compensatory slowing of the heart when there is a rise in pressure, and an acceleration with a fall. In addition there is the direct effect of pressure within the heart itself. The clinical value of pulse rate as an indicator depends little or not at all upon its rôle as a sympathetic-parasympathetic indicator (Henderson, Haggard and Dolley, 1927). Even as an index of emotional changes it is of less value than blood pressure (Armstrong, 1938), and its physiologic interpretation is questionable (Gantor, 1925; Shock and Schlatter, 1942). Recorded along with simultaneous changes in blood pressure, however, it may provide valuable indication of compensatory activity by the moderator nerves which should be taken into account in the interpretation of an autonomic change. Pulse rate in the chronically denervated heart is of course determined by humoral mechanisms, to be considered later.

D. *Vasomotor activity.* This is a most important variable determining blood pressure, though obviously not the only one. The inference that there has been vasoconstriction when rise in blood pressure is the sole observation is at best a loose manner of speech. And the frequent identification of vasoconstriction with sympathetic activity and of vasodilatation with parasympathetic action is likewise often in disregard of the facts. Not only do vasomotor functions represent in many instances the resultant of a balance between opposed neurohumoral influences, a change in either one of which may alter the vasomotor tone, but the existence of both sympathetic cholinergic vasodilators (Euler and Gaddum, 1931; Bulbring and Burn, 1934, 1935; Sherif, 1935) and adrenergic vasodilators (Rosenblueth and Cannon, 1935; Wyman and Tum Suden, 1936) is always a threat to such interpretation. Sympathetic vasodilatation has long been recognized as a common characteristic of muscle (Hoskins, Gunning and Barry, 1916; Hartman and collaborators, 1928a, b, and Clark, 1934) where it obviously may serve an emergency function. It is particularly marked in the dog and the hare, "animals of the chase" not only in muscle but in other structures (Langley and Dickenson, 1890; Burn, 1938) and is demonstrable without ergotoxin or eserin. Room (1938) indicated that at least in some cases adrenergic dilatation may be confined to the capillaries and constriction to the arteries and arterioles. However, the skin and splanchnic region of most animals including man most frequently and under most conditions manifest sympathetic adrenergic vasoconstriction and cholinergic vasodilatation.

Of great importance is the fact that evidence indicates the presence of sympathetic cholinergic vasodilator activity in many blood vessels where there are no demonstrable parasympathetic nerve connections. It thus becomes possible readily to explain in these structures the vasodilator effects of parasympathetic drugs and to account at the same time for the depressor effects of weak sympathetic nerve stimulation and of small doses of adrenalin. It is probable that only with strong stimulation or with larger doses of adrenalin will the inhibitory action of sympathin I or inhibitory adrenalin become strong enough completely to counteract this sympathetic cholinergic vasodilator action. The depressor action of adrenalin after ergotamine will later receive a similar explanation. Another mechanism of adrenalin depressor effects is of course the adrenalin sensitization of the carotid sinuses.

Tests of vasomotor function have become of very great concern to the physiologist and clinician because of their usefulness in the attack on the problems of hypertension and other neurocirculatory disorders. These are discussed in reviews by Brown (1936) and by Weiss (1939). They are given consideration under the present heading because of the predominantly sympathetic hyperactivity apparently involved, and the use of sympathetic nerve section as a therapeutic procedure.

Tests of sympathetic vasomotor function are urgently needed to determine the probable benefits of sympathectomy. The question is always whether such radical intervention would sufficiently restore normal circulation to be justified. The use of nerve block (White, 1930; Scott and Morton, 1931) to determine the probable effects of nerve section appears logical. The employment of spinal anesthesia and general anesthesia (Scott and Morton, 1930) and sleep-inducing barbiturates (Craig, 1938) to test the effect of temporary elimination of central sources of sympathetic activity also provide a relatively direct approach. The rationale behind those other tests which employ what appear to be active vasodilatation technics is not so obvious, inasmuch as their operation may be quite independent of an effect on the sympathetic system. The use of fever (Brown, 1926; Adson and Brown, 1929; Adson, 1936), placing the hands in hot water (Landis and Gibbin, 1933), and the employment of cholinergic drugs are examples of this approach. In so far as these latter methods are satisfactory tests of the possible benefits of sympathectomy it must be inferred that they operate by effecting a central impairment or reflex inhibition of sympathetic tone, or that they work peripherally by opposing the action of inhibitory sympathin and adrenalin on the cholinergic vasodilators.

A test of sympathetic reactivity which has had wide application in the diagnosis of hypertension is the cold pressor test of Hines and Brown (1932, 1933), White and Gildae (1937). For this test, the patient rests for 30 minutes after which one hand is immersed in ice water for 2 minutes. A rise in pressure of over 22 mm. is considered indicative of a tendency toward hypertension. Recovery of the pre-test level should occur in the normal person within two minutes. Of special value in the diagnosis of hypertension also is the ophthalmoscopic observation of the eyegrounds (Weiss, 1939; Keith, Wagener and Kernohan, 1928; Wagener, 1933; Hallum, 1936; and Hallum and Gibson, 1938). Tests of skin temperature (Craig, Horton and Sheard, 1933), plethysmographic volume and plethysmographic blood flow are of course useful as are also photoelectric plethysmographic technics (Hertzman and Dillon, 1938, 1940) especially when combined with stimulating procedures of the types described above.

CHESTER W. DARROW

III. *Assay of the output of humoral mediators adrenalin or sympathin and acetylcholine.* The evidence that the transmission of nerve impulses to the effector organs depends upon the mediation of the humoral agents acetylcholine and sympathin needs no elaboration (Dale, review, 1935; Cannon and Rosenblueth, 1937; Butt, review, 1937). The assay of the humoral mediators may be accomplished *in vitro* either by chemical tests or by strips of excised sensitized tissue, and it may be accomplished *in vivo* either in the same or in a second animal by registration of effects on denervated sensitized organs. It should perhaps be pointed out that any humorally determined autonomic response in the absence of nerve activity is, in effect, an *in situ* biological assay of humoral mediator.

A. *Assay of acetylcholine.* Space permits only mention of some of the organic preparations which have been employed. Quoting from Cannon and Rosenblueth (1937):

> According to Gaddum (1936) the relative sensitiveness, measured in γ (0.001 mgm.) per liter, of common indicators of acetylcholine, is as follows:
> Leech muscle (isolated and treated with eserine)..........................   2
> Rabbit auricle (isolated and treated with eserine)..........................   4
> Frog heart (Straub method)..   10
> Mouse intestine...   10
> Rabbit intestine...   20
> Frog's rectus abdominis (isolated and treated with eserine).................   20
> Cat's denervated gastrocnemius... 100
> Since none of these organs is strictly specific, the suggestions of Chang and Gaddum (1933) as to ways of distinguishing between their reaction to acetylcholine and to other substances become important.

Other tests may be mentioned, such as the slowing of the denervated heart and the hypotensive effect (blocked by atropine) of acetylcholine on the blood pressure of the eviscerated chloralose cat.

B. *Excitatory and inhibitory sympathin and adrenalin.* The fact that sympathin, mediating the sympathetic effects is of two types, E and I, excitatory and inhibitory (Cannon and Rosenblueth, 1933, 1935, 1937) must be given more than passing attention. The more rarely mentioned evidence that adrenalin itself is also of two types (Bacq, 1933, 1934, 1940; Greer, Pinkston, Baxter and Brannon, 1938) one of which is primarily excitatory and the other of which is both excitatory and inhibitory is of no less importance.[2]

It has been pointed out by Bacq (1934) that the two types of sympathin, E and I, correspond in their effects to those of an undifferentiated adrenalin and those of an adrenaline, "nor adrenalin," partially oxidized (Bacq, 1935) which has thus been deprived of its inhibitory action.

Even more significant is the usually unmentioned fact that *the inhibitory action of either inhibitory sympathin, I, or of inhibitory adrenalin appears only in structures having a parasympathetic (cholinergic) nerve supply, or those in which, in the absence of a demonstrated parasympathetic supply, the presence of cholinergically*

[2] For simplicity the excitatory and inhibitory effects of adrenalin will here be referred to as "E" and "I," respectively, analogous to Cannon and Bacq's designation of the different types of sympathin.

activated effectors is indicated by a sensitivity to parasympathetic drugs. For example, the contractions of the nerveless amnion of the fowl are inhibited by adrenalin (Langley, 1905; Bauer, 1928) but the amnion notwithstanding its absence of nerve supply is a cholinergically activated mechanism (Bauer, 1928). Even the cholinergic "pseudomotor" contractions of denervated skeletal muscle, most familiar in the Sherrington contraction, are blocked by adrenalin as shown by Gasser and Dale (1926), Dale and Gaddum (1930), Hinsey and Gasser (1930), Bulbring and Burn (1936), and Bender (1938). It should be emphasized that there is no clear evidence of an inhibitory action of adrenalin on purely *adrenergic* structures, except secondarily by way of effects of adrenalin on the cholinergic sympathetic ganglia (Marazzi, 1939) or by way of the carotid sinus and other moderator nerves (Heymans, 1929; Gellhorn, Darrow and Yesinick, 1939; Bronk, Pitts and Larrabee, 1940). Recognition that the antagonistic or inhibitory effects of inhibitory sympathin or adrenalin are functionally inhibitory of cholinergic mechanisms[3] (regardless of what the chemical, permeability, or other mechanisms of that antogonism may be) permits some simplification of the main facts of neurohumeral transmission and of pharmacologic action.

The reaction of the *denervation sensitized nictitating membrane* is that of a *relatively* pure adrenergically excitable structure. It is a sensitive indicator of excitatory (E) sympathin (Hampel, 1935; Liu and Rosenblueth, 1935; Simeone, 1937). The N. M. is little or not at all affected by inhibitory (I) sympathin or the inhibitory action of adrenalin. Extensive utilization of the chronically denervated nictitating membrane for the *in vivo* assay of excitatory sympathin and adrenalin by such workers as McGoun and Ranson (1937), Cattell and Wolff (1934), Rosenblueth and Morrison (1934), Partington (1936), Liu (1935), and Bender and Siegel (1940) bear testimony to its value.

Differentiation of excitatory (E) from inhibitory (I) sympathin was early provided by the differential reaction of the *non-pregnant uterus* of the cat and the *nictitating membranes*. An amount of excitatory sympathin from stimulation of hepatic nerves, which was sufficient to contract the nictitating membrane, had relatively little inhibiting effect on the non-pregnant uterus of the cat (Cannon and Rosenblueth, 1933), whereas inhibitory sympathin from stimulating inhibited structures of the gastrointestinal tract produced a marked relaxation of the uterus (see end of section) but relatively little contraction of the nictitating membrane.

Further differentiation of excitatory from inhibitory sympathin was provided by the nictitating membrane in combination with the response of the pupil. Cannon and Rosenblueth (1935) showed that an amount of excitatory (E) sympathin sufficient to produce a measured contraction of the nictitating membrane occasioned little dilatation of the pupil, although an amount of inhibitory (E plus I) sympathin sufficient to produce the same contraction of the nictitating membrane produced a large dilatation of the pupil. Only after cutting the constrictor fibers of the iris could Cannon and Rosenblueth (1935) obtain appre-

[3] Necheles and Neuwelt (1938) have demonstrated an antagonism between pituitrin and acetylcholin.

ciable pupillary dilatation with their sympathin E. They inferred from this that sympathin E must somehow stimulate the cholinergic constrictor mechanism. However, the evidence that inhibitory sympathin or inhibitory adrenalin relaxes the cholinergic constrictor mechanism of the iris, thus facilitating dilatation, as shown by Joseph (1916), Miller (1926), Poos (1927), Yonkman (1930), and Shackler, Christiansen and Schlossman (1937), offers another if not a better explanation. It is apparent that combined inhibitory and excitatory sympathin may work synergistically by relaxing the constrictor fibers while simultaneously contracting the dilator fibers to produce a greater dilatation than would be possible by excitation alone. Obviously the operation of the humoral mediators E and I adrenalin or sympathin on the pupil parallels the action of nerve stimulation where there may also be synergistic action of sympathetic excitation and inhibition of parasympathetic tone.

When both sympathetic and parasympathetic nerve supplies have been removed the pupil in the eserinized animal provides a valuable indicator of the synergistic combined effects of excitatory and inhibitory adrenalin. Bender and Weinstein (1940) have employed such a denervated iris as an adrenergic indicator along with the denervated facial musculature as a cholinergic indicator.

The gastrointestinal tract, and particularly the musculature of the large and small intestine, have provided some of the earliest and most used tests for the assay of the inhibitory action of adrenalin and sympathin. The fact is again not without significance that motility and tone are here parasympathetically or cholinergically maintained. Indeed, the intestine is itself often used as a test indicator for acetylcholine. Reflex inhibition of these structures is exemplified in the studies of King (1924), Pearcy and Van Liere (1926), Loew and Patterson (1935), and Youmans and Meek (1937). That these inhibitory effects of nerve stimulation are neurologically sympathetic is inferred from the fact that they may be abolished by splanchnicotomy and duplicated by adrenalin. Youmans, Meek and Herrin (1938) employ both innervated and denervated Thierry fistulae in the same dog for the simultaneous testing of both the neurally and the humorally transmitted effects. That the inhibitory effects of nerve stimulation may be mediated in the gastrointestinal tract by an inhibitory sympathin indistinguishable from adrenalin is suggested by the observations of Youmans (1938), Youmans, Aumann and Haney (1939).

The rate of the denervated heart has also been used as a differential indicator for the humoral effects (Cannon and Uridil, 1921; Cannon, Lewis and Britton, 1926; Newton, Zwemer and Cannon, 1931; Rosenblueth and Phillips, 1932; Whitelaw and Snyder, 1934). It is of course sensitive to both cholinergic and adrenergic humoral mediators, but in the absence of eserin or similar drugs the cholinergic effects may be assumed negligible, except as far as it is possible that resident acetylcholine may be subject to adrenergic inhibition. In any case excitatory and inhibitory actions, whether of adrenalin or of sympathin, would work synergistically.

Coagulation time of the blood may also be used as an indicator of adrenergic effects (Cannon, 1929).

Blood sugar is another frequently used indicator in which, barring important corticoadrenal and hypophyseal effects (Soskin, 1941) changes are the resultant of opposed neuro-humoral autonomic influences. The widespread identification of increased blood sugar with sympathicoadrenal function doubtless received its impetus in Cannon's early work with Britton (1925, 1927) and his emphasis on its emergency function in his book on *Bodily changes* (1929). A degree of correspondence between changes in blood sugar and other sympathetic indicators following sympathetic stimulation is shown by Chang (1937) and Bodo and Benaglia (1938). Such correspondence may be eliminated by sympathectomy (Bodo and Benaglia, 1938). Although long used as an indicator of emotion in animals (Cannon and Britton, 1925; Bömer, 1930), only strong emotion is apparently effective in increasing the blood sugar of normal human subjects (Gildae, 1905), and there is general agreement that while elevation of blood sugar may be met with in depressed human subjects, the "emotions" of schizophrenic patients tend to be devoid of hyperglycemic concomitant (Bowman and Kasanin, 1929; McCowan and Quastel, 1931; Whitehorn, 1934; Gildae, Mailhouse and Morris, 1935). The failure to obtain emotional hyperglycemia in these cases may not, as has often happened, be attributed necessarily to a defect in the sympathico-adrenal function, but may, as will appear, be equally well a consequence of an increased vagal activity and insulin secretion.

Dual neuro-humoral control of blood sugar by both sympathico-adrenal and vagal-insulin mechanisms was early shown in morphine hyperglycemia by Houssay and Lewis (1923). They demonstrated that the hyperglycemia could be abolished by splanchnicotomy and that it could then be restored by cutting the vagus. They inferred the antagonistic action of the sympathetic and the vagus. The rôle of the vagal cholinergic innervation of the pancreas (Clark, 1931; La Barre and Vesselovsky, 1933; Babkin, Hebb and Sergeyeva, 1939) as the factor determining the frequent absence of emotional hyperglycemia which has been the concomitant of excitation following adrenalectomy (Britton, 1925; Lumley and Nice, 1930; Harris and Ingle, 1937; McQuarrie, Ziegler, Wangensteen and Dennis, 1939; and Bodo and Benaglia, 1939) has apparently been overlooked until its recent demonstration as a general principle by Gellhorn, Feldman and Cortell. Under a wide range of conditions such as anoxia and convulsant drugs (1940), fever (1941), sham rage, and hypothalamic stimulation (1941), and heat and cold (1941) they demonstrate that after adreno-demedullation there is a consistent tendency for such conditions to produce a hypoglycemia which is reversed if there is subsequently a subdiaphragmatic section of the vagus to eliminate the parasympathetic innervation of the pancreas. Thus blood sugar is added to the list of indicators which must be interpreted as the resultant of a balance of opposed autonomic influences.

Employing the hypophysectomized-adreno-demedullated rat as an extremely sensitive indicator, Gellhorn, Feldman and Allen (1941a, b) demonstrated an abnormally high insulin content in the blood of emotionally disturbed schizophrenic patients. This probably accounts in part at least for the absence of emotional hyperglycemia in the several studies of schizophrenic patients previously cited. Related and superficially conflicting evidence will be considered later in its relation to the problem of "autonomic balance" (see section VII). *The non-pregnant uterus of the cat*, as previously noted, is another of the earlier used indicators of adrenergic inhibitory effects. This organ is unusual in that it is one of the few among inhibited structures having definite sympathetic innervation, but, at least until recently, no established parasympathetic, pelvic nerve innervation (Reynolds, 1939). However, Sheehan and Labate, according to Sheehan (1941) have now "established beyond question the presence of a parasympathetic (sacral) outflow." The important consideration is that despite its sympathetic innervation the uterus is also cholinergically activated (Reynolds, 1939). Sherif (1935) demonstrated acetylcholine secretion by hypogastric (sympathetic) stimulation in the dog.

The effects of adrenalin and sympathetic stimulation is to produce relaxation of the non-pregnant uterus of the cat as contrasted with contraction when the animal is pregnant. This action of adrenalin in the cat is perhaps not surprising in view of the prevalence of other adrenalinergic manifestations in this animal. Van Dyke and Gustavson (1929) and Robson and Schild (1938a, b) showed that the change is dependent in the cat on the secretion of the corpus luteum and may be found in pregnancy, pseudo-pregnancy, or after progesterone (see Kennard, 1937). That the effects are mediated by an altered response to the inhibitory factor in ordinary (E + I) adrenalin and sympathin is indicated by the absence of appreciable relaxation effect by either non-inhibitory sympathin from hepatic nerve stimulation (Cannon and Rosenblueth, 1933) or by non-inhibitory norepinephrine (Greer, Pinkston, Baxter and Brannon, 1933). When, however, according to these latter authors, a uterus which, for some reason, does not give the usual relaxation in response to ordinary (E + I) epinephrine, that uterus will give a contraction in response to the relatively non-inhibitory norepinephrine. In other words, when inhibition is not too pronounced, contractility may be demonstrated. In view of the apparent relation of adrenergic inhibition to cholinergic function it would seem that acetylcholine may be involved. Demonstration by Reynolds and Foster (1939) of acetylcholine in the pregnant, pseudopregnant and progesterone treated uterus of the rabbit makes this seem possible. A similar reversal of inhibitory response by physostigmine (Agar, 1940) and by the physostigmine-like action of ergotoxine (see section IV) also implicates acetylcholine. The limited available evidence suggests that animals having a low level of acetylcholine or an absence of cholinergic response to estrogens such as the nonpregnant cat (Reynolds and Foster, 1940) and the rat (Astwood, 1940; Holden, 1939) typically show relaxation in response to adrenalin, and that animals on the other hand which assay a higher acetylcholine content of the uterus during estrus or pregnancy such as the rabbit (Reynolds and Foster, 1939a, b), the dog (Sherif, 1935), and possibly by inference, the pregnant cat (?) typically show contraction in response to adrenalin. This suggests that adrenalin-inhibitory effects may become ineffective in the presence of excess acetylcholine, and that in the absence of inhibition the excitatory effects of adrenergic or cholinergic action may be clearly manifest. This is consistent with observations on the sphincter of the iris by Joseph (1916), Poos (1927), and Yonkman (1930). This is also the implication of the change of adrenergic relaxation to contraction following administration of physostigmine or of physostigmine-like ergotamine.

There is, however, the complicating fact that during pregnancy ergotamine, while itself producing near maximal contraction of the uterus (Agar, 1940), typically reverses the adrenalin response from contraction to relaxation (Dale, 1906; Cushny, 1906, 1910). This phenomenon has contributed no little to the confusion which has prevailed regarding the mechanism of adrenalin inhibition. It is not improbable, however, that notwithstanding the fact that in general blood flow and muscular activity in the uterus vary independently (Robson and Schild, 1938), the greater susceptibility of the pregnant uterus to circulatory embarrassment is an important factor in this reaction. Vasoconstrictor reactions become more pronounced at this time (Reynolds, 1939) and any deficiency of oxygenation results in a marked increase in the tendency toward uterine contraction (Reynolds, 1939) even to the point of abortion. Under such conditions adrenergic inhibition of uterine vasodilatation may decrease blood flow and occasion contraction of the uterine musculature. On the other hand, after ergotamine, the reversal of the vasomotor response to adrenalin (Robson and Schild, 1938) may favor an improvement in circulation and result in relative muscular relaxation. The rôle of ergotamine and ergotoxine in the blocking of inhibitory adrenergic effects will be considered.

IV. *Autonomic tests involving pharmacologic blocking of one or the other branches of the autonomic system.* This type of test has had application clinically as well as physiologically because the reversibility of the effects permits of their application in human subjects.

A. *Ergotamine, ergotoxine.* This drug has enjoyed a wide reputation as a "sympathicolytic" drug by which sympathetic excitatory effects could be blocked pharmacologically. This has been assumed to permit the differentiation of sympathetic excitatory from other autonomic effects. That this interpretation of its action is misleading, that ergotoxin blocks primarily not sympathetic excitatory (E) but sympathetic inhibitory (I) effects (Rothlin, 1929; Thienes, 1929; Issekutz and Lenzinger, 1928), and that this action is in fact not an action on the sympathetic mechanisms but a protection of parasympathetic activity or a "physostigmine-like" action (Loewi and Navratil, 1926; Matthes, 1930; Linegar, 1939) is supported by the following facts:

The primary action of ergotamine is the contraction of smooth muscle, especially of cholinergically (Sherif, 1935) activated smooth muscle such as that of the uterus (Dale, 1906; Sharp, 1911; Agar, 1940, intestine (Rothlin, 1929), excised sphincter iridis (Crouch and Thompson, 1939), stomach (Smith, 1918), and retractor penis (Dale, 1906). In the intact animal it increases intestinal motility (Planelles, 1925), occasions extreme miosis (Dale, 1906; Crouch and Thompson, 1939), lowers blood sugar, but not after pancreatectomy (Shpiner, 1929) and decreases blood pressure (Wright, 1930). Frequently cases of increased blood pressure have been attributed to contraction of muscular organs. Carotid sinus desensitization by ergotamine (Heymans, Regniers and Bouckaert, 1930; Bacq, Brouha and Heymans, 1930) may also be a factor in cases of increased blood pressure following this drug.

Even where sympathetic excitatory effects have appeared blocked by ergotoxine, the blocking is not impossibly, as in the case of the nictitating membrane (Rosenblueth, 1932; Rosenblueth, Leese and Lambert, 1933) and the pregnant uterus (Agar, 1940), attributable to the accompanying tonic response or contracture. The sensitivity of these sympathetically innervated structures to acetylcholine has been shown in the case of the nictitating membrane by Morrison and Acheson (1938) and in the case of the uterus by Reynolds (1939). As noted in the foregoing, even the sympathetic impulses via the hypogastric nerves to the uterus are mediated by acetylcholine in the dog according to Sherif (1935). The increased peristalsis (Planelles, 1924), increased excitability of the vagus to acetylcholine, the nausea and emesis, and the uterine contractions attending administration of ergotamine, all point to a physostigmine-like action.

It is the inhibitory effects of adrenalin or sympathetic stimulation on cholinergically activated mechanisms which are blocked by ergotoxine. It is, as already noted, the ability of adrenalin or sympathetic stimulation to relax or block the spontaneous activity and tone in the intestine or the nonpregnant uterus of the cat which is prevented by ergotoxine. Even in denervated skeletal muscle adrenalin inhibition of the cholinergic pseudomotor contraction can be blocked by ergotoxine (Hinsey and Gasser, 1928). Also in the nerve-free but acetylcholine rich human placenta (Chang and Gaddum, 1935) adrenalin constriction of the blood vessels is blocked by ergotoxine (Euler, 1938). And even the familiar reversal of vasomotor response to adrenalin and sympathetic stimulation following ergotoxine are accounted for if we accept the evidence (Burn, review, 1939) for sympathetic cholinergic vasodilator fibers. We may assume that these cholinergic vasodilators normally are inhibited by inhibitory sympathetic action or inhibitory adrenalin, resulting thereby in a constriction which is synergic with the reaction of the adrenergic constrictors. Following ergotoxine this inhibition of the vasodilators does not take place, and there is in consequence a decreased pressor, or even a depressor effect. Bulbring and Burn (1935) and Herwick, Linegar and Koppanyi (1939) showed a similar vasomotor reversal after eserine—abolished by atropine. This again suggests that inhibitory adrenergic effects may be blocked or possibly swamped in the presence of sufficient acetylcholine. That ergotamine may likewise potentiate the depressor effects of acetylcholine and that this action may be reversed to a pressor action by atropine is shown by Linegar (1939) and by Herwick, Linegar and Koppanyi (1939). The previously considered (section III) relation of ergotamine to the reversal of adrenergic response in the pregnant and non-pregnant cat is consistent with this point of view.

That ergotamine may have considerable value as a means of testing for the presence of sympathetic inhibitory and adrenalin inhibitory effects on parasympathetic cholinergic functions appears to be indicated.

B. *Atropine.* The employment of atropine to block the action of cholinergic or parasympathetic mechanisms is the most familiar of pharmacologic blocking technics. Two types of measurements have been sought by this means—1, an index of the normally present parasympathetic activity derived from the changes induced when that activity is blocked, and 2, an index of sympathetic function derived from the magnitude of the total residual activity after parasympathetic opposition is eliminated.

Both of these effects are to some extent obscured or damped by the possible effect of the drug upon cholinergic transmission of nerve impulses within the sympathetic ganglia and adrenals, as well as in the central nervous system, and by the possible compensatory action of the carotid sinus and other moderator nerves.

As early as 1870, Schmiedeberg demonstrated that atropine blocked the inhibitory effects of the vagus on the heart. Escudro (1923) and Danielopolu (1926) devised tests of sympatheticotonia and parasympathecotonia based on the effects of atropine in blocking the parasympathetic control of the heart. Fentress and Solomon (1936) have applied the procedure in the study of autonomic function in psychoneurotic patients.

The contrasting effects of atropine, of parasympathicomimetic and sympathicomimetic drugs have been used as autonomic tests by Myerson, Loman and Dameshek (1937) and by Brohoff, Grosse and Kaldenberg (1938) in the study of the synergistic and antagonistic pharmacologic responses of human subjects. In physiological experiments the use of atropine to determine the rôle of cholinergic mechanisms in a given response is, of course, so common as to be almost routine.

V. *Equating of effects in differentially sensitive autonomic indicators.* The classic instance of derivation of autonomic activity from differential effects on peripheral autonomic indicators is Cannon and Rosenblueth's (see p. 9) differentiation of sympathin E from sympathin I on the basis of the differential effects on the iris or uterus and nictitating membrane.

Darrow and Gellhorn (1939) used a somewhat similar equating technic in contrasting the effects of nerve stimulation on a sympathectomized pupil having only a parasympathetic nerve supply with that of the normal pupil of the opposite side having both parasympathetic and sympathetic innervations. From the denervated pupil it was possible to determine the presence of inhibition of parasympathetic tone following stimulation, while from the difference between that and the normal pupil it was possible to infer the presence of sympathetic excitation.

Darling and Darrow (1938) and Darling (1938) attempted a similar derivation from the differential effects of stimulation upon blood pressure and palmar sweating (galvanic) activity. As the method is more recently being applied (Darrow and Solomon, 1939, 1940) the rationale depends upon the assumption *1*, that blood pressure change represents the difference between opposing effects of sympathico-adrenal and parasympathico-cholinergic influences. Galvanic or sweating activity on the other hand, depends upon both sympathetic nerve conduction and upon cholinergic transmission at the effector (see p. 3). These relationships are symbolized in the equations:

$$B.P. = S - P$$

$$\text{and Galv.} = S + P$$

where S represents sympathico-adrenal activity, and P represents parasympathico-cholinergic activity.

Given simultaneous galvanic and blood pressure responses to stimulation these simultaneous equations may be solved for either S or P. Or, if desired, the data may be plotted into two-dimensional graphs or "autonomograms." The results of the method indicate simultaneous effects on both sympathetic and parasympathetic activity in the normal individual with sympathetic effects predominating. They indicate, further, the presence of decreased sympathetic responses and a tendency toward the inhibition of parasympathetic tone following stimulation in "resistant" hostile, inhibited, unco-operative psychotic patients. Evidence from the studies of Darrow and Gellhorn (1939a, b, c) that the presence of adrenalin in the circulating blood disposes toward exaggeration of responses of the type involving inhibition of parasympathetic tone, as well as a diminution of sympathetic responses, suggests that adrenalin may be a factor in determining the reaction pattern of the "resistant" psychotic patients. A possible rôle of adrenalin in accounting for the condition of these patients will be considered under "Autonomic balance" (see section VII).

VI. *Electrical recording of autonomic potentials.* Action potentials of the autonomic effectors or of their innervating nerves provide valuable indications of autonomic activity. A familiar example is the electrical recording of sweat gland activity by the use of endosomatic potentials (Tarchanoff, 1890) (See reviews of galvanic response literature, Landis and Dewick 1929; Landis, 1932; Darrow, 1936, 1937). The nictitating membranes and pilomotor muscles have been recorded electrically (Orias, 1932; Rosenblueth, Leese and Lambert, 1933; Rosenblueth, Davis and Rempel, 1936a, b; Eccles and Magladery, 1937a, b). Effects of ovulation have been registered as abdominal or vaginal action potentials by Burr, Hill and Allen (1935); Reboul, Davis and Friedgood (1937), and Bourdillon (1939). Effects of pharmacologic agents on uterine potentials have been studied by Bozler (1938), Morrison (1940) and Balassa and Gurd (1941). Gastrointestinal motility was studied by Bozler (1938, 1939, 1941), and paccinian corpuscle potentials of the mesentary by Gammon and Bronk (1935). Gastric impulses in the vagus are reported by Partridge and Wilson (1933) and vagal (carotid sinus?) effects by Fischer, Gantt and Lowenback (1934). Comparison of electrical responses in various types of smooth muscle such as the nictitating membranes, pilomotors, intestine, bladder, uterus and ureter by Rosenblueth, Leese and Lambert (1933), Lambert and Rosenblueth 1935, and Davis, Rosenblueth and Rempel (1936), and Bozler (1938) indicate that the initial potentials, types I and II of Cannon and Rosenblueth (1937) are associated with excitation, whether in the case of the sympathetic nerves or in the case of the parasympathetic ones.   The effects of various pharmacologic agents on the magnitude of these potentials relates to effects on permeability (Rosenblueth and Cannon, 1936). Inhibitory effects are accompanied only by type III delayed and prolonged potentials, identified by Cannon and Rosenblueth with actual contraction.   In the salivary glands the possibility of differential negative as opposed to positive potentials, associated respectively with parasympathetic as opposed to sympathetic stimulation, is indicated by Bronk and Gesell (1926).   Pharmacologic effects on the potentials of the submaxillary gland were studied by Rosenblueth, Forbes and Lambert (1933).

Effects of adrenalin, atropine and other drugs in damping cholinergic transmission in sympathetic (cholinergic) ganglia, as well as the facilitating effect of moderate concentrations of parasympathetic drugs on the ganglia have been studied electrically by Marazzi (1939a, b).   Potentials from several different autonomic nerves as a means toward the solution of problems of autonomic control have been employed by Hinsey and Gasser (1930), Corbin and Hinsey (1935) and Bishop, Heinbecker and O'Leary (1934).

Especially important are the records of sympathetic action potentials and the correlation of these with cardiovascular control from the hypothalamus and carotid sinus as reported by Bronk, Ferguson, Margaria and Solandt (1936), Bronk, Lewy and Larrabee (1936), Pitts, Larrabee and Bronk (1941), and Pitts and Bronk (1942).   The rhythmic character of these potentials and their frequency at about that of the cortical potentials (notwithstanding anesthesia) is of particular interest in view of the evidence assembled by Darrow, Jost, Solomon and Mergener (1942) for an association of alpha potentials with cerebral vasoconstrictor tone.

Of great interest also is the recording of potentials from the carotid sinus and the demonstration of specific functional relationships to sympathetic regulation which could have been derived only by electrical methods (Bronk, 1931; Bronk and Stella, 1932, 1935; Fischer and Löwenback, 1934; Bogue and Stella, 1934, 1935; Samaan and Stella, 1935, and Pitts, 1942).   The possible applications of such electrical recording technics (Bronk, Pitts and Larrabee, 1940) are as extensive as the ramifications of the autonomic system.

VII. *Autonomic balance—dynamic equilibrium.*   Autonomic dysfunction is often times referred to as "autonomic imbalance."   This may be begging the question, for obviously in a balanced system abnormal activity would be recognized only if it were sufficient to upset the balance.   A dysfunction of one part of the autonomic system, balanced by a compensatory dysfunction of another part of the system might conceivably constitute a double liability, and yet not be demonstrable as an "imbalance."   The futility of treating symptoms under such conditions is obvious, and it is likely that many of the baffling problems of autonomic dysfunctions are of this type.

Although the Eppinger and Hess (1909) concept of balance, of sympathicotonia, and of parasympathicotonia has served a useful purpose in directing and stimulating research, the actual clinical and physiological consequences of its application have unquestionably been disappointing.   Without detracting from the importance of the concept in the development of our thinking, it should be pointed out that present day knowledge of the physiological processes involved in maintenance of "balance" dicatates that discussion to be profitable must be concerned but little with "balance" in the abstract and concentrated rather on specific neurophysiological mechanisms of homeostatic control.

Since the discovery by Hering in 1923 of the main mechanisms of autonomic regulation or maintenance of balance and the confirmation by Koch (1923) and by Heymans (1928) our knowledge of carotid sinus, aortic and abdominal vasosensory mechanisms has advanced so rapidly and the specific determinants of sympathicatonic and vagotonic effects have been sufficiently defined that reference to such terms as "autonomic balance," "sympathicotonia," and "parasympathicotonia" without physiologic qualification partakes almost of mysticism. Such terms are too general and too indefinite, though on occasion it is conceded that they may be useful for purposes of classification.

The carotid sinus mechanism, and aiso the carotid bodies, at the bifurcation of the internal and external carotid arteries, the vasosensory zone located in the arch of the aorta, and the less important, less well localized "vasotatic" receptors in the abdominal region established by Heymans (1929a, b), Heymans, Bouckaert, Farber and Hsu (1936), and Hsu and Chu (1937) supply neurosensory impulses for the reflex control of circulatory and respiratory equilibrium. The carotid sinuses exercise control by maintaining and varying the tonic inhibition over these most essential life-maintaining functions as well as over the more general emergency functions of the sympathetic system. They determine, as it were, the varying *negative bias* required to "modulate" or moderate oscillations in the circulatory system. In general, optimal conditions of oxygenation and blood pressure which favor bodily activity *activate* carotid sinus function also, and the carotid sinus in turn lowers blood pressure to that minimum which is commensurate with the maintenance of its own activity. Conditions of low oxygen, low blood pressure, or excess carbon dioxide (Bielinski and Wierzuchowski, 1939) in the carotid sinus, on the other hand, tend to reduce or *inactivate* carotid sinus inhibitory processes and release the restrained sympathetic mechanisms from tonic inhibition. At the same time tonic parasympathetic impulses from the carotid sinus are reduced. Such conditions tend, like denervation, toward hypertension, and in more extreme conditions they may occasion hyperpnea (Heymans and Bouckaert, 1930a, b; Winder, 1937a, b, 1938; Schmidt, 1932). The terms *activation* and *inactivation* are here employed relative to the carotid sinus because of the current confusion with respect to the word "sensitization" as applied for example to Vercauteren's (1932) demonstration that in the presence of carbon dioxide the added embarrassment of a standard reduction in intrasinusal pressure will produce a larger compensatory hypertensive effect than a similar change in pressure without the carbon dioxide. Since usage has designated this effect a "sensitization" it is pointed out that in this case one agent merely potentiates the *inactivation* produced by the other (Bielinski and Wierzuchinski, 1939). This general interpretation of carotid sinus function is offered with full consideration of the fact that in extremely low pressure, "paradoxical" reactions with failure of respiration and blood pressure may obscure normal carotid sinus compensations. It is not assumed that these principles apply equally to the chemoreceptors of the carotid bodies, for these apparently operate by a positive rather than by an inhibitory mechanism of control.

Gesell and collaborators have recently called attention to still another buffering action on ganglionic structures. They point out that acetylcholine is rapidly destroyed by cholinesterase in an alkaline medium, but that it is conserved, increasing its duration and intensity of action, in an acid medium. This provides a direct biochemical buffering mechanism in which accumulation of acetylcholine with its facilitation of myoneural and ganglionic transmission parallels carotid sinus disinhibition of sympathetic activity.

Not only do the moderator nerves normally maintain a regulatory inhibitory control over sympathetic activity, actually reducing the magnitude of vasomotor and other reactions to afferent nerve stimulation (see Rosenblueth and Schwartz, 1935, for nictitating membrane, Izquierdo, 1920, for vasomotor effects) but there is evidence likewise of a positive control by way of the parasympathetic system (Hering, 1927; Heymans, 1928, Bernthal and Motley, 1939). Of effects (blocked by atropine) via the vagus on the heart there can be no question, and even increased intestinal motility and tone has been reported following carotid sinus stimulation (Tournade and Malmajac, 1929). Evidence to the contrary (Thomas and Brooks, 1937; Grimson, 1940) that reflex carotid sinus control is completely lost following sympathectomy does not disprove the existence of normal parasympathetic regulation by the carotid sinus, for the reason that carotid sinus function is dependent both upon the presence of adequate internal pressure, and on the presence of sensitizing adrenalin, either or both of which may be eliminated by sympathectomy.

Adrenalin secretion, so often identified as an emergency blood pressure raising device, apparently plays an important, and not always considered, rôle in the carotid sinus limitation and homeostatic regulation of autonomic activity. The presence of circulating adrenalin in the carotid sinus tends to sensitize that mechanism and increase inhibitory effects both on blood pressure and respiration (Heymans, 1929a, b). This was attributed by Stella (1932) to the increase of blood pressure and the effect of adrenalin on the "centers," but Malmajac, Donnet and Desanti (1935a, b), Battencourt (1935) and Chu and Hsu (1938) showed that the presence of adrenalin actually increases the sensitivity of the carotid sinus mechanisms to the existing pressure. Thus may adrenalin occasion a depressor blood pressure reaction independently of its depressor peripheral effects previously considered. Thus adrenalin by increasing carotid sinus inhibition of the sympathetic may exercise an inhibitory control over medulliadrenal secretion. It thereby provides homeostatic limitation of its own output. In like manner may adrenalin limit the reactivity of other sympathetic functions (Darrow and Gellhorn, 1939; Gellhorn, Darrow and Yesinick, 1939).

Conversely, the action of acetylcholine in the carotid sinus may decrease inhibition of sympathetic activity as shown by Heymans, Bouckaert, Farber and Hsu (1935) resulting in hypertension. This may be considered a cholinergic inactivation of the carotid sinus, since the effects are similar in direction if not in degree to those of denervation. The same apparently may be said of the physostigmine-like action of ergotamine in the carotid sinus, which may also result in hypertension according to Bacq, Brouha and Heymans (1932), again probably as an effect of disinhibition of the sympathetic by depression of carotid sinus reflexes, as demonstrated after ergotamine by Heymans, Regniers and Bouckaert (1930). The increased blood pressures observed in human subjects following ergotamine by Freeman and Carmichael (1936) are possibly so accounted for.

Inhibitory control by the carotid sinus apparently extends likewise over the activities of those tonic postural mechanisms which are sometimes associated with sympathetic function. Not only will increase of intra-carotid pressure block respiration (Bouckaert and Heymans, 1930; Schmidt, 1932) but it will halt shivering (Tournade and Malmajac, 1929) decrease action potentials in skeletal muscle (Spychela, 1935) eliminate the knee jerk (Schweitzer and Wright, 1937) reduce other skeletal reflexes (Kaufman, 1938; Koch, 1932) occasion relaxation and sleep (Koch, 1932), halt convulsions and/or induce sleep in previously narcotized animals aroused by metrazol (Gellhorn, Darrow and Yesinick, 1939). Effects such as hyperpnea, convulsions, increased muscle potentials, increased somatic reflexes and convulsions have been observed following decrease of blood pressure by the same authors. Thus conditions of autonomic equilibrium within the carotid sinus may exert a most important direct influence over the activities of the central nervous system.

The most definitely identified clinical effects of carotid sinus dysfunction are probably the syncopal attacks attributed to carotid sinus hyperirritability (Weiss and Baker, 1933a, b). Ferris, Capps and Weiss (1935, 1936) following Weiss and Baker, have subdivided such attacks into 1, cerebral; 2, cardiac, and 3, vasomotor types, depending upon the probable mechanisms of precipitation. In "cerebral" attacks there is apparently a direct action of carotid sinus reflexes upon the brain or its circulation. In the other types the syncope is secondary to the embarrassment of general circulation. Convulsions in these latter cases are consequent to the syncopal attack (Freedberg and Sloan, 1937) and not directly an effect of carotid sinus hyperirritability, although Lennox, Gibbs and Gibbs demonstrate the possibility of attacks without cerebral anoxemia, by direct action of the carotid sinus on the brain. Weiss and Baker (1933) note that in idiopathic epilepsy (150 cases) carotid sinus pressure does not produce seizures. Marinesco and Kraindler (1931a, b) offer further evidence that epilepsy is actually associated not with carotid sinus hypersensitivity but with hyposensitivity and that it may often be a result of failure of that mechanism to protect the brain from mechanical shocks transmitted by the circulation. That a deficiency of the buffering mechanism is an etiologic factor in some cases of epilepsy is indeed not unlikely, but it seems to the author that electroencephalographic evidence suggests that it is the inadequate buffering of the autonomic discharges to the brain, rather than the lack of hydrodynamic control, which is probably most frequently involved.

The complexity of the problem of testing and interpreting the equilibrium which is the final product of the moderator nerves is further illustrated in certain cases of schizophrenia. Hypersensitivity and over-regulation by the carotid sinus are here possibly indicated. There is a relative absence of sinus arrhythmia (Whitehorn and Richter, 1937) which, according to Regniers (1920), is a sign of carotid sinus activity. Sympathetic functions are depressed (Darrow and Solomon, 1934, 1939, 1940; Gellhorn, 1938). Blood pressure tends to be low (Truman, Hoskins and Sleeper, 1932). Pulse tends to be slow (Hoskins and Welch, 1932). Postural activity may be inhibited as is evident in many of the so-called "withdrawal" symptoms. The vago-insulin secretion is increased (Gellhorn, Feldman and Allen, 1941) and emotional hypoglycemia is the rule (Bowman and Kasanin, 1929; McCowan and Quastel, 1931; Whitehorn, 1934; Gildae, Mailhouse and Morris, 1935). Insulin desensitization with the development of an anti-insulin factor may occur (Meduna and Gerty, 1932), just as insulin hypersensitivity may follow carotid sinus denervation (Casas and Hinsberg, 1932). And a possible mechanism for such a carotid sinus sensitization in resistant hostile unco-operative patients is the secretion of adrenalin suggested by the studies of Darrow and Solomon (1940). This is further supported by the aggravation of schizophrenic symptoms by subcutaneous adrenalin as reported by Lindeman (1935) and the decreased sensitivity to it (Kanner, 1918, and Freeman and Carmichael, 1935) which is a natural consequence of adrenalin adaptation according to Hoskins and Rowley (1915) and Rudolph (1938). Ergotamine which desensitizes the carotid sinus has proved effective as therapy (Baber and Tietz, 1937).

We may seek, then, tests of autonomic balance in terms of specific moderator compensatory mechanisms. Symptoms of imbalance may conceivably arise *1*, from exaggeration or displacement of one type of autonomic activity such that the normal buffering mechanisms are unable to restore equilibrium; *2*, from a deficiency or insensitivity of the moderator mechanisms; *3*, displacement of activity in one part of the autonomic system and an overcompensation by the buffer mechanisms as far as other activities of the organism are concerned; and possibly *4*, from overactive or oversensitive moderator mechanisms. A tabulation of symptoms might not differentiate these conditions, yet treatment would properly differ according to the cause of the dysfunction.

Tests of autonomic balance which have had wide application are in general of two types (A) those which examine the reaction of the organism or of some of its organs to a specific autonomic stimulus, and (B) those which impose a more or less non-specific load on the organism and attempt to measure the efficiency of the equilibrium maintaining machinery under conditions of regulated stress. Such are really tests, not of static "balance" but of dynamic equilibrium. Space permits only the mention of some of the more common tests of these two types.

A. *Tests of reaction to a specific autonomic stimulus.* Among such tests probably should be included the *oculo-cardiac* test (Aschner) in which pressure on the eyeballs elicits slowing of the heart, said to be marked in "vagotonic" individuals. The effects are different from those for carotid sinus pressure (Mandelsturm and Lipschutz, 1932a, b; Regueiers, 1930; Wright, 1932). The oculocardiac effects, probably primarily vagal, apparently affect pulse more than blood pressure. Carotid sinus pressure causes both vagal stimulation and sympathetic inhibition. Jacobivici and Nitzescu (1929) employ electrical stimulation of the carotid sinus producing effects similar to pressure. The cold-pressor test previously described (p. 7) is probably effective primarily as a means of sympathetic stimulation. That this test may be effective because it provides a harmless though moderately severe pain stimulus has probably been given less than due consideration. Orthostatic tests, with or without a tilting table may be mentioned in this connection because of action on the carotid sinus. Correspondence of findings with those obtained by carotid sinus pressure appear not too good. The use of autonomic drugs by various routes should doubtless also be included in this group of tests. In the case of intravenous injections interpretation is always complicated by the fact that peripheral effects and central and carotid sinus compensatory effects may work in opposition. The compensatory effect is often the important one. Reactions to intravenous adrenalin and "wheal" and "flare" reactions to subcutaneous adrenalin may have quite different significance. Tests of reaction to carbon dioxide and to overventilation and attempts to shift the acid-base equilibrium as for example with bicarbonate or ammonium chloride deserve mention in this connection, not only because of the relation of ionic equilibrium to ganglionic and myoneural transmission, but more especially because of the activation by hypocapnia, high pH and calcium of the carotid sinus complex.

It must be emphasized that *a priori* interpretations of such tests involving autonomic stimulation is hazardous. For example, the fact that pressure on the eyes produces marked vagal-like effects in certain individuals does not automatically render this a valid test of "vagotonia." Only demonstration of the correlation of these stimulation effects with results of other valid indicators can be justification for such an interpretation.

B. Tests which attain significance because they impose an effective load on the organism and thus provide a means of gauging the effectiveness of various homeostatic mechanisms in handling the load are almost too non-specific to be included as autonomic tests. We should perhaps mention the Schneider (1920) test of cardiovascular efficiency, with its regulated mounting and demounting of a standard stairstep. Tests in which the ability of the organism to cope with a low oxygen pressure and acapnia also deserve mention. Apparently it makes little difference whether the subject ascends high altitudes by breathing a low percentage of oxygen from a Douglas bag, by being subjected to reduced pressure in a tank, or by boarding a plane. This adds to the facility and convenience of making such studies. A third class of tests worthy of special mention are the so-called "neurosis" producing tests which permit study of equilibrium maintaining mechanisms which may be upset in emotion.

Such tests tend to go afield from the category of strictly autonomic tests. Metabolic activity, brain function, electroencephalographic activity, electrocardiographic activity, biochemistry and other functions without number may be and are on occasion properly measured in pursuit of information regarding autonomic functions. The only limitation is what can be measured and what is the aspect of autonomic function under consideration.

Batteries of autonomic tests have been employed for the study of autonomic function and balance with a view toward determining individual differences and to throw light on the rôle of the autonomic system in the broader clinical adaptive and psychological relations. The clinical-pathological studies of Peterson and collaborators (1930–1938) provide an exploration in this field with clues to possible relationships which should be mentioned. The pharmacologic studies of Meyerson, Loman, Dameshek et al. also provide a systematic approach. The correlational studies employing factorial analysis by Darling and by Wenger (1941) suggest possibilities for the application of modern mathematical technics to the solution of autonomic problems where results from batteries of autonomic tests are available. The latter method should reveal any tendency for autonomic test results to be grouped according to any principle. For example, if sympathetic and parasympathetic activities play different and determining rôles these should be derivable by such factorial analyses as indeed they were in the results of Darling. Factorial analysis, it should be pointed out, may reveal relationships which otherwise might escape attention. They cannot, however, impart autonomic significance to tests which are not themselves valid according to acceptable physiologic criteria. Such correlational procedures should nevertheless provide tests for the validity of accepted test technics and assist in the identification of still undiscovered autonomic indicators.

REFERENCES

ACHESON, G. H., A. ROSENBLUETH AND P. F. PARTINGTON. Some afferent nerves producing reflex responses of the nictating membrane. Am. J. Physiol. 115: 308, 1936.

ADSON, A. W. AND G. E. BROWN. The treatment of Raynaud's disease by resection of the upper thoracic and lumbar sympathetic ganglia and trunks. Surg., Gynec. and Obst. 48: 577, 1929.

ADSON, A. W. Indications for operation on the sympathetic nervous system. J. A. M. A. 106: 360, 1936.

AGAR, W. T. The action of adrenalin upon the uterus of the guinea pig and its modification by eserine. J. Physiol. 98: 492, 1940.

ANDERSON, H. K. Reflex pupil dilatation by way of the cervical sympathetic nerve. J. Physiol. 30: 15, 1904.

ARMSTRONG, H. G. The blood pressure and pulse rate as an index of emotional stability. Am. J. Med. Sci. 17: 211, 1938.

ASTWOOD, E. B. Factors influencing the early action of estrogen upon the uterus. Am. J. Physiol. 129: 302, 1940.

BABER, E. A. AND E. B. TIETZ. The effect of ergotamine tartrate on the behavior of psychotic patients. Ohio J. Med. 17: 551, 1937.

BABKIN, B. P., C. O. HEBB AND M. A. SERGEYEVA. The parasympathetic-like effect of splanchnic nerve stimulation on pancreatic secretion. Quart. J. Exper. Physiol. 29: 217, 1939.

BACQ, Z. M., L. BROUHA ET C. HEYMANS. Reflexes vaso-moteurs D'origine sino carotidienne chez le chat sympathectomise. Compt. Rend. Soc. de Biol. 111: 152, 1932.

BACQ, Z. M. Les propriétés biologiques et physico-chemiques de la sympathine comparées a celles de l'adrenaline. Liege, 1933.
La Pharmacologie du systéme nerveux autonome, et particulierement du sympathique d'apres la théorie neurohumorale. Ann. de Physiol. 10: 467, 1934.
La Transmission chimique des influx dans le systeme nerveux autonome. Ergebn. d. Physiol. 37: 82, 1935.

BACQ, Z. M., L. BROUHA AND C. HEYMANS. Réflexes vasomoteurs d'origine sino-carotidienne et actions pharmacologiques chez le chat et le chien sympathec-tomisés. Arch. Internat. Pharmacodynam. **48**: 429, 1934.

BAIN, W. A., J. T. IRVING AND B. A. McSWINEY. The afferent fibres from the abdomen in the splanchnic nerves. J. Physiol. **84**: 322, 1935.

BALASSA, G. AND M. K. GURD. Action of adrenaline and potential changes in the cat uterus. J. Pharmacol. and Exper. Therap. **72**: 63, 1941.

BARD, P. A diencephalic mechanism for the expression of rage with special reference to the sympathetic nervous system. Am. J. Physiol. **84**: 490, 1928.
The neuro-humoral basis of emotional reactions. Foundations of Experimental Psychology, Chap. 12, pp. 449–487. Clark Univ. Press, 1929.

BARGETON, D. Some effects of acute anemia on the transmission of impulses through a sympathetic ganglion. Am. J. Physiol. **121**: 261, 1938.

BAUER, M. Versuche am Amnion von Huhn and Gans. Arch. f. exper. Path. u. Pharmacol. **134**: 49, 1928.

BENDER, M. B. Sensitized pupillary dilator and facial muscles as indicators of sympa-thetic and parasympathetic substances in blood. Proc. Soc. Exper. Biol. **39**: 62, 1938.
Fright and drug contractions in denervated facial and ocular muscles of monkeys. Am. J. Physiol. **121**: 609, 1938.

BENDER, M. B. AND S. SIEGEL. Release of autonomic humoral substances in hypoglycemic cats and monkeys. Am. J. Physiol. **128**: 324, 1940.

BENDER, M. B. AND E. A. WEINSTEIN. Actions of adrenalin and aceylcholine on the de-nervated iris of the cat and monkey. Am. J. Physiol. **130**: 268, 1940.

BERNTHAL, T. AND H. E. MOTLEY. The efferent pathway of chemoreflex vasomotor re-actions of carotid body origin. Am. J. Physiol. **126**: 443, 1939.

BETTENCOURT, J. M. DE. Adrénaline et zone réflexogène carotidienne. Compt. Rend. Soc. de Biol. **120**: 541, 1935.

BIELINSKI, C. AND M. WIERZUCHOWSKI. Antagonism des gaz dans leur action sur les pres-sorecepteurs du sinus carotidien. Compt. Rend. Soc. de Biol. **130**: 1549, 1442, 1939.

BILLIGHEIMER, E. Ueber einem Antagonismus zwischen Pilokarpin und Adrenalin: Beitrag zur Innervation der Schweiss-drüsen. Arch. f. exper. Path. u. Phar-makol. **88**: 172, 1920.

BISHOP, G. H., P. HEINBECKER AND J. O'LEARY. The significance in vasomotor responses to vagus and depressor nerve stimulation in the rabbit. Am. J. Physiol. **109**: 409, 1934.

BODO, R. C. AND A. E. BENAGLIA. The effect of sympathin on blood sugar. Am. J. Physiol. **116**: 12, 1936.
Hyperglycemia produced by sympathin in emotional excitement. Am. J. Physiol. **121**: 738, 1938.

BOGUE, J. Y. AND G. STELLA. Impulses in the carotid sinus nerve. J. Physiol. **82**: 23, 1934.
Afferent impulses in the carotid sinus nerve (nerve of Hering) during asphyxia and anoxemia. J. Physiol. **83**: 459, 1935.

BÖMER, M. Ueber die Wirkung einiger Kramfgifte auf Blutzucher und Blutmilchsäure. Arch. exper. Path. u. Pharmakol. **149**: 247, 1930.

BOURDILLON, R. B. Vaginal potentials in rabbits. J. Physiol. **97**: 138, 1939.

BOWMAN, K. M. AND J. KASANIN. Sugar content of the blood in emotional states. Arch. Neurol. and Psychiat. **21**: 342, 1939.

BOZLER E. The action potentials of visceral smooth muscle. Am. J. Physiol. **124**: 502, 1938.
Electric stimulation and conduction of excitation in smooth muscle. Am. J. Physiol. **122**: 614, 1938.
Electrophysiological studies on the motility of the gastrointestinal tract. Am. J. Physiol. **127**: 301, 1939.

An analysis of the excitatory and inhibitory effects of sympathetic nerve impulse and adrenalin on visceral smooth muscle. Am. J. Physiol. **130:** 627, 1941.

BRITTON, S. W. The nervous control of insulin secretion. Am. J. Physiol. **74:** 291, 1925.
The prepotency of medulliadrenal influence in emotional hyperglycemia. Am. J. Physiol. **86:** 340, 1928.

BROCKOFF, F. G. AND F. KALDENBERG. Ueber den Antagonismus von Sympathetic und Vagus unter der Einwirkung adrenalinähnlicher Substanzen. Arch. f. Exper. Path. u. Pharmakol. **188:** 383, 1938.

BRONK, D. W. Afferent impulses in the carotid sinus and aortic nerves. Proc. Soc. Exper. Biol. and Med. **28:** 1014, 1931.

BRONK, D. W. AND G. STELLA. Afferent impulses in the carotid sinus nerve. J. Cell. and Comp. Physiol. **1:** 113, 1932.
The response to steady pressures of single end organs in the isolated carotid sinus. Am. J. Physiol. **110:** 708, 1935.

BRONK, D. W., L. K. FERGUSON, R. MARGARIA AND D. Y. SOLANDT. Activity in cardiac sympathetic centers. Am. J. Physiol. **117:** 237, 1936.

BRONK, D. W., F. H. LEWY AND M. G. LARRABEE. The hypothalamic control of sympathetic rhythms. Am. J. Physiol. **116:** 15, 1936.

BRONK, D. W. AND R. GESELL. Electrical conductivity, electrical potential, and H ion concentration measurements on the submaxillary gland of the dog recorded with continuous photographic methods. Am. J. Physiol. **77:** 570, 1926.

BRONK, D. W., R. F. PITTS AND M. G. LARRABEE. Role of hypothalamus in cardiovascular regulation. Assn. Res. Nerv. and Ment. Dis. The hypothalamus. Chap. X, pp. 323–341, 1940.

BROOKS, C. M. Reflex activation of the sympathetic system in the spinal cat. Am. J. Physiol. **106:** 251, 1933.

BROWN, G. E. Clinical tests of function of the autonomic system. J. A. M. A. **106:** 353, 1936.
The treatment of peripheral vascular disturbances of the extremities. J. A. M. A. **87:** 379, 1926.

BROWN, G. L. Conduction in the cervical sympathetic. J. Physiol. **81:** 228, 1934.

BROWN, G. L. AND J. C. ECCLES. The action of a single vagal volley on the rhythm of the heart beat. J. Physiol. **82:** 211, 1934a.
Further experiments on vagal inhibition of the heart beat. J. Physiol. **82:** 242, 1934b.

BUCY, P. C. The nictitating membrane and the superior cervical ganglion in the rabbit. J. Comp. Neurol. **43–44:** 221, 1927.

BULBRING, E. AND J. H. BURN. Cholinergic nature of sympathetic vasodilator fibers. J. Physiol. **81:** 42, 1934.
The sympathetic dilator fibers in the muscles of the cat and dog. J. Physiol. **83:** 483, 1935.
The Sherrington phenomenon. J. Physiol. **86:** 61, 1936.

BURN, J. H. Sympathetic vasodilator fibers. Physiol. Revs. **18:** 137, 1938.

BURR, H. S., R. T. HILL AND E. ALLEN. Detection of ovulation in the intact rabbit. Proc. Soc. Exper. Biol. and Med. **33:** 109, 1935.

BUTT, H. R. Chemical mediation of nerve impulses. Arch. Neurol. and Psychiat. **37:** 141, 1937.

CANNON, W. B. Bodily changes in pain, hunger, fear and rage. New York: D. Appleton, 1915, 1920.

CANNON, W. B. AND S. W. BRITTON. Pseudaffective medulliadrenal secretion. Am. J. Physiol. **72:** 283, 1925.
The influence of motion and emotion on medulliadrenal secretion. Am. J. Physiol. **79:** 433, 1927.

CANNON, W. B., J. T. LEWIS AND S. W. BRITTON. Studies on the conditions of activity in endocrine glands. Am. J. Physiol. **77:** 326, 1926.

CANNON, W. B. AND A. ROSENBLUETH. Studies on conditions of activity in endocrine organs, sympathin E. and sympathin I. Am. J. Physiol. **104:** 557, 1933.
A comparison of the effects of sympathin and adrenine on the iris. Am. J. Physiol. **113:** 251, 1935.
A comparative study of sympathin and adrenine. Am. J. Physiol. **112:** 268, 1935.
Autonomic neuro-effector systems. New York, Macmillan, 1937.

CANNON, W. B. AND J. E. URIDIL. Some effects on the denervated heart of stimulating the nerves of the liver. Am. J. Physiol. **58:** 353, 1921.

CARLSON, H. B., E. GELLHORN AND C. W. DARROW. Representation of the sympathetic and parasympathetic nervous system in the forebrain of the cat. Arch. Neurol. and Psychiat. **45:** 105, 1941.

CASAS, J. AND K. HINSBERG. Ueber Insulinempfindlichkeit und Sinus carotidiens. Klin. Wchnschr. **11:** 641, 1932.

CATTELL, M., H. G. WOLFF AND D. CLARK. The liberation of adrenergic and cholinergic substances in the submaxillary gland. Am. J. Physiol. **109:** 375, 1934.

CHANG, H. C. AND J. H. GADDUM. Choline esters in tissue extracts. J. Physiol. **79:** 255, 1935.

CHANG, S. A comparative study of the effect of adrenaline on the blood sugar, blood pressure, denervated heart, nictitating membrane, stomach, iris, hair and salivary gland in the cat. Chinese J. Physiol. **12:** 397, 1937.

CHU, L. W. AND F. Y. HSU. The effect of adrenalin on vasomotor reflexes. J. Exper. Physiol. **27:** 307, 1938.

CLARK, G. A. The influence of the vagus nerves on the secretion of insulin. J. Physiol. **73:** 297, 1931.
The vaso-dilator action of adrenaline. J. Physiol. **80:** 429, 1934.

COMROE, J. H. AND C. F. SCHMIDT. The part played by reflexes from the carotid body in the chemical regulation of respiration in the dog. Am. J. Physiol. **121:** 75, 1938.

CORBIN, K. B. AND J. C. HINSEY. Dorsal roots of spinal nerves and regulation of skin temperature. Proc. Soc. Exper. Biol. **2:** 368, 1935.

CRAIG, W. M. Hypertension and its surgical treatment. South. Surgeon **7:** 140, 1938.

CRAIG, W. M., T. HORTON AND C. SHEARD. Thermal changes in peripheral vascular diseases during sympathetic ganglionectomy. J. Clin. Investigation **12:** 573, 1933.

CROUCH, L. AND K. THOMPSON. Autonomic functions of the cerebral cortex. J. Nerv. and Ment. Disease. **89:** 328, 1939.

CUSHNY, A. R. On the movements of the uterus. J. Physiol. **35:** 1, 1906.
The action of atropine, pilocarpine, and physostignine. J. Physiol. **41:** 233, 1910.

DALE, H. H. On some physiological actions of ergot. J. Physiol. **34:** 163, 1906.
A survey of present knowledge of the chemical regulation of certain functions by natural constituents of the tissues. Bull. Johns Hopkins Hosp. **53:** 297, 1933.

DALE, H. H. AND W. FELDBERG. The chemical transmission of secretory impulses to the sweat glands of the cat. J. Physiol. **82:** 121, 1934.

DALE, H. H. AND J. H. GADDUM. Reactions of denervated voluntary muscle and their bearing on the mode of action of parasympathetic and related nerves. J. Physiol. **70:** 109, 1930.

DANIELOPOLU, D., I. MARCOU AND G. G. PROCA. Sur le Réflexe Respiratoire sinocarotidien. Filets centripètes sino-carotidiens excitable et inhibiteurs. Compt. rend. Soc. de Biol. **106:** 734, 1931.
Sur le tonus respiratoire sino-carotidienne Méchanisme du fonctionnement des centres respiratoires. Compt. rend. Soc. de Biol. **106:** 737, 1931.

DARLING, R. P. Autonomic action in relation to personality traits of children. J. Abn. and Soc. Psychol. **35:** 246, 1940.

DARLING, R. P. AND C. W. DARROW. Determining activity of the autonomic nervous system from measurements of autonomic change. J. Psychol. **5:** 85, 1938.

DARROW, C. W. Sensory secretory and electrical changes in the skin following bodily excitation. J. Exper. Psychol. **10**: 192, 1927.

The relation of the galvanic skin reflex recovery curve to reactivity resistance level and perspiration. J. Gen. Psychol. **7**: 261, 1932.

Quantitative records of cutaneous secretory reactions. J. Gen. Psychol. **11**: 445, 1934.

The galvanic skin reflex (sweating) and blood pressure as preparatory and facilitative functions. Psychol. Bull. **33**: 73, 1936.

Neural mechanisms controlling the palmar galvanic skin reflex and palmar sweating. Arch. Neurol. and Psychiat. **37**: 641, 1937.

DARROW, C. W. AND E. GELLHORN. The effects of adrenalin on the reflex excitability of the autonomic nervous system. Am. J. Physiol. **127**: 243, 1939.

DARROW, C. W., H. JOST, A. P. SOLOMON AND J. C. MERGENER. Autonomic indications of excitatory and homeostatic effects on the electroencephalogram. J. Psychol. **14**: 115, 1942.

DARROW, C. W. AND A. P. SOLOMON. Galvanic skin reflex and blood pressure reactions in psychotic states. Arch. Neurol. and Psychiat. **32**: 273, 1934.

DARROW, C. W., A. P. SOLOMON AND M. BLAUROCK. Blood pressure and palmar sweat (galvanic) responses of psychotic patients before and after insulin and metrazol therapy. Psychosom. Med. **1**: 118, 1939.

DARROW, C. W. AND A. P. SOLOMON. Mutism and resistance behavior in psychotic patients. Am. J. Psychiat. **96**: 1441, 1940.

DAVIS, H., A. ROSENBLUETH AND B. REMPEL. Interpretation of the electrogram of certain smooth muscles. Am. J. Psychiol. **116**: 35, 1936.

ECCLES, J. C. AND J. W. MAGLADERY. The excitation and response of smooth muscle. J. Physiol. **90**: 31, 1937.

ECCLES, J. C. AND J. W. MAGLADERY. Rhythmic responses of smooth muscle. J. Physiol. **90**: 68, 1937.

ELLIOTT, T. R. The control of the suprarenal glands by the splanchnic nerves. J. Physiol. **44**: 374, 1912.

The innervation of the adrenal glands. J. Physiol. **46**: 285, 1913.

EPPINGER, H. AND L. HESS. Zur Pathologie des vegetativen Nervensystems. Ztschr. f. klin. Med. **66**: 345; **68**: 205, 1909.

ESCUDRO, P. Pilocarpine and atropine tests. Endocrinology **7**: 305, 1923.

EULER, U. S. AND J. H. GADDUM. Pseudomotor contractures after degeneration of the facial nerve. J. Physiol. **73**: 54, 1931.

EULER, U. S. Action of adrenaline, acetylcholine and other substances on nerve-free vessels (human placenta). J. Physiol. **93**: 129, 1938.

FELDBERG, W., B. MINZ AND H. TSUDZIMURA. The mechanism of the nervous discharge of adrenalin. J. Physiol. **80**: 15, 1934.

FENTRESS, T. L. AND A. P. SOLOMON. Galvanic skin reflex and Danielopolu test in psychoneurotic patients. Arch. Neurol. Psychiat. **35**: 770, 1936.

FERRIS, E. B., R. B. CAPPS AND S. WEISS. Carotid sinus syncope and its bearing on the mechanism of the unconscious state and convulsions. Med. **14**: 377, 1935.

FISCHER, M. H. AND H. LÖWENBACH. Aktionsströme des Ganglion stellatum und des Nervus depressor. Pflüger's Arch. **233**: 722, 1934.

FISCHER, M. H., W. H. GANTT AND H. LÖWENBACH. Aktionsströme des Nervus vagus beim Warmblüter. Pflüger's Arch. **233**: 732, 1934.

FREEDBERG, A. S. AND L. H. SLOAN. Association of carotid sinus reflexes with syncope and convulsions. Arch. Neurol. and Psychiat. **38**: 761, 1937.

FREEMAN, H. AND H. T. CARMICHAEL. A pharmacodynamic study of the autonomic nervous system in normal men: The effects of intravenous injections of epinephrine, atropin, ergotamine, and physostigmine upon the blood pressure and pulse rate. J. Pharmacol. and Exper. Therap. **58**: 409, 1936; Arch. Neurol. and Psychiat. **33**: 342, 1935.

FREEMAN, H., R. G. HOSKINS AND F. H. SLEEPER. The blood pressure in schizophrenia. Arch. Neurol. and Psychiat. **27:** 333, 1932.

GADDUM, J. H. Gefässerweiternde Stoffe der Gewebe. Leipzig, 1936.

GAMMON, G. D. AND D. W. BRONK. The discharge of impulses from Pacinian corpuscles in the mesentery and its relation to vascular changes. Am. J. Physiol. **114:** 77, 1935.

GANTOR, G. Ueber sogenannte vagotonische and sympathikotonische Symptome. München. med. Wchnschr. **72:** 1411, 1925.

GASSER, H. S. AND H. H. DALE. The pharmacology of denervated mammalian muscle. II. Some phenomena of antagonisms and the formation of lactic acid in chemical contracture. J. Pharmacol. **28:** 287, 1926.

GELLHORN, E. The action of hypoglycemia on the central nervous system and the problem of schizophrenia from the physiologic point of view. J. A. M. A. **110:** 1433, 1938.

GELLHORN, E., R. CORTELL AND J. FELDMAN. The effect of emotion, sham rage and hypothalamic stimulation on the vago-insulin system. Am. J. Physiol. **133:** 532, 1941.

GELLHORN, E. AND C. W. DARROW. The action of metrazol on the autonomic nervous system. Arch. Internat. Pharm. and Therap. **62:** 114, 1939.

GELLHORN, E., C. W. DARROW AND L. YESINICK. Effect of epinephrine on convulsions. Arch. Neurol. and Psychiat. **42:** 826, 1939.
Effect of variation of blood pressure on the autonomic nervous system. Proc. Soc. Exper. Biol. and Med. **43:** 236, 1940.

GELLHORN, E., J. FELDMAN AND R. CORTELL. On the vago-insulin and sympathico-adrenal system and their mutual relationship under conditions of central excitation induced by anoxia and convulsant drugs. Am. J. Physiol. **131:** 281, 1940.

GELLHORN, E. AND J. FELDMAN. The influence of fever on the vago-insulin and sympathico-adrenal systems. Endocrinology **29:** 141, 1941.
The influence of cold and heat on the vago-insulin and the sympathico-adrenal systems. Am. J. Physiol. **133:** 670, 1941.

GELLHORN, E., J. FELDMAN AND A. ALLEN. Assay of insulin on hypophysectomized-adreno-demedullated rat. Endocrinology **29:** 137, 1941; Am. J. Physiol. **133:** 193, 1941.
Effect of emotional excitement on the insulin content of the blood. Arch. Neurol. and Psychiat. **47:** 234, 1941.

GEMMILL, D. L., E. W. OVERSTREET AND L. M. HELLMAN. The effect of occlusion of the carotid arteries on heart and respiratory rates before and after denervation of the carotid sinus in normal dogs. Am. J. Physiol. **105:** 36, 1933.

GESELL, R., C. R. BRASSFIELD AND M. A. HAMILTON. An acid neuro-humoral mechanism of nerve cell activation. Am. J. Physiol. **136:** 604, 1942.

GIBSON, G. G. Clinical significance of retinal changes in hypertensive toxemias of pregnancy. J. Ophthal. **21:** 22, 1938.

GILDAE, E. F., V. L. MAILHOUSE AND D. P. MORRIS. Relationship between various emotional disturbances and the sugar content of the blood. Am. J, Psychiat. **92:** 115, 1935.

GREER, C. M., J. O. PINKSTON, J. H. BAXTER AND E. S. BRANNON. Nor-epinephrine [B-(3,4-Dehydroxyphenyl)-B-Hydroxylamine] as a possible mediator in the sympathetic division of the autonomic system. J. Pharmacol. and Exper. Therap. **62:** 189, 1938.

GRIMSON, K. S. Rôle of the sympathetic nervous system in experimental neurogenic hypertension. Proc. Soc. Exper. Biol. and Med. **44:** 219, 1940; Arch. Surg. **43:** 284, 1941.

GUTTMANN, G. L. Die Schweisssekretion des Menschen in ihren Beziehungen zum Nervensystem. Ztschr. f. d. ges. Neurol. u. Psychiat. **135:** 1, 1931.

HALLUM, A. V. Eye changes in hypertensive toxemia of pregnancy. J. A. M. A. **106:** 1649, 1936.

HAMPEL, C. W. The effect of denervation on the sensitivity to adrenine of the smooth muscle in the nictitating membrane of the cat. Am. J. Physiol. **111:** 611, 1935.

HARPER, A. A. AND B. A. MCSWINEY. Ascending spinal pathways of the pupillo-dilator fibres. J. Physiol. **90:** 395, 1937.

HARPER, A. A., B. A. MCSWINEY AND S. F. SUFFOLK. Afferent fibres from the abdomen in the vague nerves. Am. J. Physiol. **85:** 267, 1935.

HARRIS, R. E. AND D. J. INGLE. The influence of destruction of adrenal medulla on emotional hyperglycemia in rats. Am. J. Physiol. **120:** 420, 1937.

HARTMAN, F. A., J. I. EVANS, B. T. MALACHOWSKI AND L. M. MICHALEK. Effect of sympathetic nerve stimulation upon the capillaries and fibers of skeletal muscle. Am. J. Physiol. **85:** 99, 1928.

HARTMAN, F. A., J. I. EVANS AND H. G. WALKER. The action of epinephrin upon the capillaries and fibers of skeletal muscle. Am. J. Physiol. **85:** 91, 1928.

HENDERSON, Y., H. W. HAGGARD, AND F. S. DOLLEY. The efficiency of the heart and the significance of rapid and slow pulse rates. Am. J. Physiol. **82:** 512, 1927.

HERING, H. E. Der Karotisdrückversuch. München. med. Wchnschr. **70:** 1287, 1923. Die Karotissinus Reflexe auf Herz u. Gefässe. Dresden, 1927.

HERWICK, R. P., C. R. LINEGAR AND T. KOPPANYI. The effect of anesthesia on the vasomotor reversal. J. Pharmacol. and Exper. Therap. **65:** 185, 1939.

HERTZMAN, A. B. Photoelectric plethysmography and sphygmography in man and animal. Am. J. Physiol. **123:** 99, 1938.

HERTZMAN, A. B. AND J. B. DILLON. Reaction of large and small arteries in man to vasoconstrictor stimuli. Am. J. Physiol. **130:** 56, 1940.

HEYMANS, C. Sur les actions vasomotrices réflexes déterminées par les variations de la pression artérielle dans la circulation céphalique. Compt Rend. Soc. de Biol. **99:** 1236, 1928.
Le sinus carotidien isolé et perfusé, zone réflexogene régulatrice de l'adrenalinosécrétion. Compt. Rend. de Soc. de Biol. **100:** 199, 1929.
Sur la régulation réflexe du tonus vasomoteur et de l'adrénalinosécretion en rapport avec la pression artérielle. Compt. Rend. Soc. de Biol. **100:** 765, 1929.
Le sinus carotidien et les autres zones vasosensibles réflexogènes. Rev. Belge d. Sc. Med. **1:** 507, 1929.
Recherchès sur la physiologie et las pharmacologie du sinus carotidien. Am. J. Physiol. **90:** 387, 1929.

HEYMANS, C. AND J. J. BOUCKAERT. Observations chez le chien en hypertension artérielle chronique et experimentelle. Comp. Rend. Soc. de Biol. **106:** 471, 1931.
Hypertension artérielle experimentale et sympathectomie. Compt. Rend. Soc. de Biol. **120:** 82, 1935.
Sinus carotidien et réflexes respiratoire. Compt. Rend. Soc. de Biol. **103:** 498, 1930.
Sinus caroticus and respiratory reflexes. J. Physiol. **69:** 254, 1930.

HEYMANS, C., J. J. BOUCKAERT, S. FARBER AND F. Y. HSU. Influence de l'acetylcholine sur recepteurs chimio-sensitifs du sinus carotidien. Compt. Rend. Soc. de Biol. **120:** 1354, 1935.
Spinal vasomotor reflexes associated with variations in blood pressure. Am. J. Physiol. **117:** 619, 1936.

HEYMANS, C., R. REGNIERS AND J. J. BOUCKAERT. Ergotamine et réflexes vasomoteurs la localisation de l'action de l'ergotomine sur les réflexes vasomoteurs du sinus carotidien. Arch. Intern. de Pharm. et de Therapie. **39:** 213, 1930.

HILL, I. G. W. Stimulation of vagus nerve and carotid sinus in man. Quart. J. Exper. Physiol. **22:** 79, 1932.

HINES, E. A. AND G. E. BROWN. A standard test for measuring the variability of blood pressure; its significance as an index of the prehypertensive state. Ann. Int. Med. **7:** 209, 1933.

A standard stimulus for measuring vasomotor reactions; its application in the study of hypertension. Proc. Staff Meet. Mayo Clin. **7:** 332, 1932.

HINSEY, J. C. AND H. S. GASSER. The component of the dorsal root mediating vasodilatation and the Sherrington contracture. Am. J. Physiol. **92:** 679, 1930. The Sherrington Phenomenon. I, II, III. Antagonism by adrenalin. Am. J. Physiol. **87:** 368, 1928.

HINSEY, J. C., R. A. PHILLIPS AND K. HARE. Observations on cats following pre-and post-ganglionic sympathectomies. Am. J. Physiol. **41:** 513, 1939.

HODES, R. AND H. W. MAGOUN. A further study of pupillary responses to electrical stimulation of the forebrain and midbrain. Am. J. Physiol. **133:** 330, 1941.

HOLDIN, R. B. Vascular reactions of the uterus of the immature rat. Endocrinology. **25:** 593, 1939.

HOLLINSHEAD, W. H. The innervation of the adrenal glands. J. Comp. Neurol. **64:** 449, 1936.

HOSKINS, R. G., R. E. L. GUNNING AND E. L. BERRY. The effects of adrenin on the distribution of the blood. Am. J. Physiol. **41:** 513, 1916.

HOSKINS, R. G. AND W. N. ROWLEY. The effects of epinephrin infusion on vasomotor irritability. Am. J. Physiol. **37:** 471, 1915.

HOSKINS, R. G. AND A. WALSH. Oxygen consumption (basal metabolic rate) in schizophrenia. Arch. Neurol. and Psychiat. **28:** 1346, 1932.

HOUSSAY, B. A. AND J. T. LEWIS. Etudes sur les hyperglycémies experimentales. Mechanisme nerveux de l'action de la morphine. Compt. Rend. Soc. Biol. **89:** 1120, 1923.

HSU, F. Y. AND L. CHU. The diffuse vasotatic reflex. Chinese J. Physiol. **12:** 37, 1937.

HYNDMAN, O. R. AND J. WOLKIN. Sweat mechanisms in man. Study of distribution of sweat fibers from the sympathetic ganglia, spinal roots, spinal cord and common carotid artery. Arch. Neurol. and Psychiat. **45:** 446, 1941a.

The pilocarpine sweating test. A valid indicator in differentiation of preganglionic and postganglionic sympathectomy. Arch. Neurol. and Psychiat. **45:** 992, 1941b.

ISSEKUTZ, B. V. AND M. V. LENZINGER. Ueber die pharmakologische Wertbestimmung des Mutterkorns. Arch. f. exper. Path. u. Pharmakol. **128:** 165, 1928.

IZQUIERDO, J. J. Influence of the aortic and carotid sinus nerves upon the height and form of the rise of blood pressure produced by peripheral stimulation of the splanchnic nerve. J. Physiol. **70:** 221, 1930.

JOCOBOVICI, J., J. J. MITZESCU AND A. POP. Experimentelle Untersuchungen über die Physiologie der carotisdrüse beim Menschen. Ztschr. f. d. ges. exper. Med. **66:** 359, 1929.

JOSEPH, D. R. The inhibitory influence of the cervical sympathetic nerve upon the sphincter muscle of the iris. Am. J. Physiol. **55:** 279, 1921.

The mutually antagonistic actions of adrenalin and physostigmin upon the sphincter muscle of the iris. J. Pharmacol. and Exper. Therap. **9:** 358, 1916–17.

KANNER, L. The adrenalin blood pressure curves in dementia praecox and emotional psychoses. Am. J. Psychiat. **8:** 75, 1918.

KARPLUS, J. P. AND A. KREIDL. Sympathicusleitung im Gehirn und Halsmark. Pflüger's Arch. **129:** 138, 1911.

KAUFMAN, W. Effects of chemical stimulation of the carotid body upon the reflex contraction of the tibialis anticus muscle. Am. J. Physiol. **123:** 677, 1938.

KEITH, N. M., N. P. WAGENER AND J. W. KERNOHAN. Syndrome of malignant hypertension. Arch. Int. Med. **41:** 141, 1928.

KENNARD, J. H. The reversal by progestin of the response of the non-pregnant uterus of the cat. Am. J. Physiol. **118:** 190, 1937.

KING, C. E. Studies of intestinal inhibitory reflexes. Am. J. Physiol. **70:** 183, 1924. The effect of double vagotomy and carotid sinus denervation on the reaction of barbitalized dogs to hyperventilation. Am. J. Physiol. **119:** 350, 1937.

Koch, E. Die Irradiation der pressoreceptorischen Kreislaufreflexe. Klin. Wchnschr. **11**: 225, 1932.

Klinische Beobachtungen zum Karotisdrückversuch. München. med. Wchnschr. **70**: 1316, 1923.

La Barre and O. Vesselovsky. Contributions à l'etude des variations physiologiques de la sécrétion interne du pancréas: le pneumogastrique nerf insulinosécrétieur chez le chat. Arch. Int. de Physiol. **37**: 188, 1933.

Lambert, E. F. and A. Rosenblueth. A further study of the electric responses of smooth muscle. Am. J. Physiol. **114**: 147, 1935.

Landis, C. and H. N. De Wick. The electrical phenomena of the skin (psychogalvanic reflex). Psychol. Bull. **26**: 64, 1929.

Landis, C. Electrical phenomena of the skin. Psychol. Bull. **29**: 693, 1932.

Landis, E. M. and J. H. Gibbon. A simple method of producing vasodilatation in the lower extremities with reference to its usefulness in studies of peripheral vascular disease. Arch. Int. Med. **62**: 785, 1933.

Langley, J. N. On the reaction of cells and of nerve endings to certain poisons (nerve endings and receptive substance). J. Physiol. **33**: 374, 1905.

Langley, J. N. and K. Uyeno. The secretion of sweat. II. The effect of vasoconstriction and of adrenalin. J. Physiol. **56**: 207, 1922.

Langworthy, O. R. and C. P. Richter. The influence of efferent cerebral pathways upon the sympathetic nervous system. Brain **53**: 178, 1930.

Lennox, W. G., F. A. Gibbs and E. L. Gibbs. Relationship of unconsciousness to cerebral blood flow and to anoxemia. Arch. Neurol. and Psychiat. **34**: 1001, 1935.

Lieben, S. and R. H. Kahn. Die emotionelle Reaction der Pupille. Pflüger's Arch. **225**: 699, 1930.

Linegar, C. R. The effect of ergotamine on the hemodynamic actions of acetylcholine. J. Pharmacol and Exper. Therap. **66**: 22, 1939.

Lindemann, E. The psychopathological effect of drugs affecting the vegetative system. I. Adrenalin. Am. J. Psychiat. **91**: 983, 1935.

List, F. and M. M. Peet. Sweat secretion in man. Arch. Neurol. and Psychiat. **39**: 1228, 1938; **40**: 27, 269, 443, 1938; **42**: 1098, 1939.

Liu, A. C. The coöperative action of sympathetic nerve impulses, adrenine and sympathin on the nictitating membrane of the cat. Am. J. Physiol. **112**: 690, 1935.

Liu, A. C. and A. Rosenblueth. Reflex liberation of circulating sympathin. Am. J. Physiol. **113**: 555, 1935.

Loewi, O. and E. Navratil. Ueber humorale Uebertragbarkeit der Herznervenwirkung: Ueber den Mechanissmus der Vaguswirkung von Physostigmin und Ergotamin. Pflüger's Arch. **214**: 689, 1926.

Loew, E. R. and T. L. Patterson. The reflex influence of the lower portion of the large gut on the tonus and movements of the empty stomach in dogs. Am. J. Physiol. **113**: 89, 1935.

Lumley, F. H. and L. B. Nice. Blood sugar of adrenalectomized rats. Am. J. Physiol. **93**: 152, 1930.

MacFarland, W. E. and H. A. Davenport. Adrenal innervation. J. Comp. Neurol. **75**: 219, 1941.

Magoun, H. W., S. W. Ranson and N. M. Hetherington. The liberation of adrenin and sympathin induced by stimulation of the hypothalamus. Am. J. Physiol. **119**: 615, 1937.

Malméjac, J., V. Donnet and E. Desanti. Sur un des méchanismes par lequel une injection continue d'adrénaline reduit l'adrénalino-sécrétion. Compt. Rend. Soc. de Biol. **119**: 1155, 1935.

Injection continue d'adrenalin et adrénalino-sécrétion. Compt. Rend. Soc. de Biol. **119**: 1152, 1935.

MANDELSTAMM, M. AND S. LIFSCHITZ. Die Wirkung der Augenreflexe (des Aschnerschen Bulbusdrücksversuches) auf der Blutdruck. Wien. Arch. f. inn. Med. **22:** 435, 1932.

Die Wirkung der Karotissinusreflexe auf den Blutdruck beim Menschen. Wien. Arch. f. inn. Med. **22:** 397, 1932.

MARINESCO, G. AND A. KREINDLER. Les reflexes du sinus carotidien en pathologic nerveus. J. de Physiol. et de Path. **29:** 77, 1931.

MARINESCO, G., A. KREINDLER AND A. BRUCH. Weitere Beiträge zum Studium der Reflexe des Sinus caroticus in der Epilepsie. Ztschr. f. d. ges. exper. Med. **79:** 333, 1931.

MARRAZZI, A. S. A self-limiting mechanism in sympathetic homeostatic adjustment. Science **90:** 251, 1939.

Electrical studies on the pharmacology of autonomic synapses. J. Pharmacol. and Exper. Therap. **65:** 18, 1939.

MATTHES, K. The action of blood on acetylcholine. J. Physiol. **70:** 338, 1930.

McCOWAN, P. K. AND J. H. QUASTIL. Blood sugar studies in abnormal states. J. Ment. Sc. **77:** 525, 1931.

McQUARRIE, I., M. R. ZEIGLER, O. H. WANGENSTEEN AND C. DENNIS. Mechanism of insulin convulsions. III. Effects of varying partial pressures of atmospheric gases after adrenalectomy. Proc. Soc. Exper. Biol. Med. **42:** 513, 1939.

McSWINEY, B. A. AND S. F. SUFFOLK. Segmental distrbution of certain visceral afferent neurones of the pupillodilator reflex in the cat. J. Physiol. **93:** 104, 1938.

MEDUNA, L. J., F. J. GERTY AND V. G. URSE. Biochemical disturbances in mental disorders; anti insulin effect of blood in cases of schizophrenia. Arch. Neurol. and Psychiat. **44:** 38, 1942.

MILLER, G. H. The effect of cocaine on the iris compared with its effect on certain other structures containing smooth muscle. J. Pharmacol. and Exper. Therap. **28:** 219, 1926.

MINOR, V. Ein neues Verfahren zu der klinischen Untersuchung der Schweissabsonderung. Zeitschr. f. Nervenhk. **101:** 302, 1928.

MORISON, R. S. The effects of adrenalin and of nerve stimulation of the mechanical and electric responses of uterine muscle. Am. J. Physiol. **128:** 372, 1940.

MORISON, R. S. AND G. H. ACHESON. Effects of acetylcholine and adrenalin on nictitating membrane. Am. J. Physiol. **121:** 149, 1938.

MYERSON, A., J. LOMAN AND W. DAMESHEK. Physiologic effects of acetyl-beta-methylcholine (mecholyl) and its relationship to other drugs affecting the autonomic nervous system. Am. J. Med. Sc. **193:** 198, 1937.

NECHELES, H. AND F. NEUWELT. Antagonism between posterior pituitary secretion and acetylcholine. Am. J. Physiol. **124:** 142, 1938.

NEWTON, H. F., R. L. ZWEMER AND W. B. CANNON. The mystery of emotional acceleration of the denervated heart after exclusion of known humeral accelerators. Am. J. Physiol. **96:** 377, 1931.

ORIAS, O. Response of the nictitating membrane to prolonged stimulation of the cervical sympathetic. Am. J. Physiol. **102:** 87, 1932.

PARTINGTON, P. P. The production of sympathin in response to physiological stimuli in the unanesthetized animal. Am. J. Physiol. **117:** 55, 1936.

PARTRIDGE, R. C. AND M. J. WILSON. Gastric impulses in the vagus. J. Cell. and Comp. Physiol. **4:** 123, 1933.

PEARCY, J. F. AND E. J. VAN LIERE. Studies of the visceral nervous system: Reflexes from the colon. 1. Reflexes to the stomach. Am. J. Physiol. **78:** 64, 1926.

PETERSON, W. F. AND S. A. LEVINSON. The skin reactions, blood chemistry and physical status of "normal" men and of clinical patients. Ann Arbor, Edwards Bros., 1930.

PETERSON, W. F. AND M. E. MILLIKEN. The patient and the weather. Vols. I-IV. Ann Arbor, Edwards Bros., 1934–1938.

PITTS, R. F.   Excitation and inhibition of phrenic motor neurones.   J. Neurophysiol. **5:** 75, 1942.

PITTS, R. F. AND D. W. BRONK.   Excitability cycle of the hypothalamus-sympathetic neurone system.   Am. J. Physiol. **135:** 504, 1942.

PITTS, R. F., M. G. LARRABEE AND D. W. BRONK.   An analysis of hypothalamic cardiovascular control.   Am. J. Physiol. **134:** 359, 1941.

PLANELLES, J.   Ueber das Zusammenwirkung von Ergotamin und Adrenalin am Meerschweinchendarm.   Arch. f. Exper. Path. u. Pharmakol. **105:** 38, 1924.

POOS, F.   Pharmacologische und physiologische Untersuchungen an den isolierten Irismuskeln.   Arch. f. Exper. Path. u. Pharmakol. **126:** 307, 1927.

REBOUL, J., H. DAVIS AND H. B. FRIEDGOOD.   Electrical studies of ovulation in the rabbit. Am. J. Physiol. **120:** 724, 1937.

REGUIERS, P.   Nerfs cardio-aortiques et sino-carotidien; arythmies cardiaques expérimentale chez le lapin.   Influence de l'ergotamine.   Arch. Internat. de Pharmacodyn. et de Therapie. **39:** 371, 1930.
Le sinus carotidien en clinique.   Rev. Belge des sc. Med. **2:** 601, 1930.

REYNOLDS, S. R. M.   Physiology of the uterus with clinical correlations.   New York, Hoeber, 1939.

REYNOLDS, S. R. M. AND F. I. FOSTER.   Acetylcholine-equivalent content of the uterus and placenta in rabbits.   Am. J. Physiol. **127:** 343, 1939.
Relative cholinergic effects of selected estrogens.   Am. J. Physiol. **128:** 147, 1939.
Species differences in the cholinergic action of estrogen.   Am. J. Physiol. **131:** 200, 1940.

RICHTER, C. P.   The significance of changes in electrical resistance of the body during sleep. Proc. Nat. Acad. Sc. **12:** 214, 1926.
A study of the electrical skin resistance and the psychogalvanic reflex in a case of unilateral sweating.   Brain **50:** 216, 1927.

RICHTER, C. P. AND B. G. WOODRUFF.   Facial patterns of electrical skin resistance.   Their relation to sleep, external temperature, hair distribution, sensory dermatomes and skin disease.   Bull. Johns Hopkins Hosp. **70:** 442, 1942.
Changes produced by sympathectomy in the electrical resistance of the skin. Surgery **10:** 957, 1941.

ROBSON, J. M. AND H. O. SCHILD.   Response of the cat's uterus to the hormones of the posterior pituitary lobe.   J. Physiol. **92:** 1, 1938.
Effect of drugs on the blood flow and activity of the uterus.   J. Physiol. **92:** 9, 1938.

ROOME, N. W.   The effects of intra-arterial epinephrin on the blood flow in an extremity. Am. J. Physiol. **123:** 543, 1938.

ROSENBLUETH, A.   The action of certain drugs on the nictitating membrane.   Am. J. Physiol. **100:** 443, 1932.

ROSENBLUETH, A. AND P. BARD.   The innervation and functions of the nictitating membrane in the cat.   Am. J. Physiol. **100:** 537, 1932.

ROSENBLUETH, A. AND W. B. CANNON.   The adequacy of the chemical theory of smooth muscle excitation.   Am. J. Physiol. **116:** 414, 1936.
Some effects of sympathin on the nictitating membrane.   Am. J. Physiol. **99:** 398, 1932.
The chemical mediation of sympathetic-vasodilator nerve impulses.   Am. J. Physiol. **112:** 33, 1935.

ROSENBLUETH, A., H. DAVIS AND B. REMPEL.   The physiological significance of the electric responses of smooth muscle.   Am. J. Physiol. **116:** 387, 1936.
The electrograms of the pilomotor muscles.   Am. J. Physiol. **116:** 131, 1936.

ROSENBLUETH, A., A. FORBES AND E. LAMBERT.   Electric responses in the submaxillary gland.   Am. J. Physiol. **105:** 508, 1933.

ROSENBLUETH, A., C. LEESE AND E. LAMBERT.   Electrical potentials in smooth muscle. Am. J. Physiol. **103:** 659, 1933.

ROSENBLUETH, A. AND R. S. MORISON. A quantitative study of the production of sympathin. Am. J. Physiol. **109:** 209, 1934.

ROSENBLUETH, A. AND R. A. PHILLIPS. Sympathin and the hepatic sympathicomimetic hormone in the dog. Am. J. Physiol. **102:** 332, 1932.

ROSENBLUETH, A. AND H. G. SCHWARTZ. Reflex responses of the nictitating membrane. Am. J. Physiol. **112:** 422, 1935.

ROSENBLUETH, A. AND F. A. SIMEONE. The interrelations of vagal and accelerator effects on the cardiac rate. Am. J. Physiol. **110:** 42, 1934.

ROTHLIN, E. The specific action of ergot alkaloids on the sympathetic nervous system. J. Pharmocol. and Exper. Therap. **36:** 658, 1929.

RUDOLPH, G. DEM. Unusual results following the injection of epinephrine. Endocrinology **23:** 366, 1938.

SAMAAN, A. AND G. STELLA. The response of the chemical receptors of the carotid sinus to the tension of CO_2 in the arterial blood of the cat. J. Physiol. **85:** 309, 1935.

SCHMIDT, C. F. Carotid sinus reflexes to the respiratory center. Am. J. Physiol. **102:** 94, 119, 1932.

SCHNEIDER, E. C. A cardiovascular rating as a measure of physical fatigue and efficiency. J. A. M. A. **74:** 1507, 1920.

SCHNEIDER, E. C. AND D. TRUESDALE. A statistical study of the pulse rate and arterial blood pressure in recumbency, standing, and after a standard exercise. Am. J. Physiol. **61:** 429, 1922.

SCHWEITZER, A. AND S. WRIGHT. The action of adrenalin on the knee jerk. J. Physiol. **88:** 476, 1937.

SCHWARTZ, H. G. Effect of experimental lesions of the cortex on the "psychogalvanic reflex" in the cat. Arch. Neurol. and Psychiat. **38:** 308, 1937.

SCOTT, W. J. M. AND J. J. MORTON. Obliteration of vasoconstrictor gradient in the extremities under nitrous oxide-oxygen, ether, and tribromethyl alcohol anaesthesias. Proc. Soc. Exper. Biol. and Med. **27:** 945, 1930.
Sympathetic activity in certain diseases, especially those of the peripheral circulation. Arch. Int. Med. **48:** 1065, 1931.

SECKER, J. The chemical agent in the sympathetic control of retraction of the nictitating membrane of the cat. J. Physiol. **89:** 296, 1937.

SHAKLER, A. O., K. CHRISTENSEN AND A. KAPLAN. Action of drugs, nerves and electric current in iris sphincter. Proc. Soc. Exper. Biol. and Med. **34:** 399, 1936.

SHEEHAN, D. The autonomic nervous system. Ann. Rev. Physiol. **3:** 399, 1941.

SHERIF, M. A. F. Chemical transmitter of sympathetic nerves to the uterus. J. Physiol. **85:** 298, 1935.

SHOCK, N. W. AND M. J. SCHLATTER. Pulse rate response of adolescents to auditory stimuli. J. Exper. Psychol. **30:** 414, 1942.

SHPINER, L. B. The effect of ergotamine on the blood sugar level. J. Physiol. **88:** 245, 1929.

SIMEONE, F. A. The effect of regeneration of the nerve supply on the sensitivity of the denervated nictitating membrane to adrenine. Am. J. Physiol. **120:** 466, 1937.

SOSKIN, S. Metabolic function of the endocrine glands. Ann. Rev. Physiol. **3:** 543, 1941; Physiol. Rev. **21:** 140, 1941.

SPYCHALA, W. Ueber den Einfluss der pressorezeptorischen Reflexerfolge auf die Aktionsstrome von Skelettmuskeln. Verhandl. d. deutsch. Gesellsch. f. Kreislaufforsch. **25:** 140, 1933.

STELLA, G. The action of adrenaline upon the cardiac vagus centers. J. Physiol. **77:** 68, 1932–33.

TARCHANOFF, J. Ueber die galvanischen Erscheinungen an der Haut des Menschen bei Reizung der Sinnesorgane und bei verscheidenen Formen der psychischen Tätigkeit. Pflüger's Arch. **46:** 46, 1890.

THIENNES, C. H. Action of ergot alkaloids on intestine and uterus. Proc. Soc. Exper. Biol. and Med. **26:** 501, 1929.

THOMAS, C. B. AND C. M. BROOKS. The effect of sympathectomy on the vasomotor carotid sinus reflexes of the cat. Am. J. Physiol. **120**: 195, 1937.

TOURNADE, A. AND J. MALMÉJAC. Diversité des actions réflexes que déclenche l'excitation du sinus carotidien et de son nerf. Compt. Rend. Soc. de Biol. **100**: 708, 1929.

TOWER, S. S. AND C. P. RICHTER. Injury and repair within the sympathetic nervous system. I. The preganglionic neurones. Arch. Neurol. and Psychiat. **26**: 485, 1931.

II. The post ganglionic neurones. Arch. Neurol. and Psychiat. **28**: 1139, 1932.

URY, B. AND E. GELLHORN. Rôle of the sympathetic system in reflex dilatation of pupil. J. Neurophysiol. **2**: 268, 1939.

VAN DYKE, H. B. AND R. G. GUSTAVSON. On the pregnancy response of the uterus of the cat. J. Pharmacol. and Exper. Therap. **37**: 379, 1929.

VERCAUTEREN, E. Influence de l'injection sous-cutanée de cocaine sur les reflexes vasomoteurs. Compt. Rend. Soc. de Biol. **108**: 244, 1931.

Recherches sur la pharmacologie des réflexes vasomoteurs du sinus carotidien. Arch. Internat. de Pharmacodyn. et de Therap. **42**: 339, 1932.

WAGENER, M. P. Arterioles of retina in toxemia of pregnancy. J. A. M. A. **101**: 1380, 1933.

WANG, G. H. AND T. W. LU. Galvanic skin reflex induced in the cat by stimulation of the motor area of the cerebral cortex. Chinese J. Physiol. **4**: 303, 1930.

WANG, G. H., T. W. LU AND T. T. LAU. Pupillary dilatation from cortical stimulation. Chinese J. Physiol. **6**: 225, 1932.

WATKINS, A. L. Reflex responses of the nictitating membrane and the blood pressure to distention of the bladder and rectum. Am. J. Physiol. **121**: 32, 1938.

WEISS, E. Recent advances in the pathogenesis and treatment of hypertension. Psychosom. Med. **1**: 180, 1939.

WEISS, S. AND J. P. BAKER. The carotid sinus reflex in health and disease. Med. **12**: 297, 1933.

Dizziness, fainting and convulsions due to hyperactivity of the carotid sinus reflex. Proc. Soc. Exper. Med. and Biol. **30**: 614, 1933.

WEISS, S., R. B. CAPPS, E. B. FERRIS AND D. MUNRO. Syncope and convulsions due to a hyperactive carotid sinus reflex. Arch. Int. Med. **58**: 407, 1936.

WETHERELL, H. E. Hygromedry. Philadelphia, Ellis Johnson and Co., 1905 (4th ed.), pp. 1–82.

WHITE, J. C. Diagnostic blocking of sympathetic nerves to extremities with procain: A test to evaluate the benefit of sympathetic ganglionectomy. J. A. M. A. **94**: 1382, 1930.

WHITE, B. V. AND E. F. GILDEA. "Cold pressor test" in tension and anxiety: a cardiochronographic study. Arch. Neurol. and Psychiat. **38**: 964, 1937.

WHITEHORN, J. C. The blood sugar in relation to emotional reactions. Am. J. Psychiat. **13**: 987, 1934.

WHITEHORN, J. C. AND H. RICHTER. Unsteadiness of the heart rate in psychotic and neurotic states. Arch. Neurol. and Psychiat. **38**: 62, 1937.

WHITELAW, G. P. AND J. C. SNYDER. The physiological production of sympathin in the liver. Am. J. Physiol. **110**: 247, 1934.

WINDER, C. V. On the mechanism of stimulation of carotid gland chemoreceptors. Am. J. Physiol. **118**: 389, 1937.

WINDER, C. V. Pressoreceptor reflexes from the carotid sinus. Am. J. Physiol. **118**: 379, 1937.

WINDER, C. V., C. BERNTHAL AND F. WEEKS. Reflex hyperpnea and vasoconstriction due to ischemic excitation of the carotid body. Am. J. Physiol. **124**: 238, 1938.

WRIGHT, S. Recent work on afferent control of circulation in health and disease. Brit. Med. J. **1**: 457, 1932.

Studies of reflex activity in involuntary nervous system. J. Physiol. **69**: 331, 1930.

WYMAN, L. C. AND C. TUM SUDEN. The distribution of adrenergic vasodilators in the rat. Am. J. Physiol. 116: 182, 1936.

YONKMAN, F. F. Mydriasis affected by sympathomimetic agents. J. Pharmacol. and Exper. Therap. 40: 195, 1930.

YOUMANS, W. B. Similarity of effects of adrenalin and inhibitory sympathin on intestinal motility; sensitization by denervation. Am. J. Physiol. 123: 424, 1938.

YOUMANS, W. B., K. W. AUMANN AND H. F. HANEY. Relation of the various groups of the adrenalin molecule to its intestine inhibiting function in unanesthetized dogs. Am. J. Physiol. 126: 237, 1939.

YOUMANS, W. B., W. J. MEEK AND R. C. HERRIN. Extrinsic and intrinsic pathways concerned with intestinal inhibition during intestinal distention. Am. J. Physiol. 124: 470, 1938.

YOUMANS, W. B. AND W. J. MEEK. Reflex and humoral gastrointestinal inhibition in unanesthetized dogs during rectal stimulation. Am. J. Physiol. 120: 750, 1937.

*SECTION OF PSYCHOLOGY**

RESPONSE PATTERNS**

By R. C. Davis

Department of Psychology, Indiana University, Bloomington, Ind.

Although one can easily obtain wide agreement that psychology is the study of behavior, specifications of the meaning of behavior vary considerably. Frequently a piece of behavior is distinguished by an effect it has upon the organism's, or better, on the animal's environment. Consequently we have experiments in which rats press a bar, and in which humans press a key, move a lever, and speak words. In these events we distinguish one response from another; we score "success" or "failures" according to what occurs in the environment. Although such a starting point is a proper one, on brief reflection it may seem, a surprising one. Starting thus, we group together those actions of the animal that have the same effect (this, of course, is the principle of response equivalence). It seems similar to a classification of diseases according to the amount of fever they produce; on the basis, that is, of result rather than process.

It is recognized, to be sure, that various processes may achieve the same result. In fact, to some individuals, this consideration seems to justify such a classification. The end is everything, the means are nothing. However, it is no great surprise to find that the point is controversial. A well-known minority proposes that there is greater lawfulness about means than about ends, that we should do better to note the details, at least the particular limb movements, of an animal's actions.

This proposal makes a truly sporting controversy, because the facts known are so scarce that either or neither side could be right. There is a challenge to grasp the club and hand ax and join the fray, but a gentler call to take up the quest for more of our scientific substance.

The special question before us can be put quite briefly: "Can a detailed description of responses and their antecedents throw any light on an animal's action?" This question does not pose a choice of physiological information as opposed to some other sort, about either effects or causes. The question of which facts are more valuable seems hardly worth considering: one would evidently become tangled in theories of marginal utility, and in our kind of horse race it is the performance of the field that really matters.

A "detailed description" could mean simply a listing of observable

*At a meeting held by the Division of Mycology on May 24, 1957, Michael L. Furcolow presented a paper entitled "Recent Studies on the Epidemiology of Histoplasmosis." This article will appear as an Annal shortly to be published by The New York Academy of Sciences.

**This paper, illustrated with lantern slides, was presented at a meeting of the Section on May 20, 1957.

731

limb and head movements. Such a description, however, is still only a partial one, and modern instrumentation allows us to go much further. Any response one can observe with the unaided eye seems to have a wide penumbra of other components that can be brought to light by recording instruments. The records show muscular activity not only in the moving and supporting musculature, but on a smaller scale in many remote muscles; they also show concomitant changes in the other organ systems of the body. For example, consider what occurs when a subject presses a key in response to a signal, the classic simple reaction experiment, with a prior set of instructions and a warning signal. Muscular activity begins to increase shortly after the warning signal and, with the signal to respond, develops very rapidly both in the acting muscles and in the remote parts, according to a certain pattern. When the pattern presents a large enough difference between flexor and extensor action, the key is closed, and muscular activity soon begins a decline in a regular decelerated curve. Meanwhile a certain pattern of changes is occurring in other sectors: in respiration and in the autonomically controlled processes.[1] For example, sweat gland action increases, breathing becomes faster and deeper, the heart slows down, the blood vessels in the hand constrict, and pulse pressure goes up. Probably all of these changes are initiated by the warning signal. To a great extent the warning signal, if sufficiently strong, will produce such responses even if no action is required of the subject. If the subject is required to press a key, the total pattern of these responses is stronger and, qualitatively, somewhat different.

In this total complex the fact that the key was pressed appears as a direct consequence—an important one, of course—of just one small feature of the pattern: the local muscular contraction. One should ask, at this point, whether the rest of the information, as I have given it, will contribute anything to our understanding of the key press. It might be argued that this set of facts is interesting for its own sake because it shows something of the total energy expenditure that goes with the activity. In addition, however, will this kind of data help in solving the problem of whether the key press, or more generally any overt behavior, will occur; when it will occur, how forceful it will be, and how it may be modified in accordance with the experimenter's wishes? There are some promising signs of relations between what one may call the pattern and the overt response. First, a stronger, larger pattern of the right sort may be indicative of a quicker, stronger response. Second, two patterns leading to different consequences may overlap, and the amount of identity in the two could be the basis for facilitation, response generalization, transfer, conditionability, and other response interactions. Third, in the organism there are patterns that follow stimulation, but are not accompanied by any action, and patterns that remain after an action has taken place. These hidden patterns may incline the individual to execute one action rather than another, and either help or hinder the action that is the resultant. These cases may be systematized as, first, the one system case, involving just one response pattern; second, the case of two or more simultaneously activated systems; and, third, the case of one or more preactivated systems. It would be possible to give data to illustrate each of these relationships, but there is a question basic to all that should be answered. In each of the three "theories" there is a presumption of a considerable variety of different excitation patterns. Therefore, I propose to examine this question.

Half a century or more ago there would have been very little hesitation in answering it. Though the problem was formulated in quite another way, the answer, I think, would have been that different patterns occur when there are different feelings or emotions. Wilhelm Wundt had the expression of feeling and emotions, as he called it, well systematized with very few facts. His logic was quite simple: by introspection he would identify the fundamental aspects of feeling, and then corresponding states in the body must be found by the principle of parallelism. On his first point modern evidence makes it clear that Wundt was wrong: somatic response patterns are not restricted to such states as he called feelings and emotions, but are continually present. Further, his identification of affective states by introspection was much too facile. Other introspectors could and did say, "He is wrong; I observed it otherwise," and about the only reply an outsider can make is, "What are you fellows talking about, anyway?"

Actually, I doubt if there has ever been a thoroughgoing introspective attack on the number and character of the emotions. A list of them used to be considered essential in textbooks (and, alas, is still thought valuable, if the number is not greater than three[2]). However, one gathers that such lists were actually constructed backward. The mental states alleged were inferred from situations and from actions by some rather loose methods, probably influenced in great measure by popular tradition and the availability of certain names in the European languages. Even if exact introspection were possible (a condition contrary to fact, as the grammarians would say) it would not enable us to solve our problem. Self-observation could hardly be expected to reveal all the variety of the response patterns, nor can behavior nowadays be taken as a simple manifestation of a state of consciousness. We may as well, therefore, come to the point directly on response patterns on their relation to stimuli, and on overt responses.

Another overhasty answer to the question of pattern differences has had a long vogue, partly, I think, because of the forcefulness of W. B. Cannon. Cannon[3] had no doubts of emotions as mental states, nor of their variety, but he concluded on anatomical and physiological evidence that body states, in the viscera, at least, could not vary correspondingly. In these there would be only a state of vegetative functioning, or an emergency state in one degree or another, the one dominated by parasympathetic neural activity, the other by sympathetic. This extreme simplicity of action is suggested first by the manifold cross-connections within the sympathetic division and by the fact that more than one sympathetically innervated organ can be seen to respond at the same time. Then, in Cannon's own experiments, cats were found to have, so far as could be observed, the same visceral state when exposed to four or five kinds of severe stimulation. In the light of present knowledge, the argument is short of being conclusive. The parasympathetic nervous system would now have to be recognized as capable of producing excitatory states also, and various combinations of the two autonomic branches seem to be the rule.[4] We should not feel very safe in functional inferences from anatomy, and there is doubt, at least, that the sympathetic nervous system acts uniformly in all parts. Cannon's own observations of response variables were too limited in number and exactitude. For a clarification of the general question, the skeletal muscles, the sweat gland reactions, and a number of bodily states in addition to those that Cannon observed would be equally interesting. As a result we are face to face once again with the need for more facts on the pattern of responses.

The kind of work required is technically difficult in data collecting and data treatment, and expensive in time and money, but there is now an increasing number of laboratories in which it is being carried on. Apparatus engineering, data handling, and statistics all need technical improvements, but they are advanced sufficiently to make experiment possible where it would have been inconceivable a few years ago.

Different patterns in skeletal muscle action and tension are not difficult to find and relate to stimuli and responses. The problems become more difficult when other response variables are included. A first line of inquiry, including some of the autonomic variables, concerned individual peculiarities in response, called response or symptom specificities. Malmo and his co-workers[5] showed that patients with psychosomatic symptoms have their favored ways of reacting to questions about their lives and problems. The patient with psychosomatic heart trouble actually responded with circulatory system changes, and the patient with headaches responded with muscle tension in the head region. Lacey, Bateman, and Van Lehn[6] were able to show that normal persons likewise have their idiosyncracies. By an ingenious statistical method they demonstrated that an individual exposed to several kinds of stimuli will have his greatest response in one measured variable more often than can be accounted for by chance. Certain results in our laboratory provide further confirmation.[7]

Correlating responses with individuals in this way gives assurance that the pattern of somatic response is not fixed and invariant for the species. The stereotyping found in individuals might, of course, derive from the inheritance of differing anatomical structures. There is, on the other hand, the interesting possibility that patterns of reaction are subject to modification by some kind of learning, and that a person develops his own stereotype. This learning would be more than the attachment of a new stimulus to an old response; it would be a modification of the structure of the response itself with the promise of eventual intentional shaping of the responses. I do not believe we have, as yet, an experimental investigation of how this might take place in the total response pattern.

Much of interest remains to be discovered concerning these individual peculiarities, but the general questions about the relation of response patterns to overt responses cannot be answered with this kind of evidence. We must proceed to inquire about the possible variety of response patterns in the same individual on different occasions. Does a person's excitation pattern change from time to time, and are these changes referable to conditions that an experimenter can manipulate?

In the Lacey, Bateman, and Van Lehn experiment each person's response to a stimulus was expressed as a deviation from the average response to that kind of stimulus. This treatment is clearly a proper one for the study of individual differences. The very first step in the treatment is one which eliminates differential effects of stimuli that otherwise would confuse the issue. If we wish to study the effects of different stimuli on the same person, we should reverse the procedure and temporarily eliminate from consideration, the differences between individuals. The experiments on individual differences show that some of the variance of responses is attributable to individuals. Whether there is also some variance attributable to stimuli and to interaction remains an open question.

One experiment carried out by Ax[8] a few years ago gave promising results in showing a difference between two autonomic reaction patterns. The experimenter placed the subject in some rather diabolically contrived situations while he made his recordings. A general description of these and of the subject's behavior led to an identification of the patterns as "anger" and "fear." There is, I fear, some danger in using those familiar words, at least until their reference is made fairly definite. Nevertheless, it seems that two different excitation patterns were provoked by some features of the situations used in this experiment.

In our laboratory we have been carrying on certain experiments that are concerned similarly with somatic patterns. In setting up the experiments we have tried to be quite noncommittal about the number and variety of patterns to be expected. We are not, in other words, looking for the "correlates" of such patterns as "fear," "repulsion," and "sex emotion." The independent variables in the experiments are therefore explicitly the stimulus and surrounding conditions, as I suspect is always fundamentally true in this sort of experiment.

We began our studies with some very simple stimuli and with instructions to the subject that he was to do nothing.[9]While we varied the stimulus in certain systematic ways, we recorded about a dozen somatic response variables. Our method for detecting pattern change among these variables was to plot each one as a function of the stimulus variable, when that could be quantified. If these functions are similar, we assume that a pattern of response changes in intensity, but not in structure. This is approximately what happened when we varied the intensity of a brief auditory stimulus. As we approached the pain threshold the size of the responses increased faster than did our decibel input, but the responses all kept pace with one another, maintaining, as it were, the same formation. This pattern we called by an arbitrary name: the N pattern. We found one way in which this *pattern* could be modified. If we repeated stimuli at one-minute intervals, some components of the pattern adapted faster than others. Generally, the components with shortest latency are most affected by adaptation. The principal respiratory response, which has a very long latency, actually increased with repetition. The result at the end of the series was necessarily a rather different response pattern.

Simple visual stimuli, according to a later experiment,[10] also produce an N reaction. However, with cutaneous stimuli there is a difference. These, especially pressure and warmth, seem to produce a vasodilation effect in the periphery, where the N pattern calls for constriction. Our strategy of pattern detection was necessarily different in this study, because our stimuli varied qualitatively rather than quantitatively. We applied the Friedman test of agreement in ranking, a method that has been developed further in later studies. For all types of cutaneous stimuli we found that the autonomic pattern remains about the same, but that the skeletal muscle response varies in a different manner from stimulus to stimulus. For all there is an increase in tension, but not an increase proportional to the autonomic components. The typical reaction to cutaneous stimuli we designate as the C pattern.

We proceeded then to some more complicated situations.[7, 11] In one experiment the stimuli were projected pictures for the subject to look at, and in the other he was required to perform the mild task of paced key-pressing.

In the picture experiment our Friedman test shows, for male subjects, a significant agreement in the way the several autonomic variables are affected by the stimuli. This means that we have something like the first, general factor of a factor analysis. The pattern, which may be called the typical picture or P pattern, is one of great sweat gland activity, peripheral vasoconstriction, and cardiac deceleration. This pattern is produced in its purest form in male subjects presented with a picture of a nude female. There is good reason to think that other pictures have somewhat different effects, that there are, in other words, factors other than the first in our matrix. Certain response variables have good reliability correlations, but they are only slightly related to the first order pattern.

The picture of a starving man produces, not only less response, but a different sort of response with increase rather than decrease of pressure pulse, and a reversed effect on the breathing measures. These are all results for male subjects, and those for females differ from them. In our measures taken together the female response is less, even when we disregard the pictures of nudes and, so far as our statistical tests go, we cannot say, for all measures taken together, that females distinguish one picture from another. Nevertheless, I am convinced that they really do. For if we look at certain response measures, heart rate, for example, we find that females actually respond more than males, and respond differentially. This fact brings to light an important relation: an interaction between response measure, kind of subject, and the stimuli. This fact also shows that response patterns are no simple matter.

The important result of the experiment on paced tapping is, for the present purpose, the occurrence of a new dominant pattern, apparently associated with mild exercise. We have called this result the E-1 pattern because it is almost but not quite what one gets on a larger scale in vigorous activity according to standard physiological experiments. The one big difference is in the behavior of the peripheral vasculature, which constricted in our experiment instead of dilating as it does in treadmill running.

There are in our experiments four major response patterns that we may compare. To be precise, description of a pattern requires that a relation between the components be stated, and to compare patterns would be to compare relationships. However, I do not quite know how to do so at this point, but we can simplify. In TABLE 1 the patterns are described simply by using signs to show whether the function concerned is more or less

TABLE 1

COMPARISON OF RESPONSE PATTERNS

(Double signs indicate diphasic effects)

Pattern	E - 1	N	P	C
Palmar-sweating	+	+	+	+
EMG	+	+	+	+
Pulse rate	+	+ -	-	-
Volume pulse	-	-	-	-
Pressure pulse		- +	-	+
Finger volume	-	-	-	+
Chin volume		+	-	+
Respiration rate	+	-	-	+ -
Respiration amplitude	+	+	-	- +

active than in the resting condition before each stimulus. Where there are diphasic effects double signs are used. In the first two rows of the table, and in the fourth row, we see features common to all patterns. It looks as though any stimulus would produce an increase in sweat gland and muscular activity. I do not recall having seen or heard of an opposite effect. The case for volume pulse is more doubtful. More vigorous activity might reverse its response, for one thing, and for another it seems that for cutaneous stimuli the decrease means maximum vascular dilation, rather than constriction. In the other rows, columns differ a good deal from one another. Apparently the general effect of the pictures, aside from the first two variables, is to depress the activities measured. By contrast, the tapping task increases most of them. The N and C patterns are intermediate and mixed, differing from each other in the heart rate and possibly in the breathing reactions.

It is convenient to speak of patterns as though they were a denumerable set of entities, distinct from one another. I have no reason to think this is true. All the variables in the pattern are continuous, and it seems most likely that the patterns would likewise merge into one another in a series of gradations if conditions were varied appropriately. The several variables, the ones we have recorded and others, could be represented in a hyper space, with some dimensions assigned to stimulus variables and others to the response variables. Then, as we moved along a stimulus axis, it is doubtful that the accompanying response variables would behave in discontinuous, saltatory fashion.

We should expect, as a further complication, that the structure of this hyper space would change as a result of learning. Certainly, the responses become attached to new stimuli and detached from old ones, and they may change with respect to each other. Many of the problems about response patterns can be put as questions about the distribution of points in this complex space. There is, for example, the matter of a general activation state, to use E. Duffy's idea.[12] Suppose we regard the sleep state as the point of origin in all our dimensions. Then the question becomes, "Will a movement along any stimulus dimension cause us to move on all response dimensions, in the same way on one as on another?" Perhaps there is a common solid in some dimensions around the origin. Our muscle tension and galvanic skin response results given above suggest this might be a true picture, although we do not know the size of the solid.

This imaginary space is helpful, I believe, in forming problems, but naturally an experimenter could manage only a small part of it at a time. He would need to make a judicious slice somewhere and apply the microscope to the section.

We are certainly in need of the experimenter's information. Our knowledge of somatic patterns is very meager indeed. I think we do know enough of them, however, to say that earlier guesses of one, two, or three modes of variation are a long way short of the facts. Tangled as the relations are, there is an assuring hope for us in their very complexity. The peripheral patterns may provide us with a way of exposing to direct light the wealth of intermediate processes that we can suspect in a person, but cannot otherwise see.

References

1. DAWSON, H. E. & R. C. DAVIS. 1957. The effects of an instructed motor response upon somatic responses to a brief noise. J. Comp. and Physiol. Psychol. In press.
2. MORGAN, C. L. & E. STELLAR. 1950. Physiological Psychology. McGraw-Hill. New York, N. Y.
3. CANNON, W. B. 1927. The James-Lange theory of emotions: a critical examination and an alternative theory. Am. J. Psychol. 39: 106-124.
4. GELLHORN, E. 1942. Autonomic Regulation. Interscience. New York, N. Y.
5. MALMO, R. B., C. SHAGASS & J. DAVIS. 1950. Specificity of bodily reaction under stress. A physiological study of somatic symptom mechanisms in psychiatric patients. Research Publ. Assoc. Nervous Mental Disease. 29: 231-261.
6. LACEY, J. I., D. E. BATEMAN & R. VAN LEHN. 1953. Autonomic response specificity. Psychosomat. Med. 15: 8-21.
7. DAVIS, R. C., A. LUNDERVOLD & J. D. MILLER. 1957. The pattern of somatic response during a repetitive motor task and its modification by visual stimuli. J. Comp. and Physiol. Psychol. 50: 53-60.
8. AX, A. 1953. The physiological differentiation between fear and anger in humans. Psychosomat. Med. 15: 433-442.
9. DAVIS, R. C., A. M. BUCHWALD & R. W. FRANKMAN. 1955. Autonomic and muscular responses and their relation to simple stimuli. Psychol. Monogr. 69(20).
10. DAVIS, R. C. & H. KLØVE. Somatic responses to interrupted visual stimuli. Unpublished data. Indiana Univ. Bloomington, Ind.
11. DAVIS, R. C. & A. M. BUCHWALD. 1957. An exploration of somatic response patterns: stimulus and sex differences. J. Comp. and Physiol. Psychol. 50: 44-42.
12. DUFFY, E. 1951. The concept of energy mobilization. Psychol. Rev. 58: 30-40.

Reprinted from JOURNAL OF EXPERIMENTAL PSYCHOLOGY,
Vol. 58, No. 2, August, 1959
Printed in U. S. A.

INDIVIDUAL PATTERNS OF PHYSIOLOGICAL ACTIVITY AS A FUNCTION OF TASK DIFFERENCES AND DEGREE OF AROUSAL [1]

MORRIS M. SCHNORE [2]

Allan Memorial Institute of Psychiatry and McGill University

A series of studies from this laboratory, using a variety of experimental procedures, have been concerned with the relationship of physiological measures to level of motivation (Bartoshuk, 1955; Malmo & Davis, 1956; Stennett, 1957b; Surwillo, 1956b). As indicated by Malmo, in a recent review (1957), the findings of these studies can be interpreted as being consistent with the formulation of an independent "arousal" (or intensity) dimension of behavior (Duffy, 1951; Hebb, 1955; Lindsley, 1951; Schlosberg, 1954). Furthermore, the data are encouraging with respect to the proposition that physiological measures may serve to quantify this dimension of arousal.

[1] This study was aided in part by research Grant M-1475 from the National Institute of Mental Health, National Institutes of Health, U. S. Public Health Service, in part by the Research and Development Division, Office of the Surgeon General, Department of the Army, under Contract No. DA-49-007-MD-626; in part by the Defense Research Board of Canada, under Grant No. 9425-04, and in part through a graduate studentship awarded to the author by the National Research Council of Canada. This paper is based on a thesis submitted to the Faculty of Graduate Studies of McGill University in partial fulfilment of the requirements for the Ph.D. degree. The author gratefully acknowledges the generous advice and supervision of R. B. Malmo. He is also indebted to S. M. Feldman who provided helpful criticisms of the manuscript; to J. F. Davis, who designed and supervised the construction of a large part of the equipment; and to W. R. D. Ross and A. K. Bartoshuk, who assisted with the collection of the data.

[2] Now at the University of Western Ontario, London, Ontario.

The main purpose of the present experiment was to attack this general problem from the point of view of individual differences, a topic that has recently been reviewed by Duffy (1957). In part, the aims of the present investigation were similar to those of Lacey and his co-workers in their studies of "autonomic response specificity" (Lacey, Bateman, & Van Lehn, 1953; Lacey & Lacey, 1958) and those of workers in our own laboratory, in attacking the problem of "symptom specificity" (Malmo, Shagass, & Davis, 1950). The specificity principles hold that individuals differ with respect to which physiological measures show the greatest change under standard conditions of stimulation.

In extending earlier work in this area of individual differences, the present study differs from previous experiments mainly in three respects (a) additional tasks have been employed, (b) quantitative variation in arousal (intensity) level was included as a variable in addition to the qualitative differences from task to task, and (c) muscle action potentials were added to the autonomic measures. Previous work on specificity with nonpatients had not included measures of activity in the striate musculature.

In addition to the new attack on the problem of physiological specificity itself, there are other purposes of the present investigation that are chiefly bound up with our interest in the concept of arousal. In the first

117   **PRINCIPLES OF PSYCHOPHYSIOLOGY**

place, there is a rather important methodological problem to be considered. Some writers have expressed strong doubts about the possibility of finding any systematic relationships between a hypothesized unitary process such as arousal and various physiological measures, because of the lack of consistency in physiological reactions from individual to individual and from one situation to the next. However, the chief hypothesis of the present study is that although individuals will indeed exhibit idiosyncratic patterns of physiological activation, these patterns will be consistent for the individuals in qualitatively different situations, and in those designed to be differentially arousing.

In addition to the matter of individual patterns of physiological activation, the further question of individual differences in what may be called "general arousability" was also investigated. That is, the hypothesis was advanced that whatever their specific patterns might be, some individuals would characteristically show greater activation than others in all of the experimental conditions.

Finally, experimental design included a plan to compare the physiological measures with respect to their apparent power to differentiate meaningfully among the different experimental conditions. This is the question of whether, despite individual differences, some physiological measures appear superior to others in gauging level of arousal.

METHOD

Experimental Conditions

Individual differences in physiological activity were studied by varying two factors: (a) the qualitative nature of the task, and (b) the noxiousness of the experimental situation. An attempt was thus made to induce relatively low and relatively high arousal levels while Ss were doing visual pursuit

tracking and while they were doing arithmetic. The conditions were as follows: "low" arousal tracking (LT), "low" arousal arithmetic (LA), "high" arousal arithmetic (HA), and "high" arousal tracking (HT). Every S served in all four conditions.

Prior to the main experimental trials, all Ss had four practice tracking trials. They were instructed to do as well as they could and were informed of their scores after every trial.

In order to cope with the problem of administering a task to Ss and at the same time achieving a low level of arousal, the often used method of a ruse was adopted. The LT trials were presented to S as if they were not actually a part of the experiment. After the practice trials were completed, S was informed that during the next few trials he would be required to do some arithmetic. Then, before starting the arithmetic, E requested S to assist him with some adjustments and calibration of the equipment, which purportedly required S's participation.

To increase the level of arousal for the HT trials, S was required to track under conditions of intense auditory distraction and was told that he would receive a strong shock if he failed to improve his best score obtained in any of the previous trials. To impress on S that this was no hollow threat, a shock was administered 60 sec. before the beginning of the first HT trial. The S was informed that if he failed to improve his best score, he would receive a shock twice as strong as the "sample." However, no shock was actually administered after a trial. After the first HT trial Ss were informed of a score that was about 10% worse than their best score but that they would be given another try.

During the LA trials, S was required to perform multiplications of one digit numbers, e.g., $3 \times 8 = ?$ This was, of course, a task involving rote memory.

During the HA trials S was required to perform more difficult multiplications, e.g., $17 \times 18 = ?$ In addition to this, he was heckled if he provided a wrong answer or failed to respond within 5 sec., e.g., "This shouldn't take that long!" "Hurry up now!" During the arithmetic trials Ss were required to hold the tracking pointer at its maximum deflection, in order to equate the muscular demands with those for the tracking.

Subjects

The Ss were 43 male university students. They were all righthanded, and ranged in age from 16 to 23 yr., with a median age of 19.

Apparatus

Tracking system.—The apparatus used for visual pursuit tracking was a modified version of one previously reported by Surwillo (1956). The modification consisted of: (a) major changes in circuitry,[3] (b) the two microammeters were mounted one above the other, instead of side by side, which slightly increased the difficulty of the task, and (c) ball bearings were incorporated for the controller knob shaft to reduce friction.

The display unit of the tracking system consisted of two pointers (indicators of the two microammeters). The axes of these pointers were 10 cm. apart. The position of the top pointer was varied by a function generator at a constant rate from left to right and back, over a total arc of 60°. A complete cycle of this function, from 0° to 60° and back to 0°, lasted 1 min. The S's task was to control the bottom pointer, so that its reading was always equal to that of the top pointer. The torque required for a maximum deflection of the pointer was 5,000 gm.-cm. and the range of knob rotation was 8°.

The controller knob contained a mechanism which permitted continuous recording of S's grip pressure. Surwillo (1956) has provided a detailed description of its construction.

Shock administration.—A DC shock of 100 v. was administered by a single charged-condenser stimulator. A charge in a two-microfarad condenser was discharged through electrodes, which were placed on the calf of S's left leg. The resistance of S through the electrodes was not more than 10,000 ohms.

Auditory distraction.—An intense auditory distraction was presented to Ss as follows. By means of an audio oscillator, tones continuously varying in frequency between 2,000 and 3,500 cycles were recorded on a Gray Audograph disc. An amplified playback of this recording was fed through a speaker, which was located on the wall directly behind S.

Physiological Variables

Muscle activity.—Electromyograms (EMG) from the ventral surfaces of right and left forearms (*pronator teres*), and from the right side of the back of the neck (*semispinalis capitis* and *splenius capitis*) were recorded by an

[3] The electronic circuitry of this system, which employed AC amplifiers instead of DC, designed by J. F. Davis, is on file in the Laboratory for Psychological Studies, Allan Memorial Institute of Psychiatry, Montreal.

Offner Type D Electroencephalograph. Details of the placement and recording technique used in this laboratory have been reported by Davis (1952). The electroencephalograph was also used to record variations in grip pressure. The muscle potentials and the grip pressure variations were integrated once every 4 sec., and recorded as spikes on a separate chart drive.

All EMG measurements were made in terms of microvolts from the integrated records. From preperiods three spikes were measured: 32–28, 20–16, and 8–4 sec. before the beginning of a trial. Ten spikes were measured for every trial: first, 4–8 sec. after the beginning of a trial and every third spike thereafter. For grip pressure the same sampling method was used, except that measurements were taken for trial periods only. Pressure was measured in grams.

Heart rate.—A continuous recording of heart rate was obtained by an electrocardiotachograph designed by Davis.[4] A chest placement was chosen to insure maximum freedom from EMG artifact. This and the subsequent variables were recorded on a third chart drive.

From preperiods three measurements were made, at 30, 15, and 4 sec. before the beginning of a trial. Eight measurements were made during trials, one every 15 sec. Rate was expressed as beats per minute.

Blood pressure.—Systolic blood pressure was recorded using a modification[5] of an apparatus developed by Burns, Elliott, and James (1955). This method of recording required placing only a small cuff on the middle finger of S's left hand. The recording device provided a measure approximately every 4 sec.

Three measurements were made during preperiods, at 30, 15, and 4 sec. before trials. Nine measurements were made during trials; the first, 4 sec., the second, 15 sec. after

[4] Circuitry and description of this apparatus are on file in the Laboratory for Psychological Studies, Allan Memorial Institute of Psychiatry, Montreal.

[5] The modifications consisted of: (a) an industrial air-pump was substituted for the aquarium type pump, (b) an eclipse Type DO valve was substituted for the handmade solenoid valve, (c) in place of a mercury column and platinum wire, a Statham Type P23AA pressure transducer was used with an Edin Type 5110 Strain Gage Amplifier and Calibrator, and (d) an automatic recycling feature was provided by the addition of a Mercoid Switch Type DA 31.

beginning of a trial, the others—one every 15 sec. Pressure was expressed in millimeters of mercury.

Respiration.—Respiration was recorded using a standard type tambour and pneumograph made by Phipps and Bird. For the tracking trials rate was determined simply by counting the number of complete inspiration-expiration cycles. For preperiods, 30 sec. before the beginning of a trial were used.

Because during arithmetic trials *S*s gave the answers orally, rate was determined by sampling those periods when *S*s did not talk. Five samples, each consisting of three complete inspiration-expiration cycles, were chosen: one right after the beginning of a trial, and the others—one approximately every 30 sec. This method was also used for some tracking trials where regular cyclical activity for the full trial period was lacking. Rate was expressed in terms of the number of inspiration-expiration cycles per minute.

Palmar conductance.—The circuit used for recording DC skin resistance in this laboratory has been previously reported by Stennett (1957a). This technique involves a standard voltage comparator bridge with a constant current ($\pm 2\%$) over the range of resistances observed in this study. Resistance was measured between the palm and dorsum of the left hand. The *S* was grounded only through the lead from the dorsum. Resistance values were converted into micromhos and all computations were done on these conductance values.

One measure was taken during preperiods, 4 sec. before a trial. Five measurements were made during trials, the first, 4 sec., the second, 30 sec. after beginning of a trial, the others—one every 30 sec.

Skin temperature.—Variations in the temperature of the skin were recorded using a Yellow Springs Instrument Co. Model 45A Tele-Thermometer, a DC amplifier, and a recording galvanometer. The placement of the thermocouple was approximately 4 in. above the wrist on the ventral surface of the left forearm.

One measurement was made during preperiods, 15 sec. after the beginning of a trial. Three measurements were made during trials, one at the beginning, one in the middle, and one at the end of a trial. Temperature was recorded in degrees centigrade.

Testing Procedure

Upon arrival at the laboratory each *S* had a 30 min. interview with *E*. Biographical data were taken, the tracking task was explained, and reassurance given concerning physiological recording. At the end of the interview the short form of the Manifest Anxiety Scale (Taylor, 1953) was administered.[6]

After the interview *S* was taken to the testing room and seated in a special chair with adjustable arm rests, which helped to reduce postural variations from *S* to *S*. Electrodes and attachments were applied, after which routine checks were made on the operation of the recording instruments.

Each trial lasted 2 min., with a 3-min. rest period between trials. Instructions to the *S* were presented through a two-way intercom. A warning to assume the tracking position was given 45 sec. before each trial (preperiod). Altogether there were 12 trials: 4 practice tracking trials, and 2 trials each of the four experimental conditions. The entire experimental routine lasted approximately 2 hr. The tasks were always presented in the following order: practice tracking, "low" arousal tracking, "low" arousal arithmetic, "high" arousal arithmetic, and "high" arousal tracking. A balanced order of conditions was not used because that would have introduced complications for any interindividual comparison of the *S*s. The length of the experimental session would then vary from *S* to *S*, because after a high arousal condition different *S*s would require variable time intervals to recover from the effects of such conditions.

Treatment of Data

Means were computed for the preperiod and trial values from the two trials of each condition for each *S*. To make possible a direct comparison among the different variables, which had been measured in different units, the means were converted into *T* scores (Garrett, 1953). For statistical analysis two indicators of *S*'s physiological activity were computed. One represented the *level* of activity of a particular function and consisted of *S*'s *T* score obtained from his trial values. The other indicator represented a *displacement* of a particular function, which was computed by subtracting a preperiod *T* score from the corresponding trial *T* score. However, since it was found that such absolute change values depended upon the preperiod values, a procedure which partialed out the correlation between the preperiod and trial scores was adopted (Lacey, 1956).

---

[6] This aspect of the study is not reported here.

TABLE 1

COMPARISON OF MEAN PHYSIOLOGICAL ACTIVITY LEVELS AMONG
EXPERIMENTAL CONDITIONS

Variable	Condition					
	LT	LA	HA	HT	χ_r^2	P^a
Heart rate	80.7	81.7	90.4	90.5	59.6	.001
Blood pressure	114.5	120.7	128.0	131.1	54.0	.001
Palmar cond.	101.5	105.7	107.8	105.7	37.3	.001
Resp. rate	20.8	20.6	22.6	23.2	58.0	.001
Skin temp.	33.52	33.55	33.45	33.34	14.0	.005
Right forearm	38.3	40.4	47.1	49.9	45.2	.001
Left forearm	6.6	6.4	7.4	9.5	23.0	.001
Neck	20.2	20.1	20.1	22.2	11.1	.01
Grip pressure	666	791	775	866	15.4	.005

a One-tailed test.

A level score of a particular function can be said to reflect the combined influence of all antecedent events (including instructions and anticipation) and the actual performance of a task, while a change score reflects the displacement in a particular function associated only with the performance during a task.

RESULTS

Physiological effects of experimental conditions.—Before presenting the results related to the consistency of individual patterns of physiological activity, the over-all physiological effects of the experimental conditions will first be examined. Table 1 contains mean values for the nine measures of level of physiological activity

during the four conditions. Freedman's (see Siegel, 1956) two-way analysis of variance for related samples was used to test the reliability of the differences among the conditions. For all variables the differences are statistically significant.

Table 2 presents the mean changes in the different functions associated with each condition. These data parallel those presented in Table 1. Again, it can be seen that larger and statistically reliable displacements are associated with the "higher" than with the "lower" arousal conditions.

Patterning.—The consistency of each individual's pattern of physiological

TABLE 2

COMPARISON OF MEAN DISPLACEMENT IN PHYSIOLOGICAL ACTIVITY ASSOCIATED
WITH DIFFERENT EXPERIMENTAL CONDITIONS

Variable	Condition					
	LT	LA	HA	HT	χ_r^2	P^a
Heart rate	− 0.2	0.0	+ 8.2	+ 4.6	49.3	.001
Blood pressure	+ 3.1	+ 8.5	+13.1	+ 8.7	33.0	.001
Palmar cond.	− 1.9	+ 2.8	+ 4.0	+ .07	55.2	.001
Resp. rate	+ 2.8	+ 2.8	+ 4.3	+ 4.6	27.2	.001
Skin temp.	0.0	+ 0.01	+ 0.01	− 0.02	—	N.S.
Right forearm	+27.2	+29.4	+38.9	+34.1	43.32	.001
Left forearm	+ 2.4	+ 1.9	+ 3.0	+ 4.3	24.7	.001
Neck	+ 0.4	+ 0.2	− 0.3	+ 0.2	3.2	N.S.

a One-tailed test.

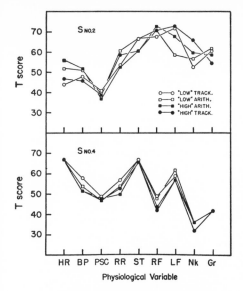

FIG. 1. Cases exemplifying consistency of patterns for physiological activity levels.

activation from condition to condition was evaluated by computing Kendall's (see Siegel, 1956) coefficients of concordance (W). In computing Ws, an individual's pattern was expressed as the rank order of his T scores for the different variables, ranked separately for each condition. For all variables, except skin temperature, high T scores signify high absolute values and large increases. For skin temperature, high T scores were assigned to low absolute values and large decreases because it has been found that anxiety is associated with decreases in finger temperature (Mittelman & Wolff, 1939).

For all Ss, except one, the Ws are statistically significant $(P < .05)$. The Ws range from .995 to .336 with a median W of .801. Two representative cases are presented graphically in Fig. 1. Note the dissimilarity between the patterns exhibited by these two Ss, while each pattern shows considerable stability from condition to condition.

The Ws, derived from T scores based on the change in activity levels associated with the experimental conditions, are statistically significant $(P < .05)$ for 22 Ss, or 51%. In this case the Ws range from .802 to .227 with a median W of .513. The results based on change in physiological activity are not as decisive as those concerning the level of activity. Fewer Ss exhibit consistency in their patterns and in general the coefficients of concordance are lower. To investigate the possibility that the low Ws are mainly due to the greater changes in physiological activity associated with the "high" arousal conditions, separate rank order correlations were computed between the two "low" and the two "high" arousal conditions. This was done only for Ss who did not exhibit significant Ws. Of the 42 such correlations only one was significant at the .05 level. It is thus evident that these Ss did not exhibit any more consistent physiological patterns during the "low" than during the "high" arousal conditions.

Intra-individual variability of physiological functions.—The cases presented in Fig. 1 also illustrate the fact that there is a considerable amount of intra-individual variability in the different physiological measures. For example, S No. 2 is below average in skin conductance, about average in heart rate, but consistently above average in neck muscle action potentials. On the basis of neck muscle action potentials this S shows high physiological activation, but in terms of skin conductance his level of activation is low.

If a group of Ss is exposed to the same experimental conditions, one might expect that all Ss would not be equally aroused, i.e., some Ss would show higher over-all physiological activity than others. In terms of

TABLE 3

P VALUES FOR COMPARISONS OF MEAN PHYSIOLOGICAL ACTIVITY LEVELS
BETWEEN EXPERIMENTAL CONDITIONS

Variable	Comparison					
	LT vs. HT[a]	LA vs. HA[a]	LT vs. HA[a]	LA vs. HT[a]	LT vs. LA	HT vs. HA
Heart rate	.001	.001	.001	.001	N.S.	N.S.
Blood pressure	.001	.001	.001	.001	.001	N.S.
Palmar cond.	.01	.01	.001	N.S.	.01	.01
Resp. rate	.001	.001	.01	.001	N.S.	N.S.
Skin temp.	N.S.	.01	N.S.	.01	N.S.	N.S.
Right forearm	.001	.001	.001	.001	N.S.	N.S.
Left forearm	.001	.05	N.S.	.001	N.S.	.01
Neck	.01	N.S.	N.S.	.01	N.S.	.05
Grip pressure	.001	N.S.	.025	N.S.	.02	N.S.

[a] One-tailed test.

individual patterns of physiological activity this means that Ss might differ with respect to the general height of their physiological patterns. That is, even though an S is high on one measure and low on another, it is possible that he is high (or low) on most measures, rather than having approximately as many values above the group mean as below. To test this, we would have to see whether the various physiological functions of each S were distributed around the group mean, or whether they were instead distributed around a personal mean, which could be either higher or lower than that for the group. A statistical test was done by computing an over-all χ^2. The null hypothesis in this case was that most Ss have as many values above 50 as below, and therefore, that one cannot differentiate among individuals in terms of their over-all physiological activity levels. Using level scores, the obtained χ^2 was 5.90, which is significant beyond the .001 level. The analogous χ^2 for change scores is 1.60, which is significant at the .05 level. Hence, the null hypothesis must be rejected.

Effectiveness of various measures in differentiating among conditions.—This

was evaluated by computing a coefficient of concordance for each S. Previously, for the pattern analysis, the Ws were computed by comparing the rank-orders of physiological measures for the four experimental conditions. In this case, the Ws were computed by ranking the four conditions for each physiological measure. With respect to the level of physiological activity the Ws are significant[7] ($P < .05$) for 24 Ss (56%). The Ws range from .041 to .733 with a median W of .317. For the change in physiological activity the Ws are significant only for 7 Ss (16%). The Ws range from .005 to .581 with a median W of .182. However, even the latter distribution of Ws differs significantly ($\chi^2 = 6.99$, $P < .01$) from the expected distribution if the population coefficient were zero (Lacey & Lacey, 1958). It can be seen, therefore, that the various physiological measures are correlated to a significant degree. Some Ss, however, show the

[7] There is no reason to expect physiological differentiation between the two "low" and between the two "high" arousal conditions, therefore, the size of these Ws is generally smaller than if different arousal levels had been induced in each of the four conditions.

predicted changes only in a few functions while others show them in all or most of the functions used in this study.

Finally, the various physiological functions were examined separately to compare their efficiency in differentiating among conditions. Table 3 contains the separate probabilities for mean differences of all measures obtained by making comparisons among the experimental conditions taken two at a time. The first four columns represent the four possible comparisons among the two "low" and the two "high" arousal conditions. In the last two columns are presented comparisons within the "low" and "high" conditions. It can be seen that only four measures consistently differentiate between the two "low" and the two "high" arousal conditions. These measures are heart rate (72% of Ss showed faster heart rate during both "high" arousal conditions as compared with the highest of the "low" arousal conditions), systolic blood pressure (72%), respiration rate (64%), and right forearm muscle tension (51%). The relatively small percentage values were obtained because Ss often failed to differ in the predicted direction on only one out

of the four possible "low"—"high" comparisons. When the above four measures were combined (16 "low"— "high" comparisons for each S) one could differentiate reliably ($P < .05$) between the "low" and "high" arousal conditions for 86% of the Ss. The other measures fail to differentiate significantly at least between one of the "low" and one of the "high" arousal conditions.

Only three measures differentiated significantly between the two "low" arousal conditions. These were systolic blood pressure, skin conductance, and grip pressure; the values being significantly higher during the arithmetic as compared with the tracking trials. The two "high" arousal conditions also showed significant differences on three measures. However, although left forearm and neck muscle tension were significantly greater during the tracking trials, Ss showed significantly higher skin conductance during arithmetic trials.

The probabilities yielded by comparing any two conditions for the amount of change are presented in Table 4. The large number of small probabilities, especially for the measures which showed high differentiation in terms of level scores, indicate

TABLE 4

P VALUES FOR COMPARISONS OF MEAN CHANGES IN PHYSIOLOGICAL ACTIVITY BETWEEN EXPERIMENTAL CONDITIONS

Variable	Comparison					
	LT vs. HT[a]	LA vs. HA[a]	LT vs. HA[a]	LA vs. HT[a]	LT vs. LA	HT vs. HA
Heart rate	.001	.001	.001	.001	N.S.	.05
Blood pressure	.001	.001	.001	N.S.	.001	.001
Palmar cond.	.001	N.S.	.001	N.S.	.001	.001
Resp. rate	.001	.001	.001	.001	N.S.	N.S.
Skin temp.	N.S.	N.S.	N.S.	N.S.	N.S.	N.S.
Right forearm	.001	.001	.001	.001	N.S.	N.S.
Left forearm	.005	.025	N.S.	.001	N.S.	.005
Neck	N.S.	N.S.	N.S.	N.S.	N.S.	N.S.

• One-tailed test.

that the probabilities in Table 3 are a result of the different arousal functions of the two types of conditions rather than only to the differences in the "alerting" response itself (instructions, anticipation).

DISCUSSION

The hypothesis that during qualitatively different stimulus situations Ss will exhibit idiosyncratic but highly stereotyped patterns of somatic and autonomic activation is clearly supported by the data. The same S might show below-average levels of activity in some functions, average in others, and above-average in still others. But no matter what the shape of the idiosyncratic pattern, Ss tend to respond with their specific hierarchy of activation to situations which require different overt responses. Even when variations in experimental situations produce increases in the over-all level of activation, significantly stereotyped physiological responses are observed.

These findings are consistent with those previously reported by Lacey et al. (1953) and Lacey and Lacey (1958) who formulated the principle of "response specificity" using autonomic variables. In view of the present results such a principle would seem to apply not only to the functioning of the autonomic nervous system but to the skeletal-muscle system as well.

The fact that during the high arousal trials a general increase in physiological activity was observed would seem to support the notion of a general arousal state. However, any given level of arousal is reflected differentially in different individuals. Such differentiation is contrary to the traditional broad classifications, such as autonomic-somatic, sympathetic-parasympathetic, since differentiation did not follow such classifications but was evident even within cardiovascular and somatic systems themselves. This lack of homogeneity indicates a need for a new approach in our thinking about the functioning of

the nervous system. Recently, Wenger (1957), in discussing some new data representing the activity of the autonomic nervous system, drew a similar conclusion.

In general, the results of this study are in accord with the notion of an arousal continuum and support the suggestion that peripheral physiological variables can be used to measure changes in arousal. Higher levels and greater increase in physiological activity were observed during the "high" than during the "low" arousal conditions. One might, however, pose the question whether varying degrees of arousal were actually induced in this experiment. To avoid circularity, one obviously can not use the physiological data themselves in support of an affirmative answer. A recourse to other observables is necessary.

The arousal theory implies that degree of arousal is a function of task difficulty and intensity of stimuli (physical or symbolic) (Duffy, 1951, p. 32). That is, other things being equal, during difficult tasks arousal is expected to be higher than during easy tasks, and noxious situations are expected to produce higher levels of arousal than relatively innocuous situations. It appears that the experimental conditions satisfy these requirements adequately. Consequently, one can interpret the data as supporting the prediction that increases in arousal will be associated with increased physiological activity.

Before continuing with this question of applying physiological measures to gauge level of arousal, an important methodological distinction deserves consideration: it is essential to be clear whether the comparisons of arousal level are inter- or intra-individual in character.

In comparison with others one S may show relatively high heart rate and relatively low muscle tension. The statement that an S's heart rate is higher than the heart rate of others, is, of course, an interindividual comparison. Similarly, the statement concerning his relatively low muscle tension is also based on comparison with other Ss. That an S may be high relative to others in one physiological function and low (again relative to others) in another physiological function is what we should expect from findings of idiosyncratic patterns of physiological activity. Such individual differences would also account for the low intercorrelations among physiological measures that have been reported by Ax (1953) and others (Lacey & Lacey, 1958; Malmo & Davis, 1956; Malmo & Smith, 1955).

But there is a point that, curiously enough, appears to have been overlooked by some writers. Despite his idiosyncratic pattern, an individual placed in an arousing situation will, according to the results of the present study, probably show a general increase in most physiological functions. The hypothetical case cited above would be expected to show increase in heart rate and also in level of muscle tension, even though, in comparison with others, muscle tension remains low, and heart rate is still high. It is possible, therefore, to obtain a zero correlation between any two variables when the correlation is computed among Ss, while the correlation between the same two variables can be perfect if computed within an S. Present data indicate that, although the correlations are generally low among Ss, there is considerably closer correspondence among different physiological measures within the same S.[8] For these reasons, self-control design (in which the same Ss are employed in all conditions) appears superior to design employing independent groups.

Another methodological point impressed on us by present findings is that whether comparisons are intra- or interindividual in character, there are significant tactical advantages in employing several physiological measures rather than in relying on only one or two. The large interindividual differences in activation, seen in all physiological functions, indicate that an individual's level of arousal, in a given situation, can not

be reliably inferred from a single physiological measure (somatic or autonomic). One would obtain a different ordering of Ss with respect to degree of arousal, depending on which physiological measure was chosen as the criterion. Although any one physiological measure appears to be an unreliable criterion of the general arousal level, by using a number of measures in combination, it seems highly probable that one can differentiate reliably among individuals. Some individuals show characteristically greater physiological activation than others in response to standard situations. In addition, even for intra-individual comparison the use of several physiological measures seems to be indicated, since individuals vary considerably in the amount of correspondence that exists among physiological measures and the significant concordance coefficients seldom approach 1.00.

Recently, several studies have been reported where the relationship between physiological activity on one hand, and MAS scores and performance data on the other hand, has been investigated (Beam, 1955; Berry & Martin, 1957; Calvin, McGuigan, Tyrrell, & Soyars, 1956; Raphelson, 1957). The results of this study suggest that the failure to find significant correlation between physiological activity and MAS, and performance might be expressly due to the undependability of a single physiological measure as an indicator of general physiological activity.

In addition to the individual differences discussed above, it was found in the present study that, for purposes of distinguishing among arousal levels, some physiological functions seem to be more adequate than others. Such differences among the physiological measures exemplify the differential sensitivity of the various functions. It appears that a given change in the general arousal state might be reflected consistently in some peripheral bodily functions and not in others. While heart rate, systolic blood pressure, respiration rate, and right forearm muscle tension differentiated consistently among conditions, skin con-

[8] Such correspondence among physiological measures is more pronounced with respect to the direction of change, rather than the amount of change.

ductance, skin temperature, left forearm muscle tension, and grip pressure failed to differentiate at least between one of the "low" and one "high" arousal condition. By combining the first four measures more reliable differentiation between the arousal levels was possible than on the basis of any one of these measures alone.

In terms of the total arousal continuum, arousal levels exhibited by *S*s of this study would seem to represent moderate degrees of arousal. Such an inference is based on two considerations. First, even during the "low" arousal conditions *S*s were required to perform a task. Second, the "high" arousal conditions were not of great enough intensity to produce a breakdown of performance; in fact, there were no striking changes in overt behavior. Accepting heart rate, blood pressure, respiration rate, and right forearm (active) muscle tension as criteria, it was possible to discriminate reliably between the "low" and "high" arousal conditions. This study indicates, therefore, that changes in the degree of arousal in the middle range of the total arousal continuum can be differentiated effectively by the combined use of these four physiological functions. It is very likely that different criteria might have to be used, depending on the amount of change of arousal one wants to detect, and in which part of the arousal continuum the given changes occur.

SUMMARY

The chief purpose of the present study was to investigate the consistency of individual differences in physiological activity. In addition, some of the problems related to the measurement of arousal were also evaluated. Nine physiological functions were recorded. Variations in experimental situation were produced by employing tracking and arithmetic tasks with two different levels of arousal for each task.

Results showed that during qualitatively and quantitatively different stimulus situations individuals exhibited idiosyncratic but highly stereotyped patterns of somatic and autonomic activation.

The present results further support earlier work which found physiological measures singularly useful in providing objective and reliable indicants of arousal. Fifty-six per cent of *S*s showed significant correlation among the physiological measures. There were four measures (heart rate, blood pressure, respiration rate, and right forearm muscle tension) which consistently differentiated between high and low arousal conditions. Present evidence suggests, therefore, that these four measures may be maximally useful as indicants of arousal, at least within the range of arousal levels studied. Although data from other experimental situations are required in order to reach a firmer conclusion concerning the relative usefulness of these measures, it seems certain that several indices are superior to only one or two in gauging level of arousal.

REFERENCES

Ax, A. F. The physiological differentiation between fear and anger in humans. *Psychosom. Med.*, 1953, **15**, 433–442.

Bartoshuk, A. K. Electromyographic gradients as indicants of motivation. *Canad. J. Psychol.*, 1955, **9**, 215–230.

Beam, J. C. Serial learning and conditioning under real-life stress. *J. abnorm. soc. Psychol.*, 1955, **51**, 543–551.

Berry, J. L., & Martin, B. GSR reactivity as a function of anxiety, instructions, and sex. *J. abnorm. soc. Psychol.*, 1957, **54**, 9–12.

Burns, B. D., Elliott, H., & James, C. E. Continuous recording of respiration, heart rate, and systolic blood pressure. *Canad. Serv. med. J.*, 1955, **9**, 509–514.

Calvin, A. D., McGuigan, F. J., Tyrrell, S., & Soyars, M. Manifest anxiety and the palmar perspiration index. *J. consult. Psychol.*, 1956, **20**, 356.

Davis, J. F. *A manual of surface electromyography.* Montreal: Lab. for Psych. Stud., Allan Mem. Inst. of Psychiat., McGill Univer., 1952.

Duffy, E. The concept of energy mobilization. *Psychol. Rev.*, 1951, **58**, 30–40.

Duffy, E. The psychological significance of the concept of "arousal" or "activation." *Psychol. Rev.*, 1957, **64**, 265–275.

Garrett, H. E. *Statistics in psychology and education.* (4th ed.) New York: Longmans, Green, 1953.

Hebb, D. O. Drives and the C. N. S. (conceptual nervous system). *Psychol. Rev.*, 1955, **62**, 243–253.

LACEY, J. I. The evaluation of autonomic responses: Toward a general solution. *Ann. N. Y. Acad. Sci.*, 1956, **67**, 123–164.

LACEY, J. I., BATEMAN, D. E., & VAN LEHN, R. Autonomic response specificity. *Psychosom. Med.*, 1953, **15**, 8–21.

LACEY, J. I., & LACEY, B. C. Verification and extension of the principle of autonomic response-stereotypy. *Amer. J. Psychol.*, 1958, **71**, 50–73.

LINDSLEY, D. B. Emotion. In S. S. Stevens (Ed.), *Handbook of experimental psychology.* New York: Wiley, 1951.

MALMO, R. B. Anxiety and behavioral arousal. *Psychol. Rev.*, 1957, **64**, 276–287.

MALMO, R. B., & DAVIS, J. F. Psychological gradients as indicants of "arousal" in mirror tracing. *Canad. J. Psychol.*, 1956, **10**, 231–238.

MALMO, R. B., SHAGASS, C., & DAVIS, F. H. Specificity of bodily reactions under stress. *Proc. Ass. Res. nerv. ment. Dis.*, 1950, **29**, 231–261.

MALMO, R. B., & SMITH, A. A. Forehead tension and motor irregularities in psychoneurotic patients under stress. *J. Personal.*, 1955, **23**, 391–406.

MITTELMAN, B., & WOLFF, H. G. Affective states and skin temperature: Experimental study of subjects with "cold hands" and Raynaud's syndrome. *Psychosom. Med.*, 1939, **1**, 271.

RAPHELSON, A. C. The relationships among imaginative, direct verbal, and physiological measures of anxiety in an achievement situation. *J. abnorm. soc. Psychol.*, 1957, **54**, 13–18.

SCHLOSBERG, H. Three dimensions of emotion. *Psychol. Rev.*, 1954, **61**, 81–88.

SIEGEL, S. *Nonparametric statistics.* New York: McGraw-Hill, 1956.

STENNETT, R. G. The relationship of alpha amplitude to the level of palmar conductance. *EEG Clin. Neurophysiol.*, 1957, **9**, 131–138. (a)

STENNETT, R. G. The relationship of performance level to level of arousal. *J. exp. Psychol.*, 1957, **54**, 54–61. (b)

SURWILLO, W. W. A device for recording variations in pressure of grip during tracking. *Amer. J. Psychol.*, 1956, **68**, 669–670. (a)

SURWILLO, W. W. Psychological factors in muscle-action potentials: EMG gradients. *J. exp. Psychol.*, 1956, **52**, 263–272. (b)

TAYLOR, J. A. A personality scale of manifest anxiety. *J. abnorm. soc. Psychol.*, 1953, **48**, 285–290.

WENGER, M. A. Pattern analysis of autonomic variables during rest. *Psychosom. Med.*, 1957, **14**, 240–244.

(Received August 15, 1958)

Reprinted from PSYCHOSOMATIC MEDICINE
Vol. XXII, No. 4, July-August 1960
Publisher by PAUL B. HOEBER, INC.
MEDICAL DIVISION OF HARPER & BROTHERS
Published by PAUL B. HOEBER, INC.
Printed in the U. S. A.

Autonomic Response Patterns During Intravenous Infusion of Epinephrine and Nor-epinephrine

M. A. WENGER, Ph.D., T. L. CLEMENS, Ph.D., M. L. DARSIE, M.D.,
B. T. ENGEL, Ph.D., F. M. ESTESS, M.D., and
R. R. SONNENSCHEIN, Ph.D., M.D.

ALTHOUGH extensive work has been reported on the differential effects of epinephrine and nor-epinephrine upon functions mediated by the autonomic nervous system (ANS),[1, 2, 4, 5, 8, 9] few variables have been measured simultaneously and most studies have used direct injection rather than controlled infusion. Drug reactions are thereby confounded with reactions to the needle. This study reports the effects of these drugs upon a number of simultaneously recorded ANS variables and isolates reactions to needle insertion, to saline at different rates of infusion, and to the drugs at different infusion rates and concentrations. It is one of a series of studies on autonomic response patterns to various stimuli, and is of particular interest in view of recent attempts to relate circulating levels of epinephrine and nor-epinephrine to emotional states such as fear and anger.[1, 3, 5, 6, 7, 9]

From the Department of Psychology, University of California at Los Angeles and the University of California Medical Center, Los Angeles. This investigation was supported by research grants M788 and M1281 from the Institute of Mental Health, National Institutes of Health. Public Health Service.

Received for publication Aug. 31, 1959.

Method

The subjects were 11 male college students, all of whom had previously served in experiments employing the same apparatus. At the beginning of each experimental session a series of measures was obtained for the determination of the subject's autonomic balance score.[11] The subject then reclined on a wooden cot covered by a foam rubber mattress, in a room adjoining that which contained the recording apparatus, and the remainder of the equipment was attached to him. He was informed that following a period of rest a physician would administer an intravenous solution of a harmless substance.

The recording apparatus consisted of an 8-channel Offner Type D3 electroencephalograph, three additional Type 133 Offner DC amplifiers, specially constructed pickups and bridges for recording ANS variables, and a Gilson automatic blood pressure recorder. Details of instrumentation are published elsewhere.[12] Table 1 summarizes the recorded variables and methods of measurement.

When a 15-minute resting period had elapsed, a physician entered the subject's room, prepared his equipment, inserted a

294

TABLE 1. RECORDED VARIABLES, UNITS AND METHODS OF MEASUREMENT

Measures	Units	Recording frequency	Method of assay
Systolic and diastolic blood pressures	mm. Hg	once per minute	once per minute
Heart rate	cycles/min.	continuously	½-min. sample every min.
Respiration rate	cycles/min.	continuously	½-min. sample every min.
Palmar skin conductance	log micromhos	continuously	mean; beginning and end of ½-min. sample every min.
Finger pulse volume	square root of μl. /stroke	continuously	mean; 2 highest and 2 lowest; ½-min. sample every min.
Finger, face and axillary temperatures	°C.	finger twice, face and axillary once every 10 seconds	mean; beginning and end of ½-min. sample every min.
Ballistocardiograph	μv.	continuously	qualitative changes
Stomach motility	sec./cycle	continuously	median; continuous minute samples
Salivary output	μl./min.	continuously	½-min. sample every min.

No. 22 hypodermic needle into the most prominent anticubital vein of the right forearm, and secured it with adhesive tape. The infusion apparatus was standard, except that a Y-valve made possible a silent transition between physiological saline and drug solutions. The infusion equipment was shielded from the subject by an opaque screen. The physician was instructed through earphones when to change the infusion procedure, and was given a minute-by-minute report of the subject's blood pressure and heart rate.

The infusion procedure is outlined in Table 2. The drugs, Suprarenin* and Levophed,† were administered to each subject in 2 experimental sessions, the order of which was counterbalanced. Following insertion of the needle, a 10-minute saline control period allowed for recovery from the effects of the needle. "Faked infusion" consisted of the physician's moving as though changing the infusion procedure but actually making no change.

Two pairs of dosage levels of epinephrine were administered, as shown at the foot of Table 2. Since the over-all effects of epinephrine on the first 5 subjects seemed to be less than the effects of nor-epineph-

*Synthetic Epinephrine solution, 1:1000 (as bitartrate), Winthrop-Stearns, Inc.
†Brand of Levarterenol bitartrate solution 0.2% (= 0.1% base), Winthrop-Stearns, Inc.

rine, epinephrine doses for the remaining subjects were doubled.

Results and Discussion

The results obtained with each infusion rate and concentration of the two drugs are presented graphically in Fig. 1-9. Table 3

TABLE 2. INFUSION SCHEDULE FOR EPINEPHRINE AND NOR-EPINEPHRINE

Event	Amount (drops/min.)	Time (min.)
Rest	..	15
Needle inserted	..	5
Saline	20	10
Faked infusion	20	5
Drug	20	5
Saline	20	5
Saline	40	5
Drug	40	5
Saline	40	5
Saline	20	5
Drug	20	5
Saline	20	10
Needle removed	..	1
Rest	..	20

Dosage levels:
(a) epinephrine single:
    1.6 μg./min. at 20 drops/min.
    3.2 μg./min. at 40 drops/min.
(b) epinephrine double:
    3.2 μg./min. at 20 drops/min.
    6.4 μg./min. at 40 drops/min.
(c) nor-epinephrine: 1.6 μg./min. at 20 drops/min.
    3.2 μg./min. at 40 drops/min.

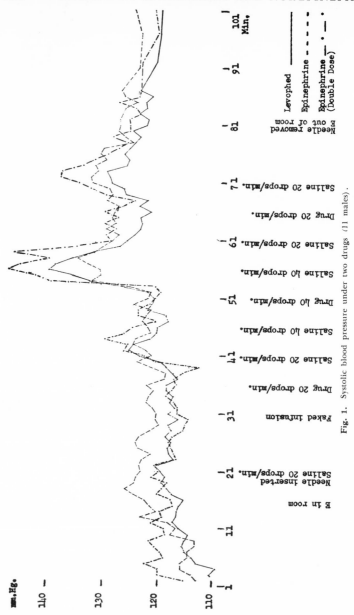

Fig. 1. Systolic blood pressure under two drugs (11 males).

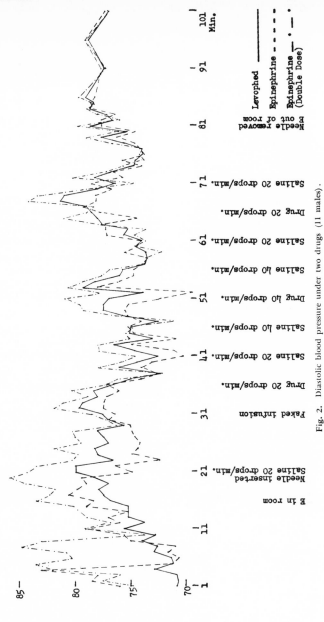

Fig. 2. Diastolic blood pressure under two drugs (11 males).

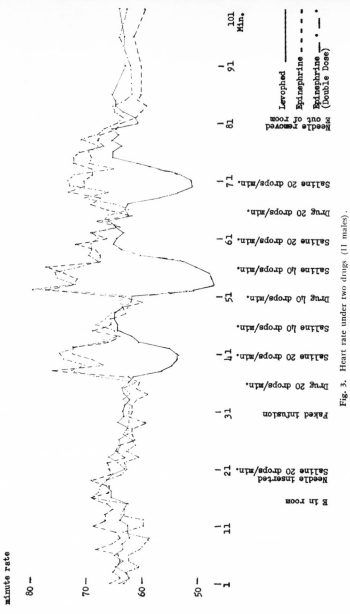

Fig. 3.   Heart rate under two drugs (11 males).

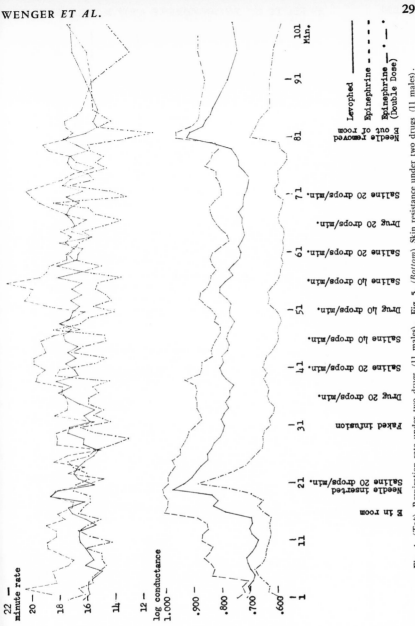

Fig. 4. (*Top*) Respiration rate under two drugs (11 males). Fig. 5. (*Bottom*) Skin resistance under two drugs (11 males).

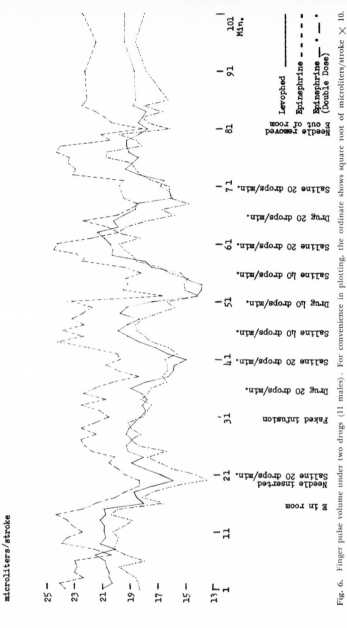

Fig. 6. Finger pulse volume under two drugs (11 males). For convenience in plotting, the ordinate shows square root of microliters/stroke × 10.

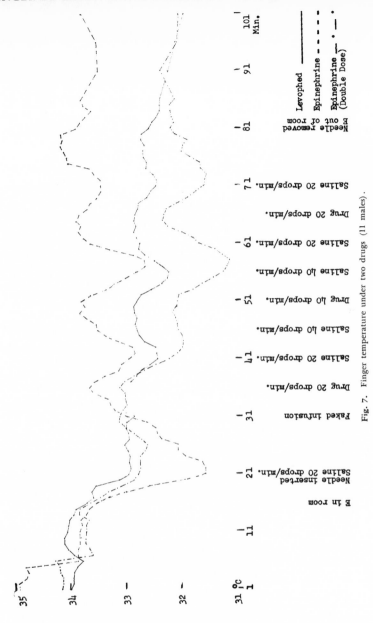

Fig. 7. Finger temperature under two drugs (11 males).

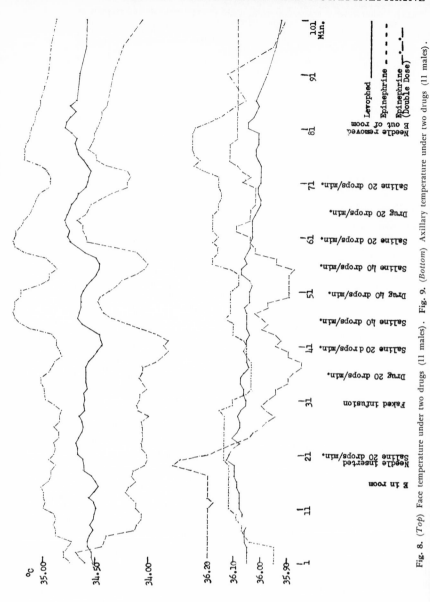

Fig. 8. (Top) Face temperature under two drugs (11 males). Fig. 9. (Bottom) Axillary temperature under two drugs (11 males).

TABLE 3. SIGNIFICANCE OF DIFFERENCES IN ANS RESPONSES OF 11 MALES TO EPINEPHRINE AND NOR-EPINEPHRINE

	Maximal response		Maximal response minus prestimulus level		Differences Nor-e. minus Epin.		
	Means		Means				
	Nor-e. Resp.	Epin. Resp.	Nor-e. Diff.	Epin. Diff.	MD	SMD	t
Systolic blood pressure	140.6	144.4	18.7	24.0	— 5.3	3.97	1.34
Diastolic blood pressure (a) *	88.5	71.2	11.3	— 5.6	16.9	3.36	5.03†
(b) *	102.7	81.4	25.5	4.6	21.0	3.26	6.44†
Heart rate	45.6	82.5	—16.4	18.7	—35.1	2.23	15.74†
Respiration rate	18.07	19.02	1.18	4.15	— 2.96	1.55	1.91
Log palmar conductance	.830	.753	.086	.059	.026	.0309	.84
Square root of finger pulse volume (c) *	1.31	1.52	— .59	— .38	— .21	.0991	2.12
(d) *	1.62	1.86	— .28	— .04	— .24	.0724	3.31†
Finger temperature	32.16	31.53	— .62	— 1.21	.52	.133	3.91†
Face temperature	34.46	34.32	— .15	— .40	.17	.0696	2.44‡
Axillary temperature	36.08	36.12	.03	.09	— .036	.0503	.72
Stomach motility	19.53	21.47	— 1.60	— 1.83	.23	1.26	.18

* (a) Maximal decrease in DBP, or lowest DBP during first 2 minutes of stimulation.
  (b) Maximal increase in DBP.
  (c) Maximal decrease in square root of finger pulse volume.
  (d) Maximal increase in square root of finger pulse volume following initial decrease.
†Significant beyond the 1% level of confidence.
‡Significant beyond the 5% level of confidence.

shows the means of the maximum changes in each variable in response to the 40-drops-per-minute infusion rate for each drug, using the combined results from the 2 epinephrine concentrations. This procedure was justified by the fact that doubling the epinephrine dosage did not have the expected effect on response magnitude, which was found to be comparable under both dosage levels for all variables. No statistically significant differences were found. (Table 4). Inspection of the graphs indicates that infusion rate had little effect upon response magnitude. Only in systolic blood pressure is a greater response to the 40-per-minute rate than to the 20-per-minute rate clearly evident. In heart rate the response is slightly greater with the higher rate of nor-epinephrine infusion than with the lower, but in the remaining variables little or no difference can be seen for either drug.

Figure 1 shows that the response in sys-tolic blood pressure is similar for both drugs in magnitude, latency, and duration. It will be noted that these subjects showed no appreciable systolic blood pressure response to insertion of the needle. The greatest differential response to the two drugs, that of heart rate, is evident in Fig. 3. Again, in this variable there was little or no reaction to needle insertion. Although the heart rate response to nor-epinephrine is typically described in the literature[4, 8] as showing no change or a slight decrease, in this study *all* subjects showed a decrease comparable in magnitude with the increase in response to epinephrine. Comparison of Fig. 1 and 3 shows that the initiation of this decrease was of shorter latency than was the systolic blood pressure rise, and therefore cannot be attributed solely to reflex action of the carotid sinus.

In Fig. 5 the greatest increases in log palmar conductance seem to be in response to the insertion and removal of the needle.

TABLE 4. Differences Between ANS Responses to Single (5 Subjects) and Double (6 Subjects) Dosage Levels of Epinephrine at Infusion Rate of 40 Drops per Minute

Variable	Maximal response Means		Maximal response minus prestimulus level Means		Differences, double minus single dosage			
	Single dosage	Double dosage	Single dosage	Double dosage	MD	SMD	t	p
Systolic blood pressure	138.2	149.5	16.8	30.0	13.2	6.43	2.05	>.05
Diastolic blood pressure (a) *	67.4	74.3	− 4.8	− 6.4	− 1.6	4.99	.32	>.10
(b) *	79.0	83.4	6.8	2.7	− 4.1	5.18	.79	>.10
Heart rate	81.6	83.3	17.2	20.0	2.8	2.68	1.04	>.10
Respiration rate	23.24	15.50	7.24	1.57	− 5.67	4.89	1.16	>.10
Log palmar conductance	.888	.641	.073	.049	− .024	.051	.47	>.10
√ finger pulse volume (c) *	1.66	1.41	− .52	− .26	.26	.133	1.95	>.05
(d) *	2.11	1.66	− .07	− .01	.06	.136	.44	>.10
Finger temperature	32.55	30.86	− 1.25	− 1.18	.07	.315	.22	>.10
Face temperature	34.88	33.96	− .35	− .41	− .06	.118	.51	>.10
Axillary temperature	35.98	36.22	.08	.10	.02	.096	.21	>.10
Stomach motility†	21.43	21.65	− .82	− 2.95	− 2.13	2.83	.75	>.10

* (a) Maximal decrease in DBP, or lowest DBP during first 2 minutes of epinephrine infusion. (b) Maximal increase in DBP following initial decrease. (c) Maximal decrease in square root of finger pulse volume. (d) Maximal increase in square root of finger pulse volume following initial decrease.
†For stomach motility, 4 subjects were given single dosage and 2, double dosage.

Only slight changes associated with drug infusion occur, and these are probably secondary responses since adrenergic stimulation in itself should not directly activate this cholinergic function.

Figures 6–8 show, under both drugs, and also in response to needle insertion, a reduction in blood flow to the skin. The fact that the decreases in face and finger temperatures, but not in finger pulse volume, were greater under epinephrine, may indicate that different mechanisms are involved in the reduction of blood flow. This is suggested by the statement, often encountered in the literature, that peripheral resistance increases under nor-epinephrine and decreases under epinephrine. It seems probable that peripheral vasoconstriction occurs under both drugs, but since neither finger pulse volume nor skin temperature can be taken as a simple indicator of the extent of such vasoconstriction, it is necessary to consider also the changes in the other circulatory variables.

Although it is not evident in Fig. 2, consistent changes in diastolic blood pressure occurred under each drug. Table 3 shows that the diastolic blood pressure increase under nor-epinephrine was greater in magnitude than the systolic blood pressure increase. The diastolic blood pressure response to epinephrine in the majority of the subjects consisted of an initial small decrease followed by a small increase above the prestimulus level. This pattern is not evident on the graph because of individual differences in the latencies of the responses. Observations of qualitative changes in the ballistocardiograph indicated that heart stroke-volume increased under epinephrine and decreased under nor-epinephrine. The difference between the heart stroke-volume responses was found by a sign test[10] to be significant beyond the 1 per cent level of confidence.

The increased heart output and increased pulse pressure under epinephrine would tend to increase both the rate of blood flow to the periphery and the change in finger volume accompanying each pulse wave. Hence the observed decrease in finger pulse volume and skin temperature must be almost entirely a consequence of vasoconstriction of the skin vessels. The decreased heart output and decreased pulse pressure under nor-epinephrine, on the other hand, would tend to decrease both blood flow and finger pulse volume. If extensive vasoconstriction were to occur also, then the decrease in skin temperature should be greater under nor-epinephrine than under epinephrine. Since the reverse is true, it can be concluded that greater vasoconstriction occurs under epinephrine, and that the decreases in finger pulse volume and skin temperature under nor-epinephrine are principally a result of reduced cardiac output and pulse pressure. This interpretation is consistent with one offered by Barcroft and Swan,[2] who state:

". . . . doses of adrenaline which reduce the blood flow . . . . accomplish this almost entirely by a skin vasoconstriction, while noradrenaline reduces the muscle blood flow in addition to decreasing the skin flow. Therefore, one can conclude that adrenaline is stronger in constrictor action on skin vessels than noradrenaline."

Since systolic and diastolic blood pressures increase under nor-epinephrine despite the decrease in cardiac output, vasoconstriction apparently occurs elsewhere than in the skin area, probably in the skeletal musculature. The small change in diastolic blood pressure under epinephrine, however, suggests that vasodilation in the muscles counteracts the pressor effects of vasoconstriction in the skin. It would therefore appear necessary to indicate whether vasomotor activity in the muscles or in the skin is involved when reference is made to changes in peripheral resistance.

As shown in Fig. 4 no consistent changes are seen in respiration rate under either drug, although there is some indication of an increase in rate under epinephrine. Table 3 shows that the mean maximal increase in rate was greater under epinephrine than under nor-epinephrine, but that

the difference was not statistically significant. The mean difference between the axillary temperature maximal increases was also insignificant; however, as Fig. 9 shows, an increase in axillary temperature occurred during each of the 3 epinephrine infusion periods, while little or no change occurred during any of the nor-epinephrine infusion periods.

Measurable stomach contraction waves were present in 9 subjects during each experimental session. Inhibition of Type I stomach contractions occurred in 5 subjects (56 per cent) during epinephrine infusion and in 2 subjects (22 per cent) during norepinephrine infusion. Table 3 shows the mean responses for the 3 subjects in whom Type I stomach contractions were present before and during stimulation in both sessions. The change in response to both drugs was a decrease in period, but there was no significant difference between the mean decreases under each drug.

No indication was found of any consistent salivary-output response to either of the drugs; however, no conclusions should be drawn from these negative results. Despite continued efforts, we remain unsatisfied with our technic for continuous recording of this variable; it was therefore omitted from Table 3.

The present results permit an indirect test of the "anger/fear" hypothesis advanced by Ax[1] and Schachter[9] and the "anger-out, anger-in, anxiety" hypothesis stated by Funkenstein *et al.*[6] Ax and Schachter, using similar procedures to produce states of "anger" and "fear," concluded that the ANS response pattern associated with fear is epinephrinelike and that the pattern associated with anger is like that produced by a combination of epinephrine and norepinephrine. Funkenstein *et al.* have made a further distinction between outward-directed anger (nor-epinephrine) and inward-directed anger, the latter being more like the anxiety (epinephrine) pattern. A comparison of their reported response patterns, our drug patterns, and other work from our laboratory, will soon be reported.

In the meantime, the following comment may be of some interest.

None of our subjects reported any emotional experience in response to either drug. Three reported that they had noticed a "pounding of the heart" during epinephrine infusion, but *none* reported any subjective experience during nor-epinephrine infusion. Certainly there was no behavioral evidence of increased anxiety, depression, or anger accompanying infusion of either drug. It should be pointed out, however, that these subjects were young, healthy, adult males who from all available information were emotionally stable. In a previous study by Clemens,[3] subcutaneous injections of USP epinephrine (approximately 20 per cent nor-epinephrine and 80 per cent epinephrine) were administered to 45 male patients hospitalized for malignant neoplasms. Twenty-two reported an increase in "nervousness" and one became angry.

Conclusions

Six of the twelve ANS variables investigated showed statistically significant differences between maximum responses to epinephrine and nor-epinephrine. The most important differences were associated with cardiac output and peripheral vasomotor activity. Epinephrine produces a marked increase in cardiac output (rate and stroke volume) while nor-epinephrine produces a decrease. A reduction of blood flow to the skin appears under both drugs, but we infer that the vasoconstrictor action of nor-epinephrine is less than that of epinephrine upon the blood vessels of the skin but greater upon the blood vessels supplying the skeletal musculature. Considering the small change in diastolic blood pressure that accompanies skin vasoconstriction in response to epinephrine, it seems likely that this drug produces vasodilation in the muscles.

Summary

Eleven male college students received in-fusions of epinephrine and nor-epinephrine. Blood pressure was sampled once a minute, and the following were recorded continuously: heart rate; respiration rate; palmar skin conductance; finger pulse volume; finger, face, and axillary temperatures; heart stroke-volume; stomach motility; and salivary output. Each drug was given in a separate experimental session in three 5-minute infusion periods, 2 at 20 drops per min. and one at 40 drops per min. preceded and followed by infusion of saline solution.

Statistically significant differences between the maximum responses to epinephrine and nor-epinephrine were found in diastolic blood pressure, heart rate, finger pulse volume, finger temperature, face temperature, and heart stroke-volume. Epinephrine produced a marked increase in both heart rate and stroke-volume while nor-epinephrine produced a decrease in both. The vasoconstrictor action of nor-epinephrine was inferred to be greater upon the blood vessels supplying the skeletal musculature but less than that of epinephrine upon the blood vessels of the skin.

References

1. Ax, A. F. The physiological differentiation between fear and anger in humans. *Psychosom. Med. 15:*433, 1953.

2. Barcroft, H., and Swan, H. J. C. *Sympathetic Control of Human Blood Vessels.* London, Arnold, 1953.

3. Clemens, T. L. Autonomic nervous system responses related to the Funkenstein Test. I. To epinephrine. *Psychosom. Med. 19:*267, 1957.

4. Von Euler-Chelpin, U. S. *Noradrenaline, Chemistry, Physiology, Pharmacology and Clinical Aspects.* Springfield, Ill., Thomas, 1956.

5. Funkenstein, D. H., Greenblatt, M., and Solomon, H. C. Nor-epinephrine-like and epinephrine-like substances in psychotic and psychoneurotic patients. *Am. J. Psychiat. 108:*652, 1952.

6. Funkenstein, D. H., King, S. H., and Drolette, M. Intrapunitive and extrapunitive reactions to stress and their physiological concomitants. *J. Nerv. Ment. Dis. 118:*267, 1953.

7. Funkenstein, D. H., King, S. H., and Drolette, M. The direction of anger during a laboratory

stress-inducing situation. *Psychosom. Med.* *16:*404, 1954.

8. GOLDENBERG, M., PINES, K. L., BALDWIN, E. DE F., GREENE, D. G., and ROH, C. E. The hemodynamic response of man to nor-epinephrine and its relation to the problems of hypertension. *Am. J. Med. 5:*792, 1948.

9. SCHACHTER, J. Pain, fear and anger in hypertensives and normotensives: a psycho-physiological study. *Psychosom. Med. 19:*17, 1957.

10. WALKER, H. M., and LEV, J. *Statistical Inference.* Henry Holt and Co., New York, 1953.

11. WENGER, M. A. Studies of autonomic balance in Army Air Forces personnel. *Comp. Psychol. Monogr.,* 19 No. 4, Univ. of Calif. Press, Berkeley, 1948.

12. WENGER, M. A., ENGEL, B. T., and CLEMENS, T. L. Studies of autonomic response patterns; rationale and methods. *Behavioral Science* 2:216, 1957.

PSYCHOPHYSIOLOGY
Copyright © 1964 by The Williams & Wilkins Co.

Vol. 1, No. 2
Printed in U.S.A.

HABITUATION OF THE ORIENTING RESPONSE IN ALERT AND DROWSY SUBJECTS

DAVID G. McDONALD, LAVERNE C. JOHNSON, AND DAVID J. HORD

U. S. Navy Medical Neuropsychiatric Research Unit, San Diego, California

ABSTRACT

Alert and drowsy subjects (by EEG criterion) were compared in two experiments for psychophysiological habituation of the orienting response. Subjects in Experiment I (N = 30) received 10 presentations of a doorbell-type buzzer, and in Experiment II (N = 69) they received 10 presentations of a 500-cps tone. Comparisons were made of: (1) galvanic skin response (GSR); (2) spontaneous GSRs between trials; (3) heart rate (HR) responses; (4) finger vasoconstriction responses; (5) finger temperature responses; and (6) respiration. Results showed that there were no differences between groups in GSR; however, the drowsy group showed consistently fewer spontaneous GSRs. Cardiovascular response measures of the drowsy groups showed consistently and significantly greater responses on the later trials and, therefore, no habituation of these responses. This finding was more consistent for HR than vasomotor response. In the discussion of these results, the authors were able to rule out several possible explanations, hence the reasons for this differential autonomic response are as yet unknown.

DESCRIPTORS: Habituation, Orienting response, Arousal, EEG, GSR, HR, Vasoconstriction, Respiration. (D. G. McDonald)

The orienting response (OR) was originally reported by Pavlov (1927), who observed that his subjects showed an orientational or "What is it?" response to novel stimuli. Some of the components of the OR which have been observed are turning of the head and eyes, electroencephalogram (EEG) α-desynchronization, galvanic skin response, and finger vasoconstriction. More recently, scientific interest in the OR has been re-kindled by the work of the Russian scientist, Sokolov (1959, 1960, 1963a), who has published a review of the literature on this subject (1963b).

While most of the work in Western countries has been concerned with habituation of the OR in awake Ss (Scholander, 1961), there also has been an interest in the OR of sleeping subjects. The work of Ackner and Pampiglioni (1955, 1957), Jung (1954), and Sokolov and Paramonova (1961), show that sleeping humans continue to exhibit an orienting response, although some components of the response may not appear at some stages of sleep. Ackner and Pampiglioni found plethysmographic responses during light sleep but not during deep sleep.

This research was supported in part by grant GB-922 from the National Science Foundation to the San Diego State College Foundation and in part by the U. S. Navy Bureau of Medicine and Surgery, Research Task MR 005.12-2304. The technical assistance of Marion T. Austin is gratefully acknowledged.

Address request for reprints to David G. McDonald, Department of Psychiatry, University of Missouri School of Medicine, Columbia, Missouri.

163

PRINCIPLES OF PSYCHOPHYSIOLOGY

Sokolov and Jung observed both a vasomotor response and a skin potential response during deep sleep and reported that these responses are actually greater during sleep and require significantly more trials to produce habituation. Unfortunately, the scientific rigor of these reports (but perhaps not the experiments) has been less than ideal since results were reported in summary form. Thus, it is difficult for the experimenter in another laboratory to evaluate this work, and the exact nature of the changes in autonomic responsiveness of sleeping Ss remains somewhat obscure.

It is of interest to note that a number of investigators of the OR, such as Davis et al. (1955), and Dykman et al. (1959), referred to their subjects as alert subjects, but did not record the EEG and therefore have no measure of the drowsiness of their subjects. Since, as indicated above, sleeping subjects may respond in a different fashion, their results may have been affected by this uncontrolled variable.

The following is a report of two studies in which the psychophysiological habituation of the OR to two simple stimuli was evaluated simultaneously with the recording of EEG activity. Subjects who remained awake and those who showed EEG evidence of drowsiness were compared with respect to the magnitude and habituation of the OR.

Experiment I

Procedure. Subjects in Experiment I were 30 male Caucasian students in the U. S. Naval Hospital Corps School, San Diego, California. Average age was 19.3 years, with a range from 17 to 27 years.

Subjects were seated in a semi-soundproof, darkened room and were given a preliminary explanation of the procedures while the recording electrodes were being applied. All subjects were instructed to sit quietly with eyes closed but to remain awake. The experimenter then left the room, and the recording began after the 5 to 10 minutes required to adjust and calibrate the recording.

After 5 minutes of resting recording, each subject received a series of 10 presentations of a relatively loud doorbell type buzzer of 3 seconds duration with intertrial intervals varying from 30 to 60 seconds on a predetermined random schedule.

All measures were recorded continuously during the session on a 12-channel Offner Type R Dynograph. Four channels of EEG were recorded although only two of these (right and left occipital) were used to monitor the depth of sleep. The autonomic measures were: (1) skin resistance, using palm-to-palm electrodes coated with agar zinc sulfate electrode paste, and a Darrow-type bridge with a 40 μa current impressed across the electrodes; (2) heart rate (HR), recorded with an Offner Type 9851 cardiotachometer; (3) finger vasoconstriction, using a photocrystal (Clairex CL-605) plethysmograph attached to the left index finger; (4) respiration, recorded with a strain-gauge belt around the chest; and (5) finger temperature, obtained from a thermistor taped to the left middle finger. A more detailed description of the equipment and recordings has been published by Johnson (1963).

Responses in the autonomic variables were defined in the following manner.

Two measures of skin resistance were used: (1) ohms change in response to the stimulus, and (2) number of "spontaneous" or "non-specific" GSR's occurring between each trial. The measure of HR response, described in detail by Lang and Hnatiow (1962), was the difference between the HR of the *fastest* beat during beats 2 to 6 after stimulus onset, minus the *slowest* beat during beats 7 to 20 after stimulus onset. This difference score is a measure of the empirically observed biphasic cardiac response. Vasoconstriction was measured as the maximum millimeters of pen deflection of those plethysmographic responses with a latency of 2 to 6 seconds after stimulus onset. A constant level of amplification and dry cell strength was used for all subjects. Respiration response was measured as a decrease in the period of the respiratory cycle, (increase in breathing rate), using the means of the three cycles immediately preceding stimulus onset and the three cycles immediately after stimulus onset. Finger temperature response was defined as the largest decrease, in degrees centigrade, during the 30 seconds after onset of the stimulus.

Results. EEG recordings were scanned visually and each of the 10 trials was rated from 0 to 4 for depth of sleep. *S*s who showed EEG evidence of sleep on any trial were classified as drowsy, and the remainder of the *S*s were classified as alert. Nineteen of the 30 subjects showed EEG evidence of sleep on at least one trial, with some showing EEG indications of sleep on all ten trials. The group mean sleep ratings per trial are illustrated in Figure 1. Figure 1 also includes the ratings for Sample II which will be described below. The ratings show a progressive increase in the sleep ratings for these two groups of subjects. The depth of sleep, however, was usually not marked and the term "drowsy" was

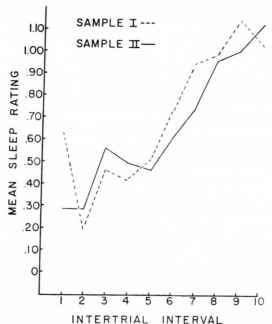

FIG. 1. Mean EEG sleep ratings per trial for drowsy groups of Experiments I and II

deemed the most appropriate description of the sleep stage shown by most subjects. The EEGs of these subjects were characterized by waves of four to seven cycles per second with occasional bursts of sleep spindles in a few subjects.

The validity of the sleep ratings was tested by measuring the amplitude of the EEG response to buzzer onset. This was done by taking the mean of the amplitude of three consecutive EEG waves during the one second prior to buzzer onset, and subtracting the mean of the amplitude of three consecutive waves during the first second after stimulus onset. Thus a positive score reflected EEG α-desynchronization in response to buzzer onset. The means of these scores per trial for each group were computed, and it was found that the drowsy group means showed α-enhancement on each of the 10 trials, and that the α-enhancement response tended to increase, albeit irregularly, over trials in agreement with the increase of the mean sleep ratings. The means of the alert group, however, showed α-desynchronization on 9 of the 10 trials, with a tendency toward habituation of this response over trials; that is, the means were closest to zero on the last four trials, showing little if any EEG response to buzzer on the later trials in the alert group. There was thus good agreement between the sleep ratings and the EEG response measures.

The alert and drowsy groups were then compared on a number of extra-experimental variables with the finding, without exception, of no significant difference between the groups. These variables, with the means of the drowsy and alert groups, respectively, were: (1) age, 19.2 and 19.4 years; (2) MMPI K scores, 15.9 and 16.1; (3) Taylor Manifest Anxiety Scale scores, 7.5 and 8.3; (4) self-ratings from 0 to 8 of adjustment, 4.8 and 4.8; and (5) self-ratings of anxiety from 0 to 8, 5.7, and 6.1.

In addition, there were no differences between the two groups on several physiological measures taken during the 5-minute period prior to the presentation of the first buzzer. These measures, with the means for the drowsy and alert groups respectively, were (1) skin resistance, 192.8 K ohms and 193.7 K ohms; (2) heart rate, 73.7 and 77.6 beats per minute; (3) finger temperature, 32.71° and 33.81° C; (4) respiration period, 92.8 mm and 95.6 mm; and (5) number of spontaneous GSRs, 5.4 and 10.7. The difference in mean number of spontaneous GSRs was nearly significant ($t = 1.93$, two-tailed $p < 0.10$), consistent with the previous findings by Johnson (1963).

The general finding of no difference between the groups on a number of psychological and pre-experimental physiological variables led us to conclude that we were not comparing "drowsy characters," but rather that comparisons between the groups on psychophysiological habituation to the 10 presentations of the buzzer were actually comparisons between the normal states of alertness and drowsiness *in general*.

Several analyses were then conducted, in order to compare the groups' psychophysiological habituation to the 10 buzzer presentations. First, to determine whether there was a significant habituation of a group on any of the five autonomic measures, the mean of the first three trials and the mean of the last three trials for each group were compared for each variable by means of a *t*

TABLE 1
Means and results of t tests for Experiment I
Tests for habituation within each group

	Alert				Drowsy			
	$\bar{X}$ 1st 3	$\bar{X}$ last 3	t	p^a	$\bar{X}$ 1st 3	$\bar{X}$ last 3	t	p^a
GSR	18.93 Ω	6.69 Ω	5.06	0.001	26.33 Ω	9.62 Ω	4.90	0.001
Spontaneous GSR	2.54	1.46	2.42	0.05	0.79	0.83	1.00	N.S.
HR	13.11 bpm	6.70 bpm	3.85	0.01	11.82 bpm	12.75 bpm	1.00	N.S.
Plethysmo-gram	8.73 mm	5.47 mm	1.85	0.10	12.21 mm	8.73 mm	2.34	0.05
Skin temperature	0.113°C	0.025°C	4.80	0.001	0.05°C	0.047°C	1.00	N.S.

Tests of level of response between groups

	$\bar{X}$ alert	$\bar{X}$ drowsy	t	p^a
GSR	11.00 Ω	15.73 Ω	1.27	N.S.
Spontaneous GSR	1.63	0.77	1.93	0.10
HR	8.30 bpm	11.57 bpm	1.71	0.10
Plethysmogram	7.30 mm	10.10 mm	1.21	N.S.
Skin temperature	0.053°C	0.046°C	1.28	N.S.

a All *p* values are two-tailed.

test for correlated means. Second, to determine whether there was an over-all difference between groups, the mean response for 10 trials for each subject was used to compute a *t* test between the alert and drowsy groups. All tests in Experiment I were two-tailed.

The results of these analyses are presented in Table 1. (Graphic presentation of the results is limited to Experiment II of the present report as results of the two experiments are highly similar. Exceptions to this rule are noted in the text.) The tests for habituation shown in Table 1 indicate that in general, the alert group showed significant adaptation, whereas the drowsy group did so only in the measures of GSR and finger vasoconstriction. In the drowsy group few spontaneous GSR responses were observed on both early and late trials, and for HR, the magnitude of response *increased* over the 10 trials. This is also reflected in the comparisons of the group means for 10 trials, where only spontaneous GSR and HR response comparisons approached significance. Respiration response data are not included in Table 1, since there were no differences between groups, and neither group showed systematic trends over trials.

EXPERIMENT II

Procedure. Experiment II was conducted in order to cross-validate in part the findings of Experiment I under similar but not identical conditions. The chief difference in procedure was in the stimulus used to produce habituation. The subjects in Experiment II consisted of 69 Caucasian male *S*s drawn in the same manner from the same source, the U. S. Naval Hospital Corps School, San Diego. Mean age was 19.1, with a range from 17 to 24.

All preliminary procedures were the same as in Experiment I, except that in addition to telling the *S*s to stay awake, they were also given a simple time estimation task in order to increase alertness. Subjects were instructed to tap on a microphone (taped to the arm of the chair in which *S* was seated) once every 30 seconds and three times every 15 minutes, but to refrain from tapping during the presentation of a stimulus.

After the usual 5 to 10 minutes required for adjustment and calibration of the equipment, the subject received a series of ten presentations of a 500-cps tone at 75 to 80 db (ref. = 0.0002 dynes/cm^2). Each tone lasted for 10 seconds, and intertrial intervals varied from 60 to 90 seconds on a predetermined random schedule.

All recordings, definitions of response, and statistical analyses of the data were the same as in Experiment I.

Results. The EEG recordings between each trial were again rated 0 to 4 for depth of sleep, and all *S*s who showed any EEG evidence of sleep were classified as drowsy, while the remainder were classified as alert. Thirty-two of the 69 *S*s showed EEG signs of drowsiness on from one to ten of the trials, leaving 37 *S*s classified as alert. The actual number of subjects varied somewhat in the analyses which follow (as indicated in Figs. 2 to 5), since a small percentage of the records were incomplete due to recording artifacts. In Figure 1 are the mean ratings of the drowsy group for each of the ten trials, showing high similarity between the two drowsy groups of Experiments I and II, in terms of both amount and rate of development of sleep.

As in Experiment I, there was no significant difference between the ages of the two groups, the means of the drowsy and alert groups being 19.1 and 19.2, respectively. Other psychological measures were not taken in the second sample since the virtual identity of the two groups on these measures in Experiment I suggested that such comparisons were not necessary.

Statistical tests for habituation of the autonomic measures were computed in the same manner as in Experiment I, and the group means and results of the *t* tests are presented in Table 2. Since it was now possible to predict the direction of the differences, all *p* values in Table 2 are one-tailed.

Group means per trial for the two groups are shown in Figures 2 to 5.

As in Experiment I, the alert group of Experiment II showed significant adaptation on the autonomic measures, with the exception of the finger temperature response (not shown) which did not change significantly over the ten trials. In the drowsy group there was again no significant habituation of the HR response, but rather an increase (Fig. 4) in the level of HR response over trials. The mean HR response of the drowsy group was also significantly greater than that of the alert group. Contrary to the findings in Experiment I, the drowsy group did show a significant decrease in number of spontaneous GSRs, although the drowsy group still showed significantly fewer spontaneous GSRs over the entire ten trials.

The changes noted in the HR response were seen in the only other measure

TABLE 2
Means and results of t tests for Experiment II
Tests for habituation within each group

| | Alert | | | | Drowsy | | | |
	$\bar{X}$ 1st 3	$\bar{X}$ last 3	t	p^a	$\bar{X}$ 1st 3	$\bar{X}$ 1st 3	t	p^a
GSR	10.55 Ω	3.98 Ω	5.86	0.001	15.65 Ω	4.06 Ω	6.21	0.001
Spontaneous GSR	2.50	1.39	3.35	0.001	0.97	0.46	2.37	0.02
HR	8.84 bpm	7.23 bpm	2.52	0.02	9.42 bpm	10.67 bpm	1.28	N.S.
Plethysmo-gram	10.02 mm	5.00 mm	5.32	0.001	12.81 mm	9.99 mm	1.93	0.05

Tests of level of response between groups

	$\bar{X}$ alert	$\bar{X}$ drowsy	t	p^a
GSR	6.60 Ω	8.29 Ω	<1.00	N.S.
Spontaneous GSR	1.78	0.74	1.65	0.05
HR	8.16 bpm	10.02 bpm	1.97	0.05
Plethysmogram	7.26 mm	10.31 mm	1.88	0.05

^{a} All p values are one-tailed.

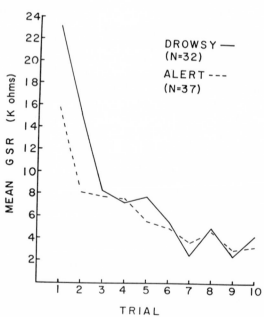

FIG. 2. Mean GSR per trial of alert and drowsy groups in Experiment II

reflecting cardiovascular function, the plethysmogram, which showed highly similar changes (Fig. 5) but at a lesser level of significance. That is, the mean vasoconstriction of the drowsy subjects showed some tendency to increase on later trials (even though the test for habituation of this response was significant),

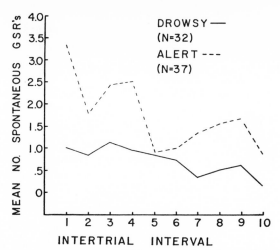

Fɪɢ. 3. Mean number of spontaneous GSR's per trial of alert and drowsy groups in Experiment II.

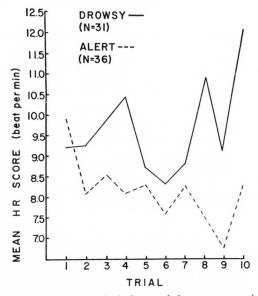

Fɪɢ. 4. Mean HR response per trial of alert and drowsy groups in Experiment II

and the mean vasoconstrictive response of the drowsy subjects for the ten trials was significantly greater than that of the alert subjects. Comparison of Figures 4 and 5 shows this similarity most clearly.

Dɪsᴄᴜssɪᴏɴ

For these two samples, no difference in the GSR (both in terms of level of response and amount of habituation) of drowsy and alert subjects to either a buzzer or a tone was found. In contrast, the heart rate response, and to a lesser

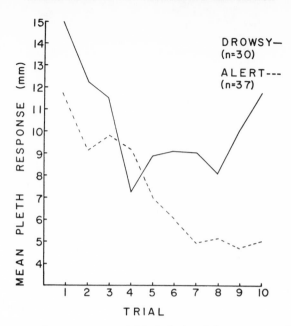

FIG. 5. Mean vasomotor response per trial of alert and drowsy groups in Experiment II.

extent the vasomotor response, of the drowsy subjects was larger than that of the alert subjects and also increased over trials. Drowsy subjects also showed consistently fewer spontaneous GSRs, both before and during the habituation trials.

The mechanism behind the increased cardiovascular response is unclear at the present time, although several alternatives can be ruled out. The first alternative is related to the so-called "Law of Initial Value" (LIV) originally discussed by Wilder (1958). In brief, response systems which obey the LIV are reported to show a negative correlation with the initial (prestimulus) level of the system; e.g. a low resting heart rate is associated with a larger heart rate response, and vice versa. One might suspect then that the data of the present experiments could be explained by the LIV, since sleeping subjects generally show lower resting heart rates (cf. Kleitman, 1963). To test this hypothesis, t tests were computed between the mean resting heart rates (taken from intertrial intervals of all ten trials during the period just before stimulus onset) of the two groups in both experiments; the t tests were not significant. In addition, the Pearson correlation coefficients between resting HR and HR response in all groups were not significant, being close to zero in magnitude. It should be remembered that we are not attempting to explain a difference between groups with greater and lesser responses, but rather between a group which *ceases to respond* and a group whose responses *become larger*.

Another conceivable explanation of the results of the present report is that the HR response measure is in reality just a measure of the amount of sinus arrhythmia (which might have increased in the drowsy subjects) rather than a true measure of the response to the stimulus. To test this hypothesis, we obtained a second "HR response" by going backwards 15 seconds on the records (in Experiment II only) for each trial, and, from that point, taking the fastest beat in beats 2 to 6 and subtracting the slowest beat in beats 7 to 20. This measure gave us an estimate of "interstimulus HR variability." The means of these variability measures were then computed for each group, and on plotting the curves it was observed that the measures were relatively constant over the ten trials for both groups. There was no significant difference between the HR variability means of the groups (7.28 and 7.96 for the drowsy and alert, respectively). Hence there was no evidence of increased sinus arrhythmia in the records of the drowsy subjects. Further, the mean HR response of the drowsy group was significantly greater than the mean interstimulus HR variability measure of the drowsy group (means of 10.02 and 7.28, respectively, $t = 3.81$, $p < 0.001$).

This left one final hypothesis to be ruled out, viz. that the drowsy subjects were being awakened or startled with each presentation of the stimulus and hence showed greater responses. Startle responses could be easily ruled out, since we excluded from the analyses any trials in which the Ss recording showed evidence of muscle artifact or unusual breathing. Inspection of the EEG tracings also indicated that there were numerous trials on which the subjects did not awaken. More important, however, the fact that the drowsy subjects showed habituation of the GSR and consistently fewer spontaneous GSRs supports the conclusion that these subjects were not experiencing greater general autonomic arousal on the later trials.

The present results, thus, cannot be explained on the basis of (1) the "Law of Initial Value," (2) amount of sinus arrhythmia, or (3) differential startle or awakening value of the stimulus for drowsy Ss.[1] On the other hand, the present results do indicate what one could miss in research of this nature by failing to monitor the EEG and, thus, the level of sleep in the subjects. For example, Dykman et al. (1959) did not include EEG, and they also concluded that there was no habituation of the HR response in the total group. Certainly we would have obtained the same result if we had combined the alert and drowsy groups in both samples.

REFERENCES

ACKNER, B., & PAMPIGLIONI, G. Combined EEG, plethysmographic, respiratory and skin resistance studies during sleep. *Electroenceph. clin. Neurophysiol.*, 1955, **7**, 153. (Abstract)

ACKNER, B., & PAMPIGLIONI, G. Some relationships between peripheral vasomotor and EEG changes. *J. Neurol. Neurosurg. Psychiat.*, 1957, **20**, 58–64.

DAVIS, R. C., BUCHWALD, A. M., & FRANKMAN, R. W. Autonomic and muscular responses, and their relation to simple stimuli. *Psychol. Monogr.*, 1955, 69, Whole No. 405.

DYKMAN, R. A., REESE, W. G., GALBRECHT, C. R., & THOMASSON, PEGGY J. Psychophysiological reactions to novel stimuli: measurement, adaptation, and relationship of psychological variables in the normal human. *Ann. N. Y. Acad. Sci.*, 1959, **79**, 43–107.

---

[1] Consistent with this last conclusion, recent data now being collected by the authors suggest that the vasomotor response persists during sleep and may increase during deeper levels of sleep, but the GSR does not return after initial habituation. Heart rate and respiratory responses are now being analyzed.

JOHNSON, L. C. Some attributes of spontaneous autonomic activity. *J. comp. physiol. Psychol.*, 1963, **56**, 415–422.

JUNG, R. Correlation of bioelectrical and autonomic phenomena with alterations of consciousness and arousal in man. In De la Fresnaye, J. F. (Ed.) *Brain mechanisms and consciousness.* Oxford: Blackwell Scientific, 1954. Pp. 310–344.

KLEITMAN, N. *Sleep and wakefulness.* (Rev. ed.). Chicago: University Chicago Press, 1963.

LANG, P. J., & HNATIOW, M. Stimulus repetition and the heart rate response. *J. comp. physiol. Psychol.*, 1962, **55**, 781–785.

PAVLOV, I. P. *Conditioned reflexes; An investigation of the physiological activity of the cerebral cortex.* London: Oxford Univer. Press, 1927.

SCHOLANDER, T. Habituation processes. *Ann. Acad. Reg. Sci. Uppsaliensis*, 1961, **5**, 5–34.

SOKOLOV, E. N. The orienting reflex. In E. N. Sokolov (Ed.), *The orienting reflex and problems of higher nervous activity.* Moscow: Akad. Pedag. Nauk RSFSR, 1959. Pp. 5–51.

SOKOLOV, E. N. Neuronal models and the orienting reflex. In Brazier, M. A. B. (Ed.), *The central nervous system and behavior.* New York: Josiah Macey, Jr. Foundation, 1960. Pp. 187–276.

SOKOLOV, E. N. *Perception and the conditioned reflex.* New York: Pergamon Press, 1963a.

SOKOLOV, E. N. Higher nervous functions: the orienting reflex. *Ann. Rev. Physiol.*, 1963b, **25**, 545–580.

SOKOLOV, E. N., & PARAMONOVA, N. P. Progressive changes in the orienting reflex in man during the development of sleep inhibition. *Zh. vyssh. nervn. Deyatel.*, 1961, **11**, 206–215.

WILDER, J. Modern psychophysiology and the law of initial value. *Amer. J. Psychotherapy*, 1958, **12**, 199–221.

Reprinted from *Psychosomatic Medicine*
Vol. 26, 701–709 (1964).

Body Image and Physiological Patterns in Patients with Peptic Ulcer and Rheumatoid Arthritis

ROBERT L. WILLIAMS, Ph.D., and ALAN G. KRASNOFF, Ph.D.

Cross-validation of Fisher and Cleveland's body-image scoring schema was achieved and its theoretical importance was extended to include physiological activity. As predicted, peptic ulcer patients had higher heart rates than rheumatoid arthritic patients under all experimental conditions. No significant differences between these groups were found for GSR or EMG activity. In comparing these groups on the basis of difference scores between experimental conditions, however, limited positive results were obtained for EKG and EMG variables. Modest support was found for a positive relationship between Ss classified on the basis of a body-image dimension and physiological arousal. These findings support the view that body-image theory has heuristic value in accounting for physiological arousal patterns. A more satisfactory theory, however, would have to encompass the principle of relative response specificity and the specific attitude hypothesis in relation to psychosomatic disorders.

THE PRESENT STUDY was undertaken to determine if an individual's attitudes toward his body, as reflected in body-image scores, are systematically and quantifiably associated with physiological reactivity patterns. Little is known about the development of physiological patterning that occurs in response to psychological variables. There is convincing evidence, however, that these psycho-

logical variables have physiological correlates. The precise relationships of these two variables remain, however, to be determined.

The major impetus for the present research is derived from the work of Fisher and Cleveland,[7] who demonstrated that rheumatoid arthritic and peptic ulcer patients could be distinguished from one another on the basis of a body-image scoring schema. Fisher and Cleveland[3–9] also demonstrated that body image is related to a variety of diverse phenomena, such as choice of psychosomatic symptoms, style of life, the Zeigarnik effect, ability to tolerate stress, level of aspiration, and sexual behavior. Davis[2] extended findings on body image in relation to physiological patterning in nor-

This investigation was supported in part by a Fellowship (MF-12, 954) from the National Institute of Mental Health, U. S. Public Health Service granted to the senior author. The authors wish to express appreciation to Dr. John A. Stern for his cooperation and assistance.

Presented in part at the Annual Meeting of the American Psychological Association, St. Louis, September 1961.

Received for publication Mar. 30, 1964.

701

mals. An initial phase of the present study serves to cross-validate the Rorschach body-image scores devised by Fisher and Cleveland in distinguishing between peptic ulcer and rheumatoid arthritic patients.

Another source of interest relevant to the present investigation involves the question of differential reactivity of physiological responses—i.e., the fact that, under stressful stimulation, certain organs respond more frequently and more intensely than others. Intraindividual and interindividual differences of physiological reactivity have been reported by Malmo et al.[14] and Lacey et al.[12] In this respect, differential reactivity is viewed as a corollary problem of organ choice in psychosomatic disorders and is, therefore, considered to be associated closely with a breakdown in an overactive area of body functioning. The factors contributing to differential reactivity or overactivity, are, however, obscure. Thus, the second phase of this research is concerned with extending the findings with regard to body-image scores for rheumatoid arthritic and peptic ulcer patients to assess the question of the existence of differential physiological patterns between these groups.

Three hypotheses were formulated and tested:

1. Individuals whose symptoms involve the body exterior, such as rheumatoid arthritics, will tend to perceive their body boundaries as being firm, as shown by their Rorschach responses, whereas individuals whose symptoms involve the body interior, such as peptic ulcer patients, will perceive their body boundaries as being indefinite.

2. Individuals whose symptoms involve the body exterior will show unique physiological responses when compared with individuals whose symptoms involve the body interior.

3. Individuals who picture their body boundaries as being firm, as shown by

Rorschach responses, will manifest unique physiological responses when compared with individuals who perceive their body boundaries as indefinite.

In operational terms, the hypotheses state that rheumatoid arthritics will produce a greater number of "barrier" responses, indicating more body definiteness, than will peptic ulcer patients. Conversely, peptic ulcer patients will give a greater number of "penetration of boundary" responses, indicating more boundary indefiniteness, than will arthritic patients. Further, the arthritic or high-barrier groups would be expected to show more electromyographic and galvanic skin responses than ulcer or low-barrier groups, whereas the latter are expected to manifest higher heart rates than the former groups. Thus, the present hypotheses are designed to extend the theoretical importance and predictive significance of the body-image theory to physiological functions.

Method

Subjects

The subjects (Ss) were 20 male peptic ulcer and 20 male rheumatoid arthritic (RA) patients. All Ss were either inpatients at the St. Louis Veterans Administration Hospital at the time they participated in the study or had been patients at some time in the past few years and were under treatment in the outpatient clinic. In all cases the diagnoses had been confirmed by laboratory studies. Ten of the ulcer cases (referred to as MU to indicate medication) had been placed on a medical regimen of phenobarbital (15–30 mg. 4 times a day). The remaining 10 peptic ulcer patients (referred to as the NMU group to indicate no medication) were receiving no sedation during the time they participated in the study. Following the body-image classification of Fisher and Cleveland, the peptic-ulcer patients comprised the interior-symptom group and the rheumatoid arthritic sample comprised the exterior-symptom group. A comparison of the groups for variables such as age, education, and IQ revealed no significant differences.

Procedure

One of the experimenters (E) presented two psychological measures: The first consisted of Vocabulary, Arithmetic, and Digit Span of the Wechsler Adult Intelligence Scale (WAIS). All Ss who obtained an IQ below the Dull Normal range were excluded from the study. The second involved a modified Rorschach procedure. At the completion of the WAIS administration, Ss were given the Rorschach according to a technique described by Fisher and Cleveland.[7] Briefly, S was asked to give three responses to the first five cards and two responses to the last five cards. This procedure yielded 25 percepts and, therefore, controlled for the total frequency of responses from which body-image scores were derived.

Two body-image indices were used in the present study. One index, Barrier Score, was based on the number of Rorschach responses in which there was an emphasis on the containing, covering, and protective aspects of the peripheries of the percepts (e.g., "bottle," "knight in armor," "turtle with a hard shell"). A second index, Penetration of Boundary score, was based on the number of Rorschach responses in which there were references to penetration, disruption, or wearing away of the outer surfaces (e.g., "mashed bug," "person bleeding," "soft mud"). In scoring the Rorschach records the total frequency of responses falling in each of the categories above was compiled. Each response was assigned a numerical value of 1. Both body-image indices were analyzed independently in the treatment of the data.

Following administration of the Rorschach, Ss were subjected to a physiological recording session in order to obtain measures of muscle activity (EMG), heart rate (EKG), and galvanic skin responses (GSR), under the following conditions: rest, psychological stress, recovery and reassurance. All physiological measurements were made in an air-conditioned room, maintained at approximately 74° F. A Grass Polygraph, Model 5, was used in obtaining the physiological data. Continuous recordings were made with S supine. The GSR

was recorded through electrodes described by Lykken.[13] The electrodes were made by anchoring a small zinc disc in a structure of dental acrylic. The electrodes were then attached to the second and third fingers of the left hand using corn pads. These pads have a center opening, which may be filled with zinc sulphate paste. The electrodes were inserted into the opening and fixed with adhesive tape. A measure of heart rate was obtained through standard EKG electrodes from Lead III position (left arm and left leg). Recordings of muscle activity were obtained from a lateral surface of the right arm (3 cm. below the elbow) through EEG cup-type electrodes placed 2 cm. apart.

After the electrodes were attached, S was instructed to relax and to keep his eyes closed at all times. A resting record was obtained for 10 min., but only the last 3 min. of this period were evaluated. This relaxation period seemed adequate for most Ss to show trends toward physiological stability.

Following the rest period, each S was exposed to a 3-min. "psychologically stressful" situation involving tasks of mental arithmetic and repetition of digits backward. For mental arithmetic, S was required to multiply two digits by one digit and to add a two-digit number (e.g., "Multiply 48 by 4 and add 56 as quickly as you can. Remember speed and accuracy are important.") As soon as the correct response was given, another problem was presented. E repeated the problem, however, if S gave an incorrect answer. For digits backward, S was required to repeat backward a series of digits ranging in length from four to eight numbers. E read the numbers rapidly. As a means of intensifying the effects of stress, E occasionally remarked, "Please work faster. You're still too slow. We all have our bad days once in awhile. This mustn't be your day." These remarks were given in a dissatisfied tone of voice. Although the number of arithmetic problems and digit span trials varied as a function of the ability of each S, duration of exposure to stress remained constant at 3 min.

Immediately following the 3-min. stress period, S was told to relax, and a 3-min. "recovery" record was obtained. At the end of the recovery period, S was reassured as follows: "You did not do as poorly as I made it seem. Purposely, I made the problems difficult. So just relax and keep your eyes closed." After S had been reassured, a 5-min. "reassurance" record was obtained. Only the last 3 min. of this interval were quantitatively evaluated.

Before a test of the hypotheses regarding physiological arousal could be accomplished, the raw polygraphic data were converted into numerical form by the following methods. The records were marked off in terms of four reference periods: (1) rest, defined as the last 3 min. of the 10-min. resting phase; (2) stress, covering the entire 3-min. interval of stressful stimulation; (3) recovery, consisting of the 3-min. immediately following stress; and (4) reassurance, defined as the last 3 min. of the 5-min. period following recovery.

GSRs were scored during the four reference periods where the pen excursion exceeded 1 mm. (quivalent to 500 ohms) in amplitude from base line. By means of the potentiometer, S was repeatedly returned to base line when the pen fell above or below it. Care was taken to note and discount any fluctuations which might have been produced by artifacts. Thus, the GSR score is the total frequency of responses which occurred during each of the four reference periods. EKG was scored by counting the number of beats per minute for each of the 3-min. experimental periods. The EMG channel of the polygraph integrated muscle activity so that the amplitude of the continuous tracings indicated the amount of muscle output per unit time. As the base line had been established during calibration procedures, it was possible to quantify the

deviations above base line by means of a planimeter which measures the area under a curve in square centimeters. Thus, the index of EMG activity is the total amount of integrated muscle activity manifested in square centimeters per unit time. Thirty seconds of muscle activity were sampled for each reference period. The initial 10 sec. of each minute in the 3-min. intervals were evaluated.

Results

Hypothesis 1

The testing of Hypothesis 1 requires a comparison of the Rorschach responses of the RA Ss with those of the U Ss. All Rorschach protocols were evaluated for body-image on a "blind" basis by Fisher and Cleveland. In order to test Hypothesis 1, body-image scores were split at the median and cast into four-fold contingency tables.

The results of the Chi-square analyses are presented in Table 1. As predicted, the RA Ss tended to produce more barrier responses than the U Ss, but the differences were not statistically significant ($p = .10-.05$). As expected, the U Ss gave a significantly greater number of penetration of boundary responses than the RA Ss ($p = .001$). These results support the hypothesis that the Ss can be differentiated on the basis of body-image scores, substantiating previous work reported by Fisher and Cleveland.[7]

TABLE 1. Chi-Square Analyses of Differences in Body-Image Scores Between Peptic-Ulcer and Rheumatoid Arthritis Patients

Group	No.	Barrier score Above median	Barrier score Below median	Range	Penetration of boundary score Above median	Penetration of boundary score Below median	Range
Peptic ulcer	20	7	13	0–10	15	5	0–10
Rheumatoid arthritis	20	13	7	1–11	4	16	0–8
CHI SQUARE		3.60			12.10		
P		.10–.05			.001		

Hypothesis 2

A test of Hypothesis 2 involves a comparison of physiological responses between the RA and U Ss across experimental conditions. Before a reliable test of this hypothesis could be accomplished, however, certain preliminary analyses were necessary to determine if the experimental operations were effective in producing over-all changes.

Table 2 shows the probability values of a Friedman Two-Way Analysis of Variance by Ranks.[15] Examination of these data indicates that the experimental operations produced significant changes in physiological reactivity across conditions for NMU, MU, and RA groups. Because phenobarbital has an obvious dampening effect on physiological activity, the 10 patients in the MU group were evaluated separately.

Mann-Whitney U tests[15] were used to determine if differences exist between the RA and U groups with respect to over-all physiological activity and response to stress. The probabilities for the comparisons are summarized in

TABLE 2. RESULTS OF SIGNIFICANCE TESTS*
TO DETERMINE WITHIN-GROUP PHYSIOLOGI-
CAL CHANGES ACROSS EXPERIMENTAL
CONDITIONS

Group	GSR	EKG	EMG
NMU	P < .001*	P < .001	P = .10-.05
MU	P < .01	P < .001	P < .01
RA	P < .001	P < .001	P < .01

*Based on Friedman's two-way analysis of variance by ranks.

Table 3. As predicted, the NMU group shows significantly higher heart rates (p = .05) than the RA group under all the experimental conditions. Similarly, the NMU group exceeded the MU group in heart rate, except under the condition of reassurance. GSR and EMG did not significantly discriminate between U and RA Ss. In view of the lowered physiological reactivity of the MU group due to the presumed effects of phenobarbital, as suggested by the comparison between NMU and MU groups, a test of the significance of differences between the MU group and the RA group was not conducted.

The data were analyzed further to determine if a differential effect in physiological response to stress existed. Since significant differences in heart rate activity were present during the resting phase, it was necessary to determine if additional differences occurred over and above the initial effects as a consequence of stress.

To accomplish this analysis, difference scores were obtained between levels of (1) stress and rest, (2) stress and recovery, (3) recovery and rest, (4) reassurance and rest, and (5) recovery and reassurance. Comparisons between NMU and RA groups were computed for each set of difference scores.

Table 4 presents the results which demonstrate little support for differential reactivity of GSR, EKG, and EMG between NMU and RA groups. The difference scores between reassurance and rest showed that the NMU group had a significantly slower readaptation than the

TABLE 3. PROBABILITY VALUES OF MANN-WHITNEY U TESTS OF CONDITIONS BETWEEN
GROUPS FOR PHYSIOLOGICAL DATA

	Rest			Stress			Recovery			Reassurance		
	GSR	EKG	EMG	GSR	EKG	EMG	GSR	EKG	EMG	GSR	EKG	EMG
NMU vs. RA P	NS*	.05	NS	NS	.05	NS	NS	.05	NS	NS	.05	NS
NMU vs. MU P	NS	.10-.05	NS	NS	.05	NS	NS	.05	NS	NS	NS	NS

*NS indicates not significant.

RA group on the basis of EKG activity (p = .05). In other words the NMU group had a greater persistence of accelerated heart rate following stress. Furthermore, the difference scores between reassurance and rest with regard to EMG activity showed a slower readaptation for the RA group in comparison with the NMU group (p = .05). Although these results are in the predicted direction, it should be noted that only 2 of 30 statistical tests were significant and, therefore, these findings should be considered as giving only tentative and partial support to the second hypothesis.

Hypothesis 3

A test of Hypothesis 3 requires a comparison of physiological responses between those Ss whose body-image scores are classifiable as high-barrier (HB) versus those designated as low-barrier (LB). To accomplish this evaluation, median Rorschach barrier scores were obtained and Ss were classified according to whether their body-image scores fell above or below the median value. The MU group was omitted from a test of Hypothesis 3 so that 30 Ss of the total sample were classified as either HB or LB.

Mann-Whitney U analyses were made of the four experimental conditions and of the difference scores to determine if the two groups differed from each other in their over-all physiological activity, and if they showed differential reactivity patterns. As Table 5 indicates, the LB group had significantly higher heart rates under the stress condition (p = .05), whereas the HB group had significantly higher muscle activity under stressful stimulation (p = .01). These findings lend some support to the hypothesis that body-image is related to physiological reactivity patterns.

As in the analyses involving the U and RA groups, only two instances of signifi-

TABLE 4. PROBABILITY VALUES OF MANN-WHITNEY U TESTS BASED ON DIFFERENCE SCORES FOR PHYSIOLOGICAL DATA

	Stress-rest			Stress-recovery			Recovery-rest			Reassurance-rest			Recovery-reassurance		
	GSR	EKG	EMG	GSR	EKG	EMG	GSR	EKG	EMG	GSR	EKG	EMG	GSR	EKG	EMG
NMU vs. RA P	NS	NS	NS	NS	NS	NS	NS	NS	NS	NS	.05	.05	NS	NS	NS
NMU vs. MU P	NS	NS	NS	NS	NS	NS	NS	NS	NS	NS	NS	NS	NS	NS	NS

TABLE 5. PROBABILITY VALUES OF MANN-
WHITNEY U TEST OF CONDITIONS BETWEEN
GROUPS FOR PHYSIOLOGICAL DATA FOR
BODY-IMAGE GROUPS

Physiological measurement	Rest	Stress	Recovery	Reassurance
GSR	NS	NS	NS	NS
EKG	NS	.05°	NS	NS
EMG	NS	.01†	NS	NS

*Low barrier greater than high barrier.
†High barrier greater than low barrier.

cant differential activity were noted. The HB group (Table 6) showed a lower rate of readaptation than the LB group, in comparisons involving differences between reassurance and rest (p = .025) and between recovery and reassurance (p = .05) for EMG. No significant differences were found for GSR and EKG. Thus, these findings partially support the third hypothesis. As previously noted with regard to the findings on Hypothesis 2, however, these results should be interpreted cautiously.

Discussion

The present study provides experimental verification of certain assertions in body-image theory, demonstrating, first of all, that RA Ss tend to give more barrier responses than U Ss. Secondly, this study indicates that U Ss give significantly more penetration-of-boundary responses than RA Ss. These findings confirm those of Fisher and Cleveland,[7] who showed that patients with symptoms of the body exterior have perceptions of their body boundaries as firm, definite, and well-delineated, whereas patients with symptoms of the body interior have perceptions of their body boundaries as indefinite and permeable.

In addition, the present study attempted to determine if RA or HB Ss would demonstrate a greater degree of physiological activity in terms of electromyographic and psychogalvanic responsivity, in contrast to U or LB Ss. Conversely, this study predicted that U or LB Ss would show a greater degree of physiological excitation in terms of heart rate as compared with RA or HB Ss. The present findings support the general hypothesis that certain physiological functions of the body are more reactive for some medical diagnostic groups than others, and that the characteristics of an individual's body image (HB vs. LB) are closely associated with the patterning of such responses. Heart rate was found to be significantly faster for the NMU group than the RA group on all statistical tests. Electromyographic activity was significantly greater for the RA group in comparison with the NMU group for difference scores between resting and reassurance conditions. Ss with high barrier scores had significantly slower heart rates than patients with low barrier scores under the condition of stressful stimulation, whereas the opposite difference was found for electromyographic activity. Furthermore, as expected, differential electromyographic activity between reassurance and rest and between recovery and reassurance was greater for patients with HB scores than for patients with LB scores.

The present study and previous research have demonstrated some relationships between body image and physiological responses. The ways in which body image and physiological activity become linked remain unclear. A number of factors in the life history of the individual no doubt operate to bring about these relationships. Two independent theoretical approaches to the study of psychophysiological relationships have shed some light on this problem. The principle of "relative response specificity" (Lacey et al.[12]) states that individuals tend to respond with a unique pattern of autonomic activation to non-

TABLE 6. Probability Values of Mann-Whitney U Tests Based on Difference Scores for the Physiological Data for the Body-Image Groups

Physiological measurement	Stress-rest	Stress-recovery	Recovery-rest	Reassurance-rest	Recovery-reassurance
GSR	NS	NS	NS	NS	NS
EKG	NS	NS	NS	NS	NS
EMG	NS	NS	NS	.025°	.05°

*High barrier greater than low barrier.

specific stressors. They do not specify any psychological variables, but speculate that the "total life experience" of the individual coupled with "physiological factors that are gene-determined" can account for various physiological reactivity patterns. Since body imagery probably emerges out of the unique genetic background and life experience of the individual, it may well be that these factors play an important role in determining the particular hierarchial pattern of autonomic activity. Some evidence for this assumption is found in the work of Grace and Graham[10] and in Graham and Graham's specific attitude hypothesis.[11] These writers state that the reaction of an individual involves an "attitude" that can be expressed in language and is usually accompanied by bodily changes. They theorize that the bodily changes, if persistent, may lead to symptoms and later to a breakdown in a specific area of body functioning. This formulation is one of the few instances in which specific attitudes, as such, have been associated with particular body functions. An evaluation of the specific attitude hypothesis in the light of the present findings regarding body-image theory suggests that an attitude toward one's body may be the central reference point in bringing about persistent changes associated with patterns of physiological arousal.

In essence, relative response specificity, the specific attitude hypothesis, and body-image theory are considered to be complementary ways of viewing the basic nature of psychophysiological rela-tionships. The precise interactions of relationships among these viewpoints remain to be determined.

Summary

This study tested three hypotheses derived from Fisher and Cleveland's theory of body image—namely, (1) patients with peptic ulcer and rheumatoid arthritis could be differentiated on the basis of body image scores; (2) these diagnostic groups would reflect unique physiological responses; (3) patients defined on the basis of body-image scores would demonstrate physiological patterns parallel to those of the diagnostic groups. Rheumatoid arthritics showed a tendency to give more Rorschach responses which refer to perceptions of their body boundaries as being surrounded by a protective defensive barrier than did peptic-ulcer patients. The latter group gave significantly more Rorschach responses which refer to perceptions of indefinite boundaries than did the former group. As expected, peptic-ulcer patients had significantly higher heart rates than the rheumatoid arthritics, but the latter did not demonstrate greater EMG or GSR activity than the former, contrary to those predicted. In a more rigorous test of the second hypothesis, however, for differential physiological changes, the results provided limited support for the predictions. Patients with well-defined body boundaries (HB) manifested significantly more EMG activity and significantly less EKG activity (under stress) than those patients with relatively indefinite body boundaries (LB). In tests for differential physiological changes, limited support was found for the third hypothesis. Within the limitations of the present study, the following conclusions were drawn: (1) The Fisher and Cleveland body image scoring system is an efficacious discriminator between patients with exterior and interior symptoms. (2) There is a close and significant relationship between these symptom groups and physiological responses, particularly in the case of heart rate. (3) Some support was found for a relationship between an individual's attitude toward his body and his physiological responses.

Psychology Service
Veterans Administration Hospital
915 North Grand Boulevard
Saint Louis 6, Mo.

References

1. CLEVELAND, S. E., and FISHER, S. Behavior and unconscious fantasies of patients with rheumatoid arthritis. *Psychosom. Med. 16:327*, 1954.

2. DAVIS, A. D. Some physiological correlates of Rorschach body image productions. *J. Abnorm. & Social Psychol. 60:432*, 1960.

3. FISHER, S., and CLEVELAND, S. E. The role of body image in psychosomatic symptom choice. *Psych. Mongr. 69:1*, 1955.

4. FISHER, S., and CLEVELAND, S. E. Body image and style of life. *J. Abnorm. & Social Psychol. 52:373*, 1956.

5. FISHER, S., and CLEVELAND, S. E. Relationship of body-image boundaries to memory for completed and incompleted tasks. *J. Psychol. 42:35*, 1956.

6. FISHER, S., and CLEVELAND, S. E. An approach to physiological reactivity in terms of body-image schema. *Psychol. Rev. 64:26*, 1957.

7. FISHER, S., and CLEVELAND, S. E. *Body Image and Personality*. Van Nostrand, New York, 1958.

8. FISHER, S., and CLEVELAND, S. E. Body image boundaries and sexual behavior. *J. Psychol. 45:207*, 1958.

9. FISHER, S., and CLEVELAND, S. E. A comparison of psychological characteristics and physiological reactivity in ulcer and rheumatoid arthritis groups: II. Difference in physiological reactivity. *Psychosom. Med. 22:290*, 1960.

10. GRACE, W. J., and GRAHAM, D. T. Relationships of specific attitudes and emotions of certain bodily diseases. *Psychosom. Med. 14:243*, 1952.

11. GRAHAM, D. T., and GRAHAM, F. K. Specific relations of attitude to physiological change. *Unpublished Progress Report*. The Univ. of Wisconsin School of Medicine, July 1, 1961.

12. LACEY, J. I., BATEMAN, D. E., and vanLEHN, R. Autonomic response specificity: an experimental study. *Psychosom. Med. 15:8*, 1953.

13. LYKKEN, D. T. Properties of electrodes used in electrodermal measurement. *J. Comp. physiol. Psychol. 52:629*, 1959.

14. MALMO, R. B., SHAGASS, C., and DAVIS, F. H. Symptom specificity and bodily reactions during psychiatric interview. *Psychosom. Med. 12:362*, 1950.

15. SIEGEL, S. *Non-Parametric Statistics of the Behavioral Sciences*. McGraw-Hill, New York, 1956.

PSYCHOPHYSIOLOGY
Copyright © 1964 by The Williams & Wilkins Co.

Vol. 1, No. 1
Printed in U.S.A.

GOALS AND METHODS OF PSYCHOPHYSIOLOGY

ALBERT F. AX

Psychophysiology Division, The Lafayette Clinic, Detroit, Michigan

ABSTRACT

The purpose of this essay is to identify the research area of psychophysiology by abstracting the goals and methods from reports which this author believes are properly called psychophysiological. The general goal of psychophysiology is to describe the mechanisms which *translate* between psychological and physiological systems of the organism. Specific goals are to identify and describe the physiological processes directly relevant to such psychological constructs as drive, motivation, attitude, emotion, and their modification by learning.

Findings include the description by physiological patterns of several emotions, sleep, dreaming, hypnosis, psychiatric and psychosomatic conditions. Principles conceived are *individual, stimulus, emotion* and *attitude specificities* and the "law of initial values."

The progressive theme of psychophysiological method has been to extend measurement to more covert behavior with decreasing interference with the organism. Methods and special problem areas are reviewed under the categories of (a) the stimulus situation, (b) observation (sensors, recorders, signal transformation), and (c) analysis, synthesis, and interpretation. The major unsolved technical problem is the automatic detection of artifact. The chief theoretical problem is to "break the code" by which the organism translates between experience and physiology. The psychophysiological method is seen as having useful application in classification and training for motivational abilities and stress tolerance.

Goal, Method, Application, Translation, Covert, Emotion, Motivation, Attitude, Specificity, Sensor, Recorder, Conversion, Computer, Analysis, Synthesis, Interpretation, Artifact, Learning, Stress-tolerance. (A. F. Ax)

Psychophysiology is best defined by its goals and methods as they are described in the reports published by its research workers. Most articles, however, report studies of specific sub-goals and often employ only a few of the techniques which characterize the specialty. Such regular research reports usually do not mention the larger context to which the study is related. Since psychophysiological reports appear in more than 80 different journals including specialties of psychology, physiology, medicine, psychiatry, and engineering and since psychophysiology has had no journal bearing its name, it is not surprising that this area of science has had no clear public image among non-psychophysiologists. The first purpose of this essay is to identify the research area of psychophysiology by abstracting the goals and methods from reports which this writer believes are properly called psychophysiological.

Just as it is healthy sometimes to take an introspective look at ourselves, so

Address request for reprints to Albert F. Ax, Ph.D., Psychophysiology Laboratory, The Lafayette Clinic, 951 E. Lafayette, Detroit, Michigan 48207.

8   **PRINCIPLES OF PSYCHOPHYSIOLOGY**

it is useful for a research specialty to take stock of its goals and methods. We expect this to be one of several articles describing psychophysiology from different viewpoints. No one of us probably can create a truly comprehensive picture of psychophysiology, but in attempting to formulate our views and by reading each other's attempts we may come closer to the total picture.

GOALS OF PSYCHOPHYSIOLOGY

A Viewpoint for Psychophysiology. The distinctions between neighboring scientific fields is historical, heuristic, and only to some extent based on subject matter and methods of study. Physics and chemistry overlap a great deal. The physical referents for chemical concepts such as *valence* have long been known. The relationships between physiology and psychology remain somewhat more obscure because few of the physiological referents for psychological concepts are known in detail. Consider the main concepts used in psychology with regard to their physiological referents—*sensation, perception, thinking, intelligence, creativity, learning, drive, need, habit-strength, motive, attitude, repression, anxiety, emotion,* etc. Except to point in a general way to the nervous system as the referent organ, only *sensation,* and to a very small extent *emotion* and *anxiety,* have known physiological referents. The reason for this persistent hiatus between psychological concepts and physiological explanations is more than mere lack of knowledge about physiological processes. It is as if the two disciplines were attempting to describe two different systems.

A compelling analogy suggests itself. Physiology describes the physical organism like an engineer describes a computer; psychology describes the psyche, like a programmer describes the symbolic program for a computer. Symbolic programming systems like Fortran or Algol can be described, taught, and used without any knowledge of the real physical hardware computer. In fact the same symbolic system can be used on very different computers. The computer obeys commands and will communicate back to the operator in the same symbolic language. The only time one becomes aware that the *physical* computer is not in fact this *symbolic* computer is when a rule of the symbolic system is broken or a hardware failure causes the physical computer to make a mistake. The resulting behavior of the computer is mysterious and irrational from the symbolic programmer's viewpoint. The only way such irrational computer behavior can be understood and corrected is by knowing about the *translator.* In order for a specific type of physical computer to utilize a general symbolic programming system it must have a specific translator program which converts every command of the symbolic program into its own special machine language and vice versa for communication back to the operator. Whereas computers and organisms are not alike in most aspects, it is plausible that the human organism does indeed have a symbolic sub-system quite analogous to the symbolic program for computers. Whenever two systems, having a symbolic relationship, interact they must do so by means of a *translator.* A translator is more than a table of equivalent vocabularies and rules of action. It is an active system for intercommunication between the computer and its human operator and programmer. The main purpose of symbolic systems is to enable a few general principles and

A. F. AX   275 commands to be spelled out in detail at the level of concrete specificity. It enables a division of labor and the multiplication of processes by several orders of magnitude at levels of increasing specificity. The symbolic program may command "invert Matrix A"; the computer executes a million acts. The psyche hears a loud sound; the physiology executes the million adjustments of the startle response.

Two points must be kept clear. First, we are not saying men and computers are alike; only that an intriguing analogy can be seen in this aspect of symbolic relationships between systems. Second, there is no return to a mystical mind-body relationship. The symbolic program of a computer is just as real and physical as the rest of the computer. It consists of patterns of positive or negative charged cores in the computer's storage exactly like the translator's commands. The difference is only in the role they play in the computer's system and their pattern of organization. The symbolic system of the organism called the "psyche" or "person" consists of patterns of physical states in the nervous and endocrine systems quite indistinguishable from those which regulate homeostasis and other proceedings of the body of which the psyche is not cognizant. Because of the natural development of organisms by evolution and ontogentic growth there appears to be a confusing interweaving of various levels of symbolic abstraction, multiple usage of subsystems, redundancy of systems, etc., which make the "debugging" of the organismic "program" considerably more difficult than that of computers. Then, of course, the human organism is also many orders of magnitude larger and more complex than any computer or program yet conceived.

Psychophysiology fits into this analogy by studying the organismic "translator." More specifically the facts and principles of psychophysiology describe the translator systems for the organism. So far psychophysiology has made real progress only in the description of the physiology of sensation, and that is far from complete. A beginning was made by Cannon in the description of the physiology of emotion. The translation functions for the remaining long list of psychological concepts are essentially unknown.

The general goal, then, of psychophysiology is the description of the systems in the organism which transfer information between the two collections of subsystems generally referred to as psyche and soma. It is, of course, expected that present models of both psyche and soma are incomplete and in some respects erroneous, so that as the translator model develops, it will assist in the remodeling of both and, of course, be influenced by them.

A less pretentious hypothesis of the nature of the relationship between physiology and psychology was stated by the Editor of *Psychosomatic Medicine* in Vol. 1, No. 1, 25 years ago (16).

"Briefly psychosomatic medicine concerns itself with the psychological approach into general medicine. It takes for granted that psychic and somatic phenomena take place in the same biological system and are probably two aspects of the same process, that psychological phenomena should be studied in their psychological causality with intrinsically psychological methods and physiological phenomena in their physical causality with the methods of physics and chemistry."

We essentially agree with that statement, but believe it is now possible to postulate a little more precisely the nature of the relationship between the "two aspects of the same process," namely, that it is one of symbolic relationship rather than simply that of classical causality which might be expected to be described by regression and differential equations. The symbolic relationship requires *translation* of the code rather than simple *correlation*. Unfortunately, little has yet been accomplished toward "breaking the code" except in sensory phenomena, but at least if we can place the problem in the correct context more rapid progress may be anticipated.

Specific Goals for Psychophysiology. Ends and means are not independent whether in the realm of ethics or of science. Lest they be mere wishful thinking, scientific goals must be theoretically attainable by the methods at hand. Advancement of the state-of-the-art in methods accordingly may open up attainable new goals for a science. It is largely on the basis of advances in techniques that psychophysiology has raised its sights toward more ambitious goals.

One of the most important contributions psychophysiology could make would be to provide an objective measure of drive and motivation independent of the subsequent overt behavior. Robert Malmo (28) has shown that the drive state associated with sleep deprivation and a tracking task does have measurable manifestation in the peripheral variables of skin conductance, respiration, heart rate, muscle potentials, and electroencephalogram (EEG). Malmo laments that very few studies have attempted to find autonomic concomitants of the relatively "non-emotional" states of hunger, thirst, or sexual arousal. When one considers the heavy responsibility the autonomic nervous system (ANS) bears for homeostatic regulation, it is reasonable to expect that the biological drive states do have peripheral autonomic representation. However abstract and non-physiological a motive may appear to be during its incubation period, as it assumes regnancy by activating behavior it *must* utilize physiological mechanisms which should be measurable. How well the quality, type, direction, and content of a motive can be specified from peripheral physiological response patterns is, of course, a moot question at present. Graham et al. (21) is finding that "attitudes" have identifiable physiological concomitants. Wolff (38) reported unambiguous physiological conditions of the stomach to be related to the type of emotion. Davis (14) was able to show that viewing different pictures produced different physiological patterns, and Ax (3) and Schachter (33) reported physiological differentiation between fear and anger experimentally induced. There are, of course, older reports of failure to find such physiological differentiation (26). We are not claiming that the issue of physiological differentiation of emotion by peripherally available measures is a settled issue, only that it looks promising.

Much confusion exists in the definition of the concepts "emotion," "motivation," "drive," and "attitude." It may be that attempts to measure them physiologically will produce a more parsimonious operational description. Possibly they are all aspects of the same process in different stages of arousal and manifested in different situations. It may be desirable as Brown (12) has suggested to reserve *drive* for the non-directional arousal aspect of motive, and let *motive* carry the more complex meaning of both *force* and *vector* parameters. Possibly *attitude* could refer to the directional or vector aspects of a motive when it is not regnant. A man's *attitude* may be conservative in politics at all times. He is *motivated* to vote conservative only on election day. He may become *emotional* if his motive to vote is blocked. Thus an attitude becomes a motive when action is imminent and emotion is aroused if the action seeking to satisfy a motive is blocked. Many emotions are inevitable simply because consumatory behavior takes time, thus delaying the motive's satisfaction. Unlike the natural need states, many acquired or learned motives are insatiable. No amount of money may satisfy the miser's greed. Learned motives thus are especially prone to generate emotion. From this viewpoint, then, it is plausible that different attitudes may be identified by their physiological patterns when activated into motives or frustrated into emotions.

The other goals of psychophysiology in a sense are corollary to the general one of measuring the motives of man. A personal viewpoint, which may not be widely held by other psychophysiologists, is that *empathy* is an ability especially significant for personality development and social life. Empathy may be thought of as an ANS state which tends to simulate that of another person. In addition to the intensity parameter, the empathic state has a dimension of accuracy, that is, the degree to which the simulated ANS pattern in the subject matches that of the object person. One's ability to empathize accurately is probably the most important "reality principle" for healthful, creative, social life. It may be the most characteristic lack in psychopaths and sociopaths. Anticipatory empathy may be the most determining motive in kindness and compassion. Although very little has yet been done toward the measurement of empathy, psychophysiology has the methods for its objective, quantitative description. Once objective measures of empathy are created, research can examine whether indeed it does play such a significant role in personality and social interaction as I have suggested.

Learning of Secondary Emotions. Most human behavior is directed by secondary motives. Secondary motives are differentiated out of the inborn drives by as yet some poorly understood process although the mechanism may be the same as for all human learning. Certainly the autonomic nervous system too has the ability to modify its response according to schedules of reinforcement. Individuals must differ in their capacity for such modification just as they differ in capacity for intellectual learning. Intelligence has many components, which are only moderately correlated. It is plausible that the ability to learn secondary motives is also distributed differently in different individuals and may not be highly correlated with intelligence. The ability to acquire strong secondary motives rapidly and retain them faithfully, yet be able to modify them flexibly as situations change, is a very important ability for adjustment in human society. Whereas much maladjustment and neurosis may be due to the learning of the wrong motives or an incompatible combination, there also may be many people who simply learn secondary motives slowly, require much reinforcement, or retain motives poorly with the result that their behavior does not coordinate well with that of their associates. It would be valuable to have reliable and valid measures of this ability to learn secondary motives and other aspects of physiological adaptation. We propose that psychophysiological methods can be used to measure the ability for an individual to acquire secondary motivation. To the extent motivation involves the ANS, psychophysiological examination of the ANS during a suitable learning regimen should provide the desired measures. Classical conditioning of autonomic variables such as palmar sweating, peripheral plethysmogram, heart rate, salivation, and gastric motility could provide one approach to the measurement of aptitude for learning motivation. Exploration of the ability for differentiation of autonomic response patterns by instrumental conditioning procedures employing both positive and negative reinforcement will probably provide even more extensive and sensitive measures of Physiological Learning Aptitude (PLA). I propose the more general term of Physiological Learning Aptitude rather than restricting the concept to motivation, because it seems likely that physiological adaptation having to do with homeostasis and many bodily processes is involved as well as those physiological processes specifically involved in motivation. Motivation, as the concept is generally used, also has an intellectual component which may or may not be measured by the various ANS conditioning procedures proposed for the measurement of the aptitude for acquisition of secondary motives. Only future research can work out the most practical classification of the various components of the abilities involved in learning secondary motives. The concept of concern just now is the physiological components of the learning aptitude, hence the term *Physiological Learning Aptitude*.

It would be quite useful to have a measure of PLA in the management of children who show sociopathic tendencies if it should turn out that they have low aptitude for learning secondary motives and empathy. Just as we now have special classes for low intelligence quotient (IQ) students, it would be useful to have special training procedures for indoctrination of secondary motivation for the low PLA children. With an adequate metric for PLA by which the development of secondary motivation could be monitored, very likely considerable improvement over present methods of "motivation training" could also be achieved for the children with normal and superior PLA.

It appears unlikely that PLA can be measured as well as IQ by a simple cross section of present achievement in physiological differentiation, because in our culture the homogeneity of motivational opportunities is much less than it is for intellectual opportunities. The formal school system which primarily emphasizes intellectual learning tends toward homogeneity in intellectual opportunity, whereas family life and social cliques are probably more determinant for motivational learning. PLA will have to be measured in a standardized learning situation such as the classical and instrumental conditioning procedures proposed.

Many other applications of psychophysiology can be mentioned such as the monitoring of a man's physiological reactions while undergoing severe stress such as space flight. The purpose may be to study the man's ability to tolerate various intensities and types of stress whether for selection, training, or operational purposes. One purpose is to learn how stressors summate when applied simultaneously as they usually occur in real life. It may be that certain schedules of stressors resonate with the body's natural rhythm so as to produce very harmful effects as has been suggested was the case in the ulcer production in Brady's executive monkey experiments (10). The principle of "autonomic tuning" as described by Gellhorn (20) could play an important role in the production of psychosomatic states. "Tuning" is the characteristic of the two branches of the ANS (sympathetic and parasympathetic) to escalate in opposition to each other. Their response and recovery rates may differ sufficiently to permit dangerously high levels of one branch to persist after recovery of the other. This tuning phenomenon could possibly account for the ulcer production in the executive monkey. The parasympathetic arousal persisted in production of acid and stomach motility after the sympathetic recovery during the rest periods. Psychophysiology is contributing to our understanding of autonomic tuning and the natural rhythms which characterize an individual's physiological adjustment to the timing aspects of environmental stressors.

The clinician would like psychophysiology to identify psychophysiologic types (or more properly, patterns of physiological factors) which may relate to susceptibility to the various psychosomatic disorders. The proper evaluation of such susceptibilities will enable retraining or, to the extent they are not retrainable, enable the susceptible persons to be protected by avoidance of the instigating situations. Psychotherapy of psychosomatic disorder may be relatively unsuccessful because the physiological habit patterns persist even though the psychotherapy may have been successful in removing the conflict at one level of personality organization. Some physiological conditioned responses, especially as reported in the Russian literature (32), are extremely resistant to extinction. Psychophysiological extinction procedures in conjunction with psychotherapy may more successfully remove recalcitrant psychosomatic disorder.

Such an array of goals and promises for psychophysiology may appear quite Utopian in view of its modest accomplishments to date. When we have discussed the recent advances in technique, there will be more justification for optimism.

METHODS OF PSYCHOPHYSIOLOGY

An Over-View of Methods. The progressive theme of psychophysiological method has been to extend observation and measurement to ever more covert and detailed behavior with ever decreasing interference with the natural functioning of the organism. These advances in observational technique must be accompanied by a new approach in the interpretation of the findings. The new approach needed, we suggest, must abstract from the total physiological response complex those aspects which represent the psychological state, such as a motive. The total physiological complex includes the physiological processes which are translating the psychic motive into somatic action. There are many parameters of these translation codes to be explored. They include the individual uniqueness vs. species generality dimension; the range of physiological specificity as a function of stimulus specificity; the interaction of "individual" and "stimulus" specificities which might be called "definition-of-the-situation" or "set-specificity." Complex feedback within and across the psychic and somatic subsystems prevails which enables the *interaction* to account for more of the variance than does either primary variable.

Closed loop analysis of complex systems which are composed of sub-systems which are themselves complex and interact via symbolic translation is indeed difficult. Clearly ways must be devised to investigate smaller sub-systems without doing violence to the principles of system organization. Psychophysiology is now at the stage of trying to upgrade its techniques sufficiently to monitor enough observation points to encompass enough of a somatic and psychic subsystem to explore their relationships.

The Stimulus Situation. The methods of psychophysiological research like those of almost every scientific discipline may be classified into methods of stimulation, observation, and interpretation. In some psychophysiological studies the observations are made under natural or real-life conditions. The stimulus situation is then described as the contextual situation in which the observations are made. The degree of naturalism can vary widely from recording by telemetry the behavior of a subject's daily life to more contrived but nevertheless "real" situations such as jumping from planes (18), watching a movie (2), or making love. More specific laboratory stimuli may be a series of tasks to perform (24), a series of specific stimuli such as pain, sounds, etc., or still more specific experimental situations such as classical or instrumental conditioning (32).

In humans, relatively few direct psychophysiological studies of drive or motivation have been reported. Not even the basic drive states of hunger, thirst, elimination, and sex have been well observed by an adequate set of modern physiological recordings. Sleep is currently receiving a lot of attention (23, 39). Prolonged vigils of wakefulness have been studied, but the nature of the stimulus situation both for keeping the subjects awake and during the physiological observation strongly influences the findings and makes interpretation difficult. For example, Malmo reported (28) that, in subjects who had been kept awake for up to 60 hours while performing a tracking task, skin conductance level was higher than when doing the same task before the sleepless vigil began. He interpreted the raised palmar conductance as evidence that the subjects were in a higher arousal or drive state due to the multiple stimulus effect of the sleepless state (internal stimuli) and the environmental stimuli in the form of demands to perform the task. With decreased environmental stimuli, however, the skin conductance level falls to lower levels than before the sleepless vigil, almost like that of sleep (5). Exactly how the fatigue or sleep deprivation state interacts with environmental stimulation to modulate arousal, drive or motivation is the purpose of such psychophysiological studies.

The more subtle motivational stimulus situations of art appreciation, social reinforcement, empathy, and curiosity have hardly been observed physiologically. It is not at present known whether significant differentiations among such motives are represented in peripheral processes, or, if they do somehow overflow into the periphery, it has not been established that they have sufficiently coherent and organized representation to be meaningfully interpreted. Possibly they can only be measured usefully when the motive is regnantly directing the overt behavior. When measured in the overt behavior situation, they might indeed contribute very significantly to the description of type and intensity of the motive.

A. F. AX

Psychophysiology can now afford to explore systematically the unambiguous motives and proceed cautiously with adequate documentation at each step toward the more subtle stimulus situations. Only repeated failure with persistent application of the most sophisticated technique can identify the limits of peripheral representation of motives and emotions.

In all scientific experimentation ingenuity must be exercised to make sure the subject (whether a molecule or a human individual) is indeed responding principally to the stimulus the experimenter has contrived. Especially with humans the most objective and detailed description of the objective stimulus may be quite irrelevant if we do not know how the subject defined the situation and his intentions with regard to the situation. For the subjective definition of the situation, the psychophysiologist utilizes the best that clinical psychology and psychiatry have to offer. Psychophysiology, however, is not completely dependent on clinical judgment, projective tests, and rating scales for its criteria of emotional arousal. By suitable inductive examination of matrices containing both physiological and psychological data it is possible to identify "states" and "traits" which are system vectors not biased by either viewpoint (13). Clearly much screening by many replications is required to differentiate the structure of emotion and motivation.

Defining the stimulus situation in depth must include the definition of the situation by the subjects as well as by the experimenters. This is a major research front to which psychophysiology can make substantial contributions by bringing to bear information independent of the overt behavior resulting from the emotion or motivation.

Observation in Psychophysiology Methodology. A several-volume handbook could be written on this topic. Here a bare sampling will be given for illustration. The classical methods of physiology and psychology, many of which may be used by psychophysiology will be omitted for brevity. The more strictly psychophysiological methods clearly bifurcate into sensors and recorders.

Sensors. Psychophysiological sensors include electrodes and transducers by which a condition or process of the organism is sensed and transduced into electrical form (or if already a bioelectrical phenomenon simply conveyed to the recorder). Only electrical sensors are considered here. Several recent and informative publications are available (11, 15, 22, 27, 34). Electrical potentials of interest to psychophysiology include the electrocardiogram (ECG), electroencephalogram (EEG), electrodermal potential (EDP), electromyogram (EMG), electroocular potential (EOP), and potentials from several visceral organs which we might tag electrovisceral potential (EVP) for general reference. Although psychophysiology is usually limited to body surface or mucous membrane surfaces, there is no strict boundary for psychophysiology. Needle electrodes inserted into a muscle or scalp are sometimes used. Deep penetration into organs, especially the brain, on the other hand, is a classical technique of physiology. Important characteristics of an electrode are low resistance and impedance, non-polarization, reliability, and innocuousness to the subject.

Low impedance is achieved by using a metal such as silver or zinc applied to the skin with an electrolyte intermediary. A very complex bioelectric relationship must be optimized for minimum influence on the tissue and minimum polarization (the battery-like effect of producing a non-biological potential which may confuse the measurement of the true biological potential). This very complex issue is currently under intense investigation and few clearly superior methods are known. Several principles are generally useful. The electrode paste (electrolyte) must be non-corrosive to the tissue and should contain approximately the salinity of the body fluid (sweat) which will likely dilute it. It must also be directly compatible with the metal in the electrode ($ZnSO_4$ for Zn and NaCl for Silver). The best currently available "non-polarizible" electrode is silver-silver chloride[1] which is tricky to manufacture and maintain (30). If bioelectric pulses of fast rise or fall times are being investigated the capacitance component of the electrode impedance must also be considered. The area and thickness of the electrolyte, which may be in a sponge, are important parameters for capacitance, larger and thinner producing greater capacitance coupling which reduces impedance. Other considerations such as innocuousness and reliability may require small area and considerable mechanical buffering by a sponge. The best electrode must be a compromise of many parameters optimized for the specific physiological variable and purpose for the observation. Our purpose here is to warn the unwary that this is a complex issue with many parameters that may be very influential on the results obtained. One advantage of a non-polarizable electrode even for such AC variables as EEG, ECG, and EMG is that the common mode rejection of electrical noise by the balanced input amplifier is optimum only when in balance to ground. If electrodes (in bipolar recording) develop unequal potential, the imbalance reduces materially the common mode rejection of electrical noise such as 60 cps AC which may contaminate and distort the signal.

Another use of electrodes is to sense the resistance or impedance of the tissue lying between and below two electrodes such as used for the galvanic skin resistance or for impedance plethysmography (19). Here too all the considerations of potential measurement apply and, in addition, considerations of frequency, current, and voltage are important parameters. Symposia and articles in this and future issues of PSYCHOPHYSIOLOGY deal at length with this problem. For several years in our laboratory we have controlled long-term electrode polarization of the galvanic skin response (GSR) electrodes by reversing the polarity twice per second (4). By this method we are able to use small, inexpensive, zinc electrodes in plastic cups filled with sponges saturated with $ZnSO_4$ solution. These electrodes have essentially no maintenance problems.

Finally, electrodes are employed for stimulation by electricity which may be DC or AC. Sponge buffering is essential to avoid burns and blisters. Innocuous salts, such as NaCl, KCl or $ZnSO_4$ are necessary so as not to contaminate the tissues by electrophoresis. Quantified stimulation requires automatically controlled current or power because of the rapidly changing impedance of the tissue when stimulated by electricity. These tissue impedance changes are mediated both by neuronal reflexes (GSR) and by purely local effects and responses to electricity. Much research is needed to determine exactly how the current should

---

[1] Constant potential electrodes are available from the Lexington Instrument Company, 16 Mechanic St., Waltham, Massachusetts, or Silver-silver chloride pelletized electrodes, 638C, from Mennen-Greatbach Electronics, Inc., 10647 Main Street, Clarence, New York 14031.

A. F. AX

be controlled as the skin impedance changes so as to maintain constant (or some desired profile of) stimulation.

Reliability of an electrode includes its constancy of placement, effective area of contact, and impedance over long periods during various activities of the subject. Adhesive tape is generally the most satisfactory method of attachment for small electrodes except on the scalp where a heavy conductive "Bentonite" paste is often used. Very flexible wire leads that will not drag on the electrode and which will endure much flexion without breaking are essential. Comfort and lack of local disturbance of the skin is also quite important.

Transducers are of many types and can be conveniently classified by the nature of the signal. For temperature, thermistors are most commonly used since they are inexpensive, tiny, quite durable, and available over a wide range of size and resistance. Unfortunately, these facts do not eliminate serious problems in temperature measurement. Continuous measurement of internal body temperature is awkward since every available body oriface has some undesirable features for transducer placement. Skin surface temperature, as an index of peripheral blood flow, is complicated by (1) the necessity of precise control of ambiant air temperature so as to provide a suitable constant temperature gradient, (2) the degree of thermal contact achieved and maintained between thermistor and skin as sweating changes, and (3) determination of how much covering to place over the thermistor. More covering slows down response time and modifies the natural skin condition and less covering produces lower readings.

Respiration rate and tidal volume are very desirable psychophysiological variables. A mask or breathing tube is too disturbing for most psychophysiological experiments. Many devices have been used for measuring the respiration movements of the chest and abdomen including bellows operating a tambour, various displacement transducers, such as strain gauges or differential transformers and impedance changes of the thorax (1, 19, 29). In a recent study (7) we found that mercury-filled rubber tube strain gauges around the chest and abdomen when combined and under ideal conditions can sense tidal volume with a 98% accuracy when calibrated against a spirometer as the criterion. This gauge and the other indirect methods tried (impedance) all degenerate to zero accuracy during strenuous activities. Clearly even for this least covert of physiological variables there is room for improvement.

The indirect measurement of blood pressure requires two transducers—a microphone to sense the Korotkoff sounds and a pressure cuff to cut off gradually the blood flow in an artery. Automation of this normally clinical procedure has been difficult and only successful under circumstances of little activity. The procedure also does interfere somewhat by stopping or reducing blood flow in a limb for short intervals and is a moderate sensory stimulus to the subject. The determination can only be made intermittantly, thus failing to reveal fine structure in blood pressure variation. The various systolic blood pressure (BP) monitors[2] which oscillate around the systolic blood pressure and are reported to

[2] Winston systolic blood pressure follower. Winston Electronics Ltd., subsidiary of Dynamics Corporation of America, 25 W. 43rd St., New York 36, New York. Beckman Instruments, Inc., 1117 California Ave., Palo Alto, California.

obtain a reading every third heart beat, first of all, of course, do not obtain diastolic blood pressure at all and are usually quite uncomfortable. They also are quite easily corrupted by movement. Other approaches of measuring BP are constantly being attempted such as the pulse wave velocity index and tiny pressure sensors over a superficial artery. Neither has yet demonstrated its practicability.

A more exotic transducer is the telemetry capsule that can be swallowed while it transmits pressures, pH or temperature in the gastrointestinal tract. It has even been suggested (8) that a considerable number of physiological variables may be detected from a distance without any transducer near or touching the subject!

The points that need emphasis with regard to transducers for psychophysiology are the following: (1) there is a large set of transducers already able to sense many bodily conditions with only minimum interference with those processes under ideal laboratory conditions; (2) under real-life field conditions their reliability and practicability decrease very significantly; (3) with the remarkable miniaturization in electronics and with sufficient research and development it would appear that almost any physiological variable may eventually be scrutinized in the intact human.

Recorders. The outputs of the physiological sensors must be displayed for human inspection or transformed into digestible units for a computer. Instantaneous and momentary display is done by oscilloscopes which may be photographed for permanent but delayed and expensive recording. Oscillographs also provide immediate display and at the same time produce a relatively inexpensive permanent record for visual inspection but are also indigestable for the computer. Magnetic tape provides an ideal recording which is electrically retrievable for input to a computer but cannot be read by the human eye. There are also the punched paper tape and card, but these are often too slow and bulky for large amounts of data storage. They also require the on-line operation of an analog-to-digital converter which adds to the complexity of data acquisition. Whatever the method of recording, high gain amplifiers are required and available. Both oscillographs and magnetic tape recorders are now well able to record conveniently up to 14 channels simultaneously with resolution of about 1 %. The number of channels can, of course, be multiplied many fold by multiplexing or by parallel recorders. With sufficient funds just about any display or recording can be achieved.

Signal Transformation. An essential part of the recording or analysis process is the further transformation of the signal so as to abstract that particular aspect or parameter desired. Signal transformation begins with the sensor. An ideal sensor abstracts only one aspect of the total signal complex. For example, at a single pair of electrodes on the fingers of the two hands are simultaneously present (1) electrocardiogram (ECG), and (2) electrodermal potentials (EDP) of sweating. Either or both may be detected by suitable amplifier and filter settings. Clearly finger pulse and many other physical and biochemical processes are occurring at those sites which normally are not being sensed. If the pressure changes of the pulse distort the shape of the sensed EKG or EDP, it would constitute undesirable noise. But beyond the particular sensor, amplifier or filter, further abstraction can be accomplished. From the complex wave pattern of the ECG, a cardiotachometer can abstract the heart period (HP) or its reciprocal *heart rate* (HR). The pulse wave period (PWP) or its reciprocal *pulse wave velocity* (PWV) can be abstracted from the time delay between the ECG and the pressure pulse at a peripheral site. The amplitude of the IJ wave from the complex wave pattern of the ballistocardiogram (BCG) can be obtained by suitable gating, polarity sensing, and holding circuitry. Such signal transformation is essential for human understanding or computer analysis and synthesis of the data. Although *heart rate* is not a simple monotonic measure of any profound state of the organism such as "arousal" maybe thought to be, it is at least a manageable parameter of a major organ and clearly bears functional relationships to significant proceedings of the body. It can be manipulated mathematically, such as determining its functional dependencies with other parameters similarly abstracted in a way not possible with a whole complex pattern such as the ECG or BCG.

One of the most refractory problems in this parameter abstraction process is the frequent contamination or distortion of the signal by movement artifact or environmental influence. A moderate finger movement completely destroys the finger plethysmogram. A minor arm gesture may produce a body acceleration about equal in amplitude and frequency components to the BCG, but of course is quite unrelated to heart stroke force; a swinging of the arms may produce chest circumference or impedance changes such as to completely obscure the changes produced by respiration; muscle potentials can submerge the electroencephalogram (EEG), etc. In a freely moving subject monitored by telemetry, in addition to all such movement artifacts, environmental influences may rapidly change. A skin temperature reading would quickly change as the subject turns the observation site from shade to sun, toward or away from a breeze. The movement artifacts can usually be detected by skilled visual inspection but for the computer this is difficult. "Automatic editing," as we shall call this essential aspect of signal detection by machinery, can be done by a progressive series of screenings. The simplest is by filtering which is limited to artifacts differing grossly in frequency components from that of the desired signal. Editing by amplitude limits can reject artifacts too large to be real. Signals in synchrony such as the BCG or plethysmogram pulse can be gated in at their proper time with reference to the ECG, thus excluding all artifacts occurring outside the gated interval. This type of editing cannot prevent movement artifacts occurring during the gated interval from getting through. An accelorometer strategically placed can sense movement and close the gate thus rejecting artifacts, but may, at times, reject good signals that would have been acceptable. Still another approach to automatic editing is to program an analog or digital computer to compare serially each branch of a complex wave pattern with a standard pattern by a number of criteria such as slope, amplitude, and interval. Presumably this type of pattern recognition can be made as sensitive as any skilled human inspector. The circuitry or computing program designed specifically for each variable might become very complex and costly. Automatic editing for psychophysiology is a research and development task of relatively unknown scope, but it must be done if high-speed processing of physiological data is to become practicable.

After the good signal has been identified by editing (human or machine) the desired parameters may be abstracted either by analogue circuitry such as the tachometer or integrator or by digital computer programming. For input to a digital computer naturally all signals must be converted from their continuous analog form into discrete samples whose amplitudes are converted to digital form and recorded on a digital medium such as magnetic tape or punched cards. The sampling frequency should be as low as possible to faithfully follow the highest frequency components of interest in the parameter. For example, the respiration curve in humans rarely exceeds 1 response/sec. which enables a sampling frequency of 10/sec. to follow it quite accurately. Sampling faster than necessary is wasteful of digital computing time. Since most of the cardiovascular variables contain respiration frequency components, they too should be sampled about 10/sec. GSR and the temperatures can be sampled less frequently.

During the A/D conversion a second oscillogram should be made of the signals as they have been transformed by the signal conditioning circuitry and whatever automatic editing that has been achieved. This final analog record is needed to provide a visual display for human editing. It is essential that no gross artifacts be treated by the computer as if they were real data. Final editing consists simply of visually scanning the oscillogram for artifacts and noting their times which are then entered into the computer as instructions to skip that section. The time and care required for this human editing is a function of how much artifact is present, how well it was automatically screened, and how clearly the automatic editing was displayed on the final record.

In a practicable, flexible program, in addition to providing for editing, there must be provision for selection of any desired sections for computation, various methods for smoothing and further editing by the computer. For example, a brief transient possibly caused by a momentary failure or error in the A/D converter can be avoided by a slope tolerance. The computer checks each pair of samples and if any one exceeds a criterion slope it will reject the sample and simply smooth across the dropped sample.

Data Analysis, Synthesis, and Interpretation. Having finally purged the data of artifact, the analysis may proceed. The parameters of physiological variables most often used for indices of emotional arousal are amplitude and frequency of *non-specific* responses occurring spontaneously in the situation of the experiment or *specific* responses elicited by discrete experimental stimuli. In either case a *response* must be identified to be counted and measured. The definition of a response for a physiological variable can be very difficult. Each experimenter sets up his own arbitrary criteria often without very complete description or justification which often makes comparisons of results between laboratories difficult. In the case of the specific response, the criterion of latency can be used to delimit the interval over which the specific response may occur. In addition the criteria of *duration, direction, amplitude,* and *slope* may be used to specify further whether indeed a response occurred. For the non-specific responses where latency is not applicable, limits on some or all of these other parameters must be used as criteria for identifying responses. Noise level for the variable is the first consideration in setting the tolerance for amplitude. Noise is produced not only by the amplifier and recorder but also by the transducer or electrode. Frequency variations higher than those of interest produce another type of noise. A variable like heart rate may respond in either direction and with wide variation in response interval. If the experimenter is interested in HR responses not due to respiration sinus arrhythmia (SA), which in some subjects may be considerably larger than the responses being investigated, he must somehow arrange to control or eliminate the sinus arrhythmia effect. If the response of interest is known to have a duration several times as long as the respiration interval, a simple average over several respiration cycles may be appropriate. Averaging over an integral number of respirations will precisely control for SA. For short duration heart rate responses, such as those of a single heart period, the sample should be taken only at a standard part of the respiration cycle.

To the extent that the *law of initial values* (LIV) operates, that is, to the extent the level of the variable just prior to a response influences the amplitude of the response (9, 25, 31, 37), it is necessary to adjust the tolerance for detecting responses. If a constant amplitude tolerance is used, the LIV correction could then be applied to the *frequency* as well as the *amplitude* of responses detected. Almost no one uses such a correction factor for frequency because the operation of LIV is still quite unclear. Almost every set of data seems to produce a new LIV. This is really not surprising when it is realized that a variable like HR is very dependent on such other variables as blood pressure, stroke volume, and peripheral resistance which are usually not included in attempts to apply LIV. Only when LIV has been generalized to include the influence on a response of amplitude, direction, and rate of change of the other relevant variables will psychophysiological response patterns be able to reveal their best validity for the description of emotions, motives, and stress states.

Individual Physiological Response Specificity (IRS) which several investigators have described (6, 17, 24, 36) is probably related to LIV. The equations which relate the response amplitude with the base level vary from one individual to another, even at birth (9). When LIV is generalized to include several variables, the hierarchy of the variables with regard to their preferred mode of expression will inevitably influence the LIV equation. Because of the combined effects of LIV and IRS, experimental design and data analysis should provide for sufficient stimulus-response replication to enable computation of the parameters of the equations for generalized LIV. Research on this problem has barely begun.

Since *Stimulus Response Specificity* (SRS) has also been demonstrated (6, 17, 36), this too will most certainly interact with IRS and LIV. But the unknown interrelations of LIV, SRS, and IRS only begin to reveal the true complexity of the situation. When the subject's "definition of the situation" interacts with IRS, SRS and LIV, there is produced a psychophysiological complex which could be called *Motivational Response Specificity* (MRS). If, as we have argued earlier, the general goal of psychophysiology is to describe motives in objective quantitative terms, then there appears to be no escape from having to obtain and analyze sufficient data on an individual to obtain the parameters of IRS, SRS, LIV, and the subject's definition of the situation. With all this, possibly the psychophysiological response patterns can be interpreted within a sophisticated model of the organism and contribute to its further description.

Since, so far as we know, no one has yet attempted to apply simultaneously all of the above-mentioned principles to a single set of data, we cannot say whether or not there really will be a significant gain in prediction of performance or accuracy of diagnosis of an emotion or motivational state in an individual. Even with all the uncertainty, until the research has been done, it seems worthwhile to make the following points: (1) to indicate that past and much present psychophysiological research is oversimplified not because psychophysiologists are unaware of the complexity of the organism, but because techniques and verified theory have been lacking, (2) to alert neophytes that by simply recording GSR or HR they cannot expect very much help in diagnosing personality, emotion or psychiatric disorder, and (3) to explain why elaborate and costly high-speed data processing machinery is essential for psychophysiological investigation. Our studies done in 1949–1950 on the physiological differentiation between fear and anger in humans (3, 33) were lucky and useful to show that the information for describing an emotion may be present in the peripheral patterns, but it is questionable whether a similar approach repeated for many different emotional states would advance our knowledge much further. Two strong emotions under the fortunate circumstances of that experiment were able to demonstrate an unambiguous difference without the benefit of IRS, SRS, and LIV, but, as we noted in our report (3), the variance between individuals was considerably larger than that between emotions. The method was not adequate to diagnose an emotional state in an individual with any high degree of confidence, and it would be less adequate if the emotion were elicited by different stimulus situations. It would not be surprising if the physiological patterns of fear in a person while running just ahead of a hungry lion in the jungle differ considerably from those of fearing an electric shock while reclining in the laboratory. For the practicable application of psychophysiology to the diagnosis of emotion we cannot ignore the stimulus specifications, the individual specificities, the law of initial values generalized over many relevant variables nor the host of other technical problems related to electrodes, transducers, recorders, and movement artifacts. But to utilize all these known principles, and probably more yet to be discovered, it is necessary to examine in detail *many* physiological variables, in response to *many* intensities of *many* kinds of stimuli on *many* individuals. "Many" to the fourth power means a great deal of data. Surely at least as much work must be done on the psychophysiological examination as has been done on IQ tests or the ECG in heart research. To do the required research requires the help of high-speed data processing machinery.

It is now possible with suitable data processing equipment and programs to obtain quickly the base level, amplitude, slope, area, and latencies of every response and recovery of many variables recorded simultaneously on human subjects in a wide variety of stimulus situations. These parameters can be efficiently interrelated so as to define physiological response profiles useful in diagnosing acute emotional states or chronic conditions. They can be used for such methodological purposes as generalization of the Law of Initial Values, Individual, Stimulus, and Motivational Response Specificities. Several methods of measuring a physiological system such as exosomatic vs. the endosomatic measurement of the palmar sweating response can be quickly compared. Rapid identification can be done of the most useful set of physiological parameters for a specific purpose such as monitoring an astronaut, personnel selection for high-stress missions, and diagnosis of a psychosomatic or psychiatric disorder. In the past, due to the inability of anyone to compare a large number of variables for such purposes, the selection of variables has been fortuitous and arbitrary with uncertain results not conducive to confidence in the method. Imagine where intelligence testing would be if each investigator insisted on limiting his measure of IQ to one particular technique such as vocabulary, block design, similarities, or picture completion. Can we doubt that the physiological profiles of emotion and motivation are less complex than school aptitude? Psychophysiology has a big job ahead of it, but the possible rewards for the understanding and management of emotional and motivational problems justify the effort.

REFERENCES

1. ALLISON, R. D. Volumetric dynamics of respiration as measured by electrical impedance. Ph.D. Thesis, Wayne State University, Detroit, 1962.
2. Ås, A. *Mutilation Fantasies and Autonomic Response.* Oslo: Oslo University Press, 1958.
3. AX, A. F. The physiological differentiation between fear and anger in humans. *Psychosom. Med.,* 1953, **15**, 433.
4. AX, A. F., AND ZACHAROPOULOS, G. Comment on skin conductance bridge. *Psychophysiol. Newsletter,* 1960, **6**, 12.
5. AX, A. F., AND LUBY, E. D. Autonomic responses to sleep deprivation. *Arch. Gen. Psychiat.,* 1961, **4**, 55.
6. AX, A. F. Response specificity. *Psychophysiol. Newsletter,* 1961, **7**, 33.
7. AX, A.F., ANDRESKI, L., COURTER, R., DiGIOVANNI, C., HERMAN, S., LUCAS, D., AND ORRICK, W. *Validation of the AMRL 3-channel personal telemetry system.* Final report on contract AF(657)-9352 made to Aerospace Medical Laboratory, USAF. Wright-Patterson Air Force Base.
8. BERKLEY, C. Talk presented at meeting of Society for Psychophysiological Research in Detroit, October 12, 1963.
9. BLOCK, J. D., AND BRIDGER, W. The law of initial value in psychophysiology: a reformulation in terms of experimental and theoretical considerations. *Ann. N. Y. Acad. Sci.,* 1962, **98**, 1229.
10. BRADY, J. V., PORTER, R. W., CONRAD, D. G., AND MASON, J. W. Avoidance behavior and the development of gastroduodenal ulcers. *J. Exp. Anal. Behav.,* 1958, **1**, 69.
11. BROWN, C. C. *Instrumentation with Semiconductors.* Springfield, Ill.: Charles C Thomas, 1964 (in press).
12. BROWN, J. Problems presented by the concept of acquired drives. *In* M. R. Jones (Ed.), *Nebraska Symposium on Motivation.* Lincoln: Universityof Nebraska Press, 1953.
13. CATTELL, R. B., AND SCHEIER, I. H. The meaning and measurement of neuroticism and anxiety. New York: Ronald Press, 1961.
14. DAVIS, R. C. Response patterns. *Trans. N. Y. Acad. Sci.,* Sec. II, 1957, **19**, 731.
15. DONALDSON, P. E. K. *Electronic Apparatus for Biological Research.* London: Butterworth's Scientific publications, 1958.
16. Editorial. *Psychosom. Med.,* 1939, **1**, 3.
17. ENGEL, B. T., AND BECKFORD, A. F. Response specificity: stimulus-response and individual-response specificity in essential hypertension. *Arch. Gen. Psychiat.,* 1961, **5**, 478.

18. EPSTEIN, S. The measurement of drive and conflict in humans: theory and experiment. *In* M. R. Jones (Ed.), *Nebraska Symposium on Motivation*. Lincoln: University of Nebraska Press, 1962.

19. GEDDES, L. A., AND HOFF, H. E. The measurement of physiologic events by electrical impedance: a review. *Amer. J. Med. Electron.*, 1964, **3**, 16.

20. GELLHORN, E. *Autonomic Imbalance and the Hypothalamus*. Minneapolis: University of Minnesota Press, 1957.

21. GRAHAM, D. T., KABLER, J. D., AND GRAHAM, FRANCES K. Physiological response to the suggestion of attitudes specific for hives and hypertension. *Psychosom. Med.*, 1962, **24**, 159.

22. IVES, D. J. G., AND JANZ, G. J. *Reference Electrodes, Theory and Practice*. New York: Academic Press, 1961.

23. KLEITMAN, N. *Sleep and Wakefulness*. Chicago: University of Chicago Press, 1963.

24. LACEY, J. I., BATEMAN, D. E., AND VAN LEHN, R. Autonomic response specificity: an experimental study. *Psychosom. Med.*, 1953, **15**, 8.

25. LACEY, J. I. The evaluation of autonomic responses; toward a general solution. *Ann. N. Y. Acad. Sci.*, 1956, **67**, 123.

26. LANDIS, C. Emotion: II. The expression of emotion. *In* C. Murchison (Ed.), *A Handbook of General Experimental Psychology*. Worcester, Mass.: Clark University Press, 1934, Chapter 7.

27. LION, K. S. *Instrumentation in Scientific Research*. New York: McGraw-Hill Book Company, 1959.

28. MALMO, R. B. Measurement of drive: an unsolved problem in psychology. *In* M. R. Jones (Ed.), *Nebraska Symposium on Motivation*. Lincoln: University of Nebraska Press, 1958.

29. NYBOER, J. *Electrical Impedance Plethysmography*. Springfield, Ill.: Charles C Thomas, 1959.

30. O'CONNELL, D. N., AND TURSKY, B. Electrodes for the recording of skin potential. *Arch. Gen. Psychiat.*, 1960, **3**, 252.

31. OKEN, D., AND HEATH, H. A. The law of initial values: some further considerations. *Psychosom. Med.*, 1963, **25**, 3.

32. RAZRAN, G. The observable unconscious and the inferable conscious in current Soviet psychophysiology: interoceptive conditioning, semantic conditioning and the orienting reflex. *Psychol. Rev.*, 1961, **68**, 81.

33. SCHACHTER, J. Pain, fear, and anger in hypertensives and normotensives. *Psychosom. Med.*, 1957, **19**, 17.

34. Techniques of Physiological Monitoring. Technical documentary report of the Aeromedical Research Labs. No. AMRL-TDR-62-98 (1), 1962, (2) 1963.

35. WENGER, M. A. Pattern analyses of automatic variables during rest. *Psychosom. Med.*, 1957, **19**, 240.

36. WENGER, M. A., CLEMENS, T. L., COLEMAN, D. R., CULLEN, T. D., AND ENGEL, B. T. Autonomic response specificity. *Psychosom. Med.*, 1961, **23**, 185.

37. WILDER, J. Basimetric approach (law of initial value) to biological rhythms. *Ann. N. Y. Acad. Sci.*, 1962, **98**, 1211.

38. WOLFF, H. G. *Stress and Disease*. Springfield, Ill.: Charles C Thomas, 1953.

39. WOLFF, W. (Ed.). Rhythmic functions in the living systems. *Ann. N. Y. Acad. Sci.*, 1962, Art. 4, 753.

Index

Index

Italic page numbers indicate the pages on which the complete references are listed.

Acetylcholine, 14, 21, 40
Acid-base balance, 40
Acne, 143, 151
Activation, 57–73, 90–91, 93, 113, 124
Adaptation, 73–74, 76, 113, 124
Adrenaline, 14, 21–22, 28, 36, 40, 44, 63, 81–82, 84–86, 90
Adrenals, 14, 21, 23, 63, 81
Adrenergic system, 14, 21, 29–30
Alexander, F., 81, *158*
Anabolism, 23
Anger, 6, 63, 79, 81, 84, 91–92, 145
Anorexia nervosa, 143, 151
Anxiety, 70, 81, 113, 145
Aorta, 40, 70
Appetitive behavior, 72
Arousal, 57
Asthma, 28, 143, 151
Atropine, 25, 28
Attitudes, 115–116, 149–156
Autonomic balance, 27–41, 124
  correlates of, 38–40
Autonomic Lability Score, 49–54, 99
Autonomic nervous system, 5, 11–25
Ax, A. F., 84, 85, *158*
Backache, 143, 152
Ballistocardiogram, 69, 71
Barber, T. X., 119, *158*
Baroreceptors, 40–41, 70

Bateman, D. E., 98, *159*
Beecher, H. K., 123, 130, *158*
Benjamin, L. S., 51, 52, 150, *158, 159*
Bickford, A. F., 102, 103, *158*
Blood pressure, 5, 23, 36, 40, 43–44, 69–71, 75, 80, 90
Bonvallet, M., 63, *158*
Brady, J. V., 76, *160*
Brain, 11, 60–62
Brain stem, 11, 21, 61–62
Bruner, J. S., 132, *158*
Buchwald, A. M., *158*

Cameron, D. E., 97, *158*
Cannon, W. B., 14, 79, *158*
Cardiac activity, 5, 23, 27, 36, 40–41, 70
Cardiac stroke volume, 69–70, 75, 80, 82
Cardiotachometer, 48, 71
Cardiovascular system, 11, 70
Carotid sinus, 36, 40, 70
Catabolism, 23
Cholinergic system, 14, 21, 29–30
Clemens, T. L., 39, 82, 109 *161*
Cold pressor, 43–44, 85–86, 98, 101, 120
Coleman, D. R., 109, *161*
Colitis, 143, 151
Conditioning, 5, 113, 125, 131, 142–143

Conrad, D., 76, *160*
Constipation, 143, 151
Consummatory behavior, 72
Cortell, L., 18, *159*
Covariance analysis, 49, 51–54
Cullen, T. D., 39, 86, 109, *161*

Damaser, E. C., 118, *158*
Darsie, M. L., 82, *161*
Davis, F. H., 97, *160*
Davis, R. C., *158*
Dell, P., 63, *158*
Demand characteristics, 128–130
Dermographia, 29
Diastolic blood pressure, 31, 48, 69, 71, 82, 84–86, 102, 108, 116, 155–156
Directional fractionation of response, 87–89, 91–93
Dual innervation, 22, 32, 41, 54
Duffy, E., 57, *158*
Dunbar, H. F., 81, *158*

Eczema, 143, 151
Electric shock, 76, 86, 114, 121, 133, 135–137
Electrocardiogram, 7
Electroencephalogram, 5, 7, 57, 66, 68, 70, 75
Electromyogram, 5, 66, 68, 70, 75, 84, 97, 119–120
Ellington, M., 29, *161*
Embarrassment, 6, 80
Emotion, *see also* specific emotions
  area of study, 9–10
  inferred, 6, 79–81, 140–141
Endocrine system, 11, 60, 65
Energy mobilization, 57, 65
Engel, B. T., 82, 84, 101, 102, 103, 106, 109, *158, 161*
Eppinger, H., 28, *158*
Ergotamine, 28
Estess, F. M., 82, *161*
Ethnic factors, 133–137
Excitation, 57

Exercise, 73, 79–81, 85–86, 101
Experimenter bias, 128
Eysenck, H. J., 39, *158*

Factor analysis, 29
Fear, 63, 79, 84, 87, 91, 119, 145
Feedback mechanisms, 45, 63, 70, 146, 156
Feldman, J., 18, *159*
Finger pulse volume, 69, 71, 75, 85, 121
Frankmann, R. W., *158*
Funkenstein, D. H., 92, *158*

Galambos, R., 76, *160*
Galvanic skin potential, 67–68, 71, 75, 119
Galvanic skin response, 7, 22, 67–68, 71, 75, 87, 90, 102, 120–121
Ganglia, 18
Gastric activity, 5, 18, 23, 27, 76, 81, 84–85, 87, 103, 122–123, 131, 144–145
Gellhorn, E., 18, 40, *159*
Glycogen, 24, 80
Goodman, C. C., 132, *158*
Grace, W. J., 149, *159*
Graham, D. T., 115, 117, 149, 150, 152, 153, 154, 155, *159*
Graham, F. K., 115, 117, 119, 150, 154, 155, *159*
Grinker, R. R., 108, *160*
Gunderson, E., 38, *159*

Habituation, 73
Hahn, K. W., Jr., 119, *158*
Heart period, 29, 31, 36–37
Heart rate, 36–37, 40, 43–46, 48, 69, 71, 75, 80, 82, 84, 87–88, 90, 97, 99, 102, 108, 116, 119–121, 155–156
Heart rate variability, 48, 71, 97, 99, 102, 108
Heath, H. A., 108, *160*
Herrnstein, R. J., 131, *159*
Hertz, M., 108, *160*

Hess, L., 28, *158*
Hiebel, G., 63, *158*
Hives, 116, 143–144, 151, 154–156
Homeostasis, 14, 23, 27, 41, 44, 47, 51–52, 54–55, 63, 76, 124, 142, 146–147, 149, 156
Hord, D. J., 48, 53, 106, 108, *159*
Hormones, *see also* Adrenaline, Noradrenaline, 60, 65, 76
   adrenocorticotropic, 63
   corticosteroids, 64, 79
   gonadotropic, 63
   testosterone, 64
   thyrotropic, 63
   thyroxine, 63
Hunger, 63, 72, 84
Hypertension, 43, 102, 116, 143–144, 151, 155–156
Hyperthyroidism, 143, 151
Hypnosis, 92, 115, 118–121, 128, 154–156
Hypothalamus, 40–41, 62–63
Individual differences, 10, 28, 37, 106, 125
Individual response-stereotypy, 95–109, 124, 144–147, 149, 156
Instructions, *see* Sets, explicit

Jasper, H. H., 58, *159*
Johnson, L. C., 48, 53, 106, 108, *159*
Jones, F. N., 20, 31, *162*
Jones, M. H., 20, 31, *162*

Kabler, J. D., 115, 117, 150, 155, *159*
Kagan, J., 87, 89, 91, *160*
Korchin, S. J., 108, *160*
Kunish, N. O., 119, 150, *159*
Kuntz, A., 11, *159*

Lacey, B. C., 48, 87, 89, 91, 106, 108, *159, 160*
Lacey, J. I., 47, 48, 49, 50, 51, 87, 88, 89, 91, 98, 99, 100, 106, 108, *159, 160*

Law of initial values, 43–55, 124
Lewis, W. C., 150, *159*
Lindsley, D. B., 59, 61, 72, 73, *160*
Loofbourrow, G. N., 40, *159*
Lubin, A., 48, 53, 106, 108, *159*
Lundy, R. M., 150, *159*

McNemar, Q., 51, *160*
Malmo, R. B., 72, 97, 98, *160*
Markwell, E. D., Jr., 38, *160*
Mason, J. W., 76, *160*
Medulla, 40
Metabolic edema, 143, 152
Metabolism, 23, 64
Migraine, 143, 152
Mind-body, dualism, 9, 139–141, 148
Moss, H. A., 87, 89, 91, *160*
Mucus, 23
Muscle potential, *see* Electromyogram
Muscular system, 11, 65
Myelin, 18

Nervous system, 11
Neuron, 18
Noradrenaline, 14, 21–22, 81–82, 84–86, 90

Obrist, R. A., 93, *160*
Oken, D., 108, *160*
Orienting reflex, 58
Orne, M. T., 118, 128, 130, *158, 160*
Oxygen, 23, 36

Pain, 79, 84, 97, 120–122, 130–131, 133–137
Palmar conductance, 29, 31, 33–35, 46–48, 67–68, 84, 87–88, 99, 108
Paradoxical responses, 44, 51, 70
Parasympathetic nervous system, 14, 21–25
Parasympathetic overcompensation, *see* Rebound
Parasympatholytic drugs, 28
Parasympathomimetic drugs, 28

Physiological psychology, definition of, 1–3
Pilocarpine, 28
Pituitary gland, 63
Placebos, 123, 130–131
Polygraph, 3, 6, 27, 36, 43, 66
Polygraph Newsletter, 3, 9
Porter, R. W., 76, *160*
Postganglionic fibers, 20–22
Preganglionic fibers, 20–22
Prestimulus levels, 44–55, 71, 75–78, 86
Psoriasis, 143, 151
Psychophysiology, definition of, 1–3
Psychophysiology, journal, 3, 9
Psychosomatic diseases, 10, 64, 76, 96, 106, 139–157
Pulse pressure, 29, 71
Pupils, 23, 43, 131

Raynaud's disease, 28, 143, 152, 154–155
Rebound, 75–78, 124, 145, 156
Regional enteritis, 143, 152
Respiration, 29, 48, 70–71, 84, 97, 102, 116, 120, 155–156
Response levels, 46–55
Reticular formation, 60–63, 65
Rheumatoid arthritis, 143, 152
Rioch, D. McK., 76, *160*
Rosenthal, R., 128, *160*

Sabshin, M., 108, *160*
Salivary output, 29, 31–33, 84, 131
Schachter, J., 84, *160*
Schlosberg, H., 112, *162*
Schwartz, N. B., 108, *160*
Selye, H., 58, 64, 79 *160*
Sensory pathways, 60, 65
Sets
    explicit, 111–125, 154–156
    implicit, 127–138, 148–149, 156
Sexual arousal, 64, 72
Shagass, C., 97, 98, *160*

Shor, R. E., 118, *158*
Skin resistance, *see* Palmar conductance, Galvanic skin response
Skin temperature, 5, 7, 48, 84, 102, 116, 154–156
Sleep, 23, 63, 72, 86
Society for Psychophysiological Research, 3, 9
Sokolov, E. N., 58, *161*
Sonnenschein, R. R., 82, *161*
Spinal cord, 11, 21, 40, 61–62
Startle, 43–44, 58, 85
Statistics, 7–8, 38, 46–47, 105
Stern, J. A., 2, 154, 155, *159, 161*
Sternbach, R. A., 8, 43, 48, 58, 72, 85, 86, 91, 113, 115, 121, 122, 123, 133, 136, *160*
Stimulus-response specificity, 79–93, 101, 124, 145–147, 156
Sublingual temperature, 31
Sweating, *see also* Galvanic skin potential, Galvanic skin response, Palmar conductance, Volar conductance, 5, 22, 33–36, 43, 46–47, 66–67, 80, 131
Sympathetic nervous system, 14, 20–25
Sympathico-adrenal system, 14, 60
Sympathicotonia, 28–29, 96, 106
Sympatholytic drugs, 28
Sympathomimetic drugs, 28
Symptom-specificity, 97, 100, 105
Synapse, 18
Systolic blood pressure, 48, 69, 71, 82, 102, 108, 116, 155–156

Tape, data recording, 7
Tart, C. T., 128, *161*
Telemetering, 7
Thalamus, 61
Thyroid gland, 63
Troffer, S. A., 128, *161*
Tursky, B., 133, 136, *161*

Ulcers, 76, 79, 143–144, 151

Vagal rebound, *see* Rebound
Vago-insulin system, 18, 60
Vagotonia, 28–29, 96, 106
Vagus nerve, 18, 28
Van Lehn, R., 98, *159*
Vasoconstriction, 22–23, 36, 40, 43, 69–70, 82
Vasodilatation, 22–23, 36, 66, 69, 80
Volar conductance, 29, 31, 35–36

Wenger, M. A., 20, 28, 29, 30, 31, 38, 39, 82, 86, 109, *161, 162*
Wilder, J., 44, *162*
Winokur, G., 154, 155, *159*
Wolf, S., 81, 82, 83, *162*
Wolff, H. G., 81, 82, 83, *162*
Woodworth, R. S., 112, *162*

Zborowski, M., 133, *162*